FLUID MECHANICS OF INTERNAL FLOW

List of Symposia

held at General Motors Research Laboratories
published by Elsevier Publishing Company, Amsterdam

1957. *Friction and Wear* (edited by ROBERT DAVIES), published 1959.

1958. *Internal Stresses and Fatigue in Metals* (edited by GERALD M. RASSWEILER and WILLIAM L. GRUBE), published 1959.

1959. *Theory of Traffic Flow* (edited by ROBERT HERMAN), published 1961.

1960. *Rolling Contact Phenomena* (edited by JOSEPH D. BIDWELL), published 1962.

1961. *Adhesion and Cohesion* (edited by PHILIP WEISS), published 1962.

1962. *Cavitation in Real Liquids* (edited by ROBERT DAVIES), published 1964.

1963. *Liquids: Structure, Properties, Solid Interactions* (edited by THOMAS J. HUGHEL), published 1965.

1964. *Approximation of Functions* (edited by HENRY L. GARABEDIAN), published 1965.

1965. *Fluid Mechanics of Internal Flow* (edited by GINO SOVRAN), this volume.

1966. *Ferroelectricity* (edited by EDWARD F. WELLER), in preparation.

FLUID MECHANICS OF INTERNAL FLOW

PROCEEDINGS OF THE SYMPOSIUM ON THE FLUID
MECHANICS OF INTERNAL FLOW, GENERAL MOTORS
RESEARCH LABORATORIES, WARREN, MICHIGAN, 1965

Edited by

GINO SOVRAN

General Motors Research Laboratories,
Warren, Michigan (U.S.A.)

ELSEVIER PUBLISHING COMPANY

AMSTERDAM-LONDON-NEW YORK

1967

ELSEVIER PUBLISHING COMPANY
335 JAN VAN GALENSTRAAT, P.O. BOX 211, AMSTERDAM

AMERICAN ELSEVIER PUBLISHING COMPANY, INC.
52 VANDERBILT AVENUE, NEW YORK, N.Y. 10017

ELSEVIER PUBLISHING COMPANY LIMITED
RIPPLESIDE COMMERCIAL ESTATE, BARKING, ESSEX

LIBRARY OF CONGRESS CATALOG CARD NUMBER 66–20561

WITH 176 ILLUSTRATIONS AND 8 TABLES

PRINTED IN THE NETHERLANDS

Preface

These proceedings contain the papers and oral discussions presented at the Symposium on the Fluid Mechanics of Internal Flow held at the General Motors Research Laboratories in Warren, Michigan, on September 20 and 21, 1965. This international, invitational symposium was the ninth in an annual series, each one having been in a different technical discipline. The symposia provide a forum for areas of science and technology that are of timely interest to the Research Laboratories as well as the technical community at large and in which personnel of the Laboratories are active investigators. They furnish an opportunity for the exchange of ideas and current knowledge between the outstanding research specialists from educational, industrial and governmental institutions who are assembled, and serve to stimulate future research activity.

Internal fluid flows, such as those which occur in turbomachines and fluid-handling devices, have great technical importance. The bounding surfaces of these confined flows are often of complicated geometry, mechanical energy is frequently exchanged with the fluid passing within them, and the majority of the configurations are dominated by turbulent shear flows. The basis for our present understanding of such flows has come both from specific research efforts directed towards them and from the application of knowledge gained in external-flow investigations. The former have received particular emphasis because of their relevance to aircraft gas turbine engines and the latter have primarily been performed in the context of aeronautical applications. In the past decade or so, government-supported internal-flow research has greatly diminished as defense requirements have shifted the emphasis from air-breathing to non-air-breathing types of propulsion devices, and much of the aeronautical activity is now devoted to flows that are outside the scope of many fluid-handling devices of industrial importance. A large and important interest in internal flows still exists, however, and the unresolved problems in this field are large, challenging and interesting. One of the primary purposes of the present symposium was to focus attention on this phase of fluid mechanics and to stimulate increased research activity in its problem areas.

In order to emphasize the underlying physical processes, the subject matter of the symposium was restricted to that of turbulent, incompressible, subsonic flow with no energy or mass transfer. A program format was evolved that systematically covered subsonic turbulent shear flows of both the bound and free type, and in two-dimensional and three-dimensional configurations. Both the depth of our understanding of these flows and our ability to predict their behavior under general circumstances were evaluated. To extend the considerations to an actual internal-flow configuration of practical importance, the performance characteristics of diffusers of various geometric types were considered. These simple fluid-handling devices will probably be the first internal-flow systems of relatively complex fluid-mechanical behavior that will be adequately understood.

To achieve adequate coverage in depth with a minimum of overlap between contributions, all of the papers presented at the symposium were specially commissioned. Research workers of demonstrated achievement who were currently active in the particular subject areas were selected. Their objective was to critically review the subjects, present the latest research results, and provide a basis for discussion by the invited attendees. Session chairmen of outstanding and recognized technical competence were chosen to spark and lead the discussions, for which ample time was allotted. These informal discussions were recorded on tape and subsequently transcribed and edited. All discussions have been approved for accuracy and intent by the persons who presented them, and have been kept in conversational form in order to preserve their liveliness and spontaneity. By virtue of both their depth and extent, they comprise a major contribution to the technical value of the symposium proceedings.

The organization of the symposium and the contacts that it permitted with many fluid-mechanics researchers in this country and abroad have represented a tremendous professional and personal experience for the Chairman. He would like to express his appreciation to the executive staff of both his department and the Laboratories for their expression of confidence in permitting him complete freedom of personal expression with regard to the scope and detailed structure of the technical program. In the overall program planning the Chairman had the invaluable moral support and frequent technical advice of Professor STEPHEN J. KLINE, and for this he is particularly indebted. To his co-worker Mr. EDWARD D. KLOMP he expresses appreciation for his willing assistance and cooperation whenever and wherever it was required.

Those who attended the symposium can attest to the excellent manner in which the myriad details of the physical arrangements were handled. The smooth functioning of the meeting and its very pleasant atmosphere were principally the work of Mr. JAMES G. COOK of the Technical Information Department, and his efforts are gratefully acknowledged.

GINO SOVRAN

Contents

Preface V
Attendance List IX

Session I – Chairman: F. H. CLAUSER, University of California, Santa Cruz.
Aspects of Internal Flow
    J. ACKERET, Eidgenössische Technische Hochschule, Zürich 1
Observed Structure Features in Turbulent and Transitional Boundary Layers
    S. J. KLINE, Stanford University 27
Critical Review of Existing Methods for Calculating the Development of
Turbulent Boundary Layers
    J. C. ROTTA, Aerodynamische Versuchsanstalt, Göttingen 80

Session II – Chairman: H. W. LIEPMANN, California Institute of Technology.
Measurements in a Turbulent Boundary Layer Maintained in a Nearly Separating Condition
    W. G. SPANGENBERG, W. R. ROWLAND AND N. E. MEASE, National Bureau
    of Standards 110
The Applicability of Turbulence Research to the Solution of Internal Flow
Problems
    J. L. LUMLEY, The Pennsylvania State University 152

Session III – Chairman: H. W. EMMONS, Harvard University.
Turbulent Jets and Wakes in a Pressure Gradient
    B. G. NEWMAN, McGill University 170
Critical Review and Current Developments in Three-Dimensional Turbulent
Boundary Layers
    P. N. JOUBERT, A. E. PERRY AND K. C. BROWN, University of Melbourne. 210
The Applicability of Secondary Flow Analyses to the Solution of Internal
Flow Problems
    W. R. HAWTHORNE, Cambridge University 238

Session IV – Chairman: J. ACKERET, Eidgenössische Technische Hochschule,
        Zürich.
Experimentally Determined Optimum Geometries for Rectilinear Diffusers
with Rectangular, Conical or Annular Cross-Section
    G. SOVRAN AND E. D. KLOMP, General Motors Research Laboratories . . 270
Some Problems of Recognizing and Defining Separation of the Skewed
Boundary Layer
    E. S. TAYLOR, Massachusetts Institute of Technology 320

Subject Index. 333

Attendance List

F. H. Abernathy,
Harvard University

J. Ackeret,
Eidgenössische Technische Hochschule,
Zürich, Switzerland

C. A. Amann,
Research Laboratories, GMC

O. L. Anderson,
United Aircraft Research Laboratories

J. P. Appleton,
GM Defense Research Laboratories, GMC

G. E. Ball,
Chrysler Corporation

J. N. Barney,
Allison Division, GMC

A. H. Bell,
Detroit Diesel Engine Division, GMC

A. C. Bemis,
General Motors Institute

T. B. Benjamin,
Cambridge University,
Cambridge, England

T. J. Black,
Illinois Institute of Technology

L. W. Blair,
Detroit Diesel Engine Division, GMC

M. H. Bloom,
Polytechnic Institute of Brooklyn

J. W. Bracken,
Detroit Diesel Engine Division, GMC

R. O. Bullock,
AiResearch

R. H. Carmody,
Allison Division, GMC

J. L. Chiddister,
Styling Staff, GMC

F. H. Clauser,
University of California

A. B. Cocanower,
Research Laboratories, GMC

D. Coles,
California Institute of Technology

J. S. Collman,
Research Laboratories, GMC

T. F. Curran,
Diesel Equipment Division, GMC

D. W. Dawson,
Research Laboratories, GMC

R. C. Dean,
Dartmouth College

R. G. Deissler,
National Aeronautics & Space Administration

J. L. Dussourd,
Ingersoll-Rand Company

E. R. G. Eckert,
University of Minnesota

E. A. Eichelbrenner,
Laval University,
Quebec, Canada

H. W. Emmons,
Harvard University

J. R. Erwin,
General Electric Company

A. Q. Eschenroeder,
GM Defense Research Laboratories, GMC

S. Eskinazi,
Syracuse University

H. S. Fowler,
National Research Council,
Ottawa, Ontario, Canada

J. E. Fowler,
General Electric Company

R. W. Fox,
Purdue University

H. L. Garabedian,
Research Laboratories, GMC

I. S. Gartshore,
McGill University,
Montreal, Quebec, Canada

A. G. Hansen,
University of Michigan

J. I. Harris,
Research Laboratories, GMC

M. J. Hartmann,
National Aeronautics & Space Administration

W. R. Hawthorne,
Cambridge University,
Cambridge, England

M. R. Head,
Cambridge University,
Cambridge, England

P. G. Hill,
Massachusetts Institute of Technology

R. N. Hollyer,
Research Laboratories, GMC

B. A. Hopkins,
Allison Division, GMC

J. H. Horlock,
University of Liverpool,
Liverpool, England

J. P. Johnston,
Stanford University

L. E. Johnson,
Caterpillar Tractor Company

J. B. Jones,
Virginia Polytechnic Institute

P. N. Joubert,
University of Melbourne,
Melbourne, Australia

M. Kamal,
Research Laboratories, GMC

K. B. Kelly,
Styling Staff, GMC

J. C. Kent,
Research Laboratories, GMC

S. J. Kline,
Stanford University

E. D. Klomp,
Research Laboratories, GMC

R. E. Kronauer,
Harvard University

D. C. Kuzma,
Research Laboratories, GMC

J. Laufer,
University of Southern California

S. Lieblein,
National Aeronautics & Space Administration

H. W. Liepmann,
California Institute of Technology

A. L. London,
Stanford University

J. L. Lumley,
Pennsylvania State University

E. O. Macagno,
University of Iowa

J. Malina,
Electro-Motive Division, GMC

H. McDonald,
United Aircraft Corporation

G. L. Mellor,
Princeton University

R. C. Mellin,
Research Laboratories, GMC

M. L. Miller,
Allison Division, GMC

J. R. Mondt,
Research Laboratories, GMC

M. V. Morkovin,
The Martin Company

H. L. Moses,
Massachusetts Institute of Technology

B. G. Newman,
McGill University,
Montreal, Quebec, Canada

C. I. H. Nicholl,
Laval University,
Quebec, Canada

V. Nicolia,
Harrison Radiator Division, GMC

G. E. Nordenson,
Research Laboratories, GMC

R. A. Novak,
Northern Research Engineering

R. Petrof,
Ford Motor Company

F. J. Pierce,
Cornell University

R. Potter,
Harrison Radiator Division, GMC

W. C. Reynolds,
Stanford University

J. M. Robertson,
University of Illinois

M. Rogers,
Air Force Office of Scientific Research

J. C. Rotta,
Aerodynamische Versuchsanstalt,
Göttingen, Germany

C. J. Sagi,
Research Laboratories, GMC

V. A. Sandborn,
Colorado State University

D. M. Sandercock,
National Aeronautics & Space Administration

G. B. Schubauer,
National Bureau of Standards
G. K. Serovy,
Iowa State University
R. A. Serra,
United Aircraft Corporation
G. D. Skellenger,
Research Laboratories, GMC
L. H. Smith, Jr.,
General Electric Company
A. M. O. Smith,
Douglas Aircraft Company
G. Sovran,
Research Laboratories, GMC
W. G. Spangenberg,
National Bureau of Standards
J. C. Steiner,
Research Laboratories, GMC
A. H. Stenning,
Lehigh University
B. S. Stratford,
Rolls Royce Ltd.,
Derby, England

E. S. Taylor,
Massachusetts Institute of Technology
G. W. Thebert,
Detroit Diesel Engine Division, GMC
W. A. Turunen,
Research Laboratories, GMC
E. W. Upton,
Engineering Staff, GMC
P. T. Vickers,
Research Laboratories, GMC
N. Wang,
Research Laboratories, GMC
K. S. Wen,
GM Defense Research Laboratories, GMC
W. W. Willmarth,
University of Michigan
G. F. Wislicenus,
Pennsylvania State University
H. Yeh,
University of Pennsylvania
M. K. Yu,
Research Laboratories, GMC

Aspects of Internal Flow

JAKOB ACKERET

Institut für Aerodynamik, Eidgenössische Technische Hochschule, Zürich, Switzerland

INTRODUCTION

In this short introductory paper I would like to describe some peculiarities of internal, ducted, or channel flow. The difference from external flow is not one of principle, since the fundamental equations and local boundary conditions are the same. But the boundaries in the large are different. Internal flow occurs inside solid walls and does not reach infinity; consequently, there are interactions with these walls. As far as non-viscous flows are concerned, they can be treated by the standard methods of potential-flow analysis and shall not be considered here in great detail. The real problem lies in *frictional effects*. From a practical point of view internal flow is important in many fields of civil, mechanical and aeronautical engineering.

It is worthwhile to enumerate four special features of internal flow.

1. The first special feature is the predominant role of the *equation of continuity*, especially if compressibility is involved. Boundary-layer theory must consequently be modified somewhat since in ducts the presence of a boundary layer with its growing displacement thickness narrows the channel and alters the pressure distribution in the potential part of the field. So we have interaction between the potential and the frictional part of the flow, and in the general case an integral equation has to be solved. In approximately-one-dimensional problems, as for instance in not-too-long straight diffusors, a somewhat simpler approach seems to be possible. In long ducts there can be no clear distinction between boundary-layer and potential flow. Turbulence fills more or less the whole cross-section and there is not much hope for the semi-empirical treatment that works not too badly in simple turbulent boundary-layer problems.

2. In aeronautics one avoids *big deflections* of the air stream as far as possible, but in ducted flow they may be quite common. In such cases large centrifugal forces (and in rotating channels also Coriolis forces) are acting and secondary flow appears, as, for example, in bends or in rotating cascades.

References p. 24

3. Another difference from external flow lies in the behaviour of *zones of separation*. If the width of the duct is not growing too fast along its length, separation will invariably be followed by *reattachment*, since for simple geometric reasons free streamlines or wakes cannot expand indefinitely. The same geometrical conditions also stop the growth of the mixing length.

4. *Three-dimensional boundary layers* can appear as in external flow. But often they occur on rotating parts, for example discs or blades, where the centrifugal forces on the boundary layer may be considerable, since a small relative speed of the inner boundary elements may correspond to a large absolute velocity.

It would be difficult to give in so short a time a complete survey of the growing activity in the field of internal flow. Instead, I will show some typical examples which are taken mostly from experiments done in our laboratory at Zürich. Some of them are quite elementary and were used for educational work with students (mostly under the guidance of Dr. Sprenger). I would be happy if the many gaps or even inconsistencies which naturally remain in such a simplified method should stimulate criticism and discussion.

I. HISTORICAL REMARKS

Internal flow is quite an old subject for study. It developed in close association with practical hydraulics. A highly interesting historical book by Rouse & Ince (1957) contains some surprising details. Around 1500, Leonardo da Vinci made many fluid mechanical experiments and presented some flow sketches which look, to a certain degree, quite modern. Figure 1 shows for instance the division of a fluid stream into two branches, with two separations, eddy formation, reattachment and the gradual disappearance of the big eddies. We can nowadays *qualitatively* explain all of these features, but we are even now unable to calculate them exactly from first principles. Therefore experiments are necessary to obtain per-

Figure 1. Sketch by Leonardo da Vinci (1452–1519) of branched channel flow. Separation and reattachment is visible.

Figure 2. Julius Weisbach, who made a great number of ducted-flow experiments.

formance figures for practical applications. To be sure the experimental facilities have been much improved, rules of similitude are used and the presentation of results is more rational and practical.

In addition to many others, I might mention the very useful experiments of Julius Weisbach (1855) in Germany, figure 2. Weisbach gave his results for a lot of configurations of tubes, orifices, valves and diffusors in the form of dimensionless coefficients. Not too infrequently we find ourselves carefully looking at them for want of more recent investigations.

The theory of *non-viscous flow* on the other hand was well developed long ago by Bernoulli (1738), Euler (1766) and d'Alembert (1744). The one-dimensional case (tube flow) was indeed treated to complete satisfaction. I might mention Euler's theory of rotating tubes of variable section in his famous paper on turbines (1754). He studied the general non-steady problem and took into account the force afterwards named after Coriolis. He invented guide vanes and calculated the region where *cavitation* was to be expected, even warning against its deteriorating effects on efficiency.

The little machine of figure 3 was built exactly after Euler's prescriptions and its performance was measured in our laboratory. The efficiency turned out to be about 70 percent, not much less than that of modern model-turbines of the same small power (0.15 h.p.). Euler shortly afterwards, and perhaps stimulated by his turbine calculations, gave the well-known general hydrodynamic equation for frictionless

References p. 24

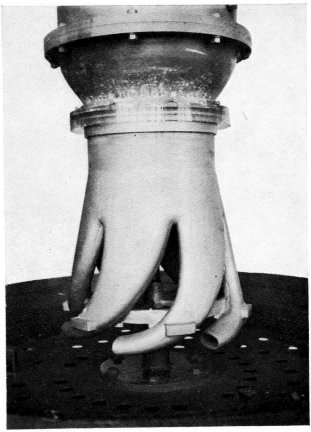

Figure 3. Reconstruction of Euler's turbine proposal. By theoretical reasoning he invented guide
vanes and also developed the famous turbine equations (1754).

flow. Curiously enough, at about the same time he proposed a theory of fluid
friction in pipes which was completely erroneous and quite in contradiction to the
experimental facts even then known by practical hydraulicians. (He assumed that
the pressure loss was proportional to the absolute pressure as with Coulomb
friction, and that even at rest a pressure difference could be maintained.)

It was at this time that the separation of practical hydraulics and "impractical"
hydrodynamics was established and it took more than 100 years to bring them back
together in a more or less unified theory of fluid motion. I need not emphasize that
an end has not yet been reached; our symposium would otherwise perhaps be
superfluous.

II. COMPRESSIBILITY EFFECTS

Turning now to some effects of compressibility which were studied much later, we can state, even in the frictionless case, some special features of internal flow. Hugoniot gave for one-dimensional tube flow the simple differential relation:

$$\frac{du}{u} = -\frac{dA/A}{1-M^2}$$

where A = area of duct
M = local Mach number
u = mean velocity along axis.

It can be seen immediately that in the neighbourhood of $M = 1$, very small changes in area give finite changes in velocity, and also in pressure.

Figure 4 shows for both a plane and a circular duct with wavy walls of small amplitude the calculated distribution across the channels of the perturbation in axial velocity due to the waviness. Linearized theory is applied and the flow is subsonic. Near the walls the deviations from the perturbation values at the center-line naturally are greatest. But when the Mach number of the mean flow approaches unity, the perturbation becomes constant across the section and the old fashioned one-dimensional theory, which assumes constant velocity over the whole section, is more and more justified, especially in the case of rotational symmetry. We could call this an internal-flow analogue of the external-flow area-rule often used in modern airplane construction.

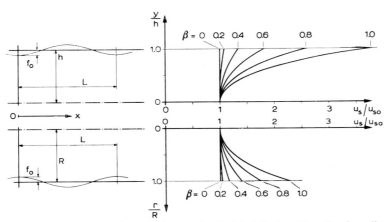

Figure 4. Frictionless gas flow through plane and cylindrical ducts with walls of small waviness. The local disturbances of axial velocity, $u_s = u - \bar{u}$, are normalized with respect to the disturbance on the centerline, u_{so}; $\beta = \sqrt{1 - M^2}$, M = Mach number of the undisturbed flow. When M nears unity, the disturbances are practically constant over the whole cross-section.

References p. 24

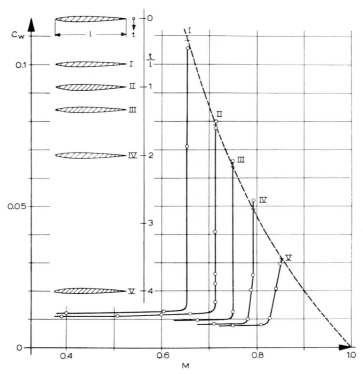

Figure 5. Drag coefficients of symmetrical profiles in unstaggered cascades. $t =$ distance between successive profiles, $l =$ chord. Blocking is shown quite clearly even at rather large distances between blades. $M =$ Mach number of flow in the undisturbed region before the cascade. Broken line: theory.

The area-rule is sometimes obeyed in a rather astonishing way. Figure 5 shows several unstaggered cascades of thin symmetrical airfoils which were tested at a constant Reynolds number of 350,000. At low inlet Mach numbers the drag coefficient decreases with increasing distance between adjacent profiles (0–I, 0–II, etc). This result can be expected. However, at a certain Mach number, depending on the blade spacing, blockage suddenly appears. If we try to apply the simple area theory neglecting viscosity, we get a maximum blockage drag (dotted line) which is in good agreement with the experimental results of Feldmann & Rott. The maximum is reached when the back pressure is lowered to a value where there is supersonic flow on the rear side of the profiles. The surface pressure diminishes monotonically along the profiles and one expects that complete laminarity and a small displacement thickness of the boundary layer are achieved. Therefore the nonviscous elementary approach might after all be expected to be valid. However, in general subsonic cases of internal flow the displacement thickness can naturally not be neglected since its constriction might have a great influence on the pressure distribution.

III. SECONDARY FLOW AND INDUCED LOSSES

The presence of a wall can change the induced drag near the tip of a rectangular wing or blade. Without the wall the secondary flow produced by lift is nearly potential and the lift reduces to zero at the end of the blade. However, when a wall is in close proximity to the tip, figure 6, the small gap (blade clearance) hinders this flow, mostly by separation, as it is forced through the gap. Therefore we have the problem of real, not potential flow through a small slot and there is a finite lift at the end of the blade. The induced drag on the blade is reduced to a value which is quite different from the potential calculations. A rather rough estimate by Betz is nicely confirmed by the measurements of Hürlimann (1963), figure 7. His drag figures contain all effects which grow with the square of the lift and may also include, therefore, some influence of pressure drag which is foreign to the classical formula for induced drag. Schlichting (1961) has found a similar linearity for what he calls tip loss.

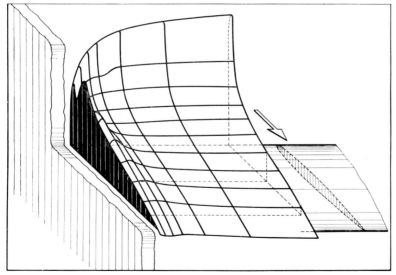

Figure 6. Pressure distribution over a wing with small gap near a wall. Contrary to the free-wing case, there is a finite lift at the end of the blade.

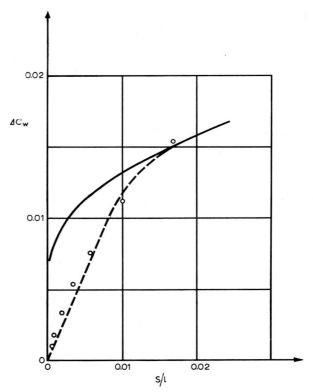

Figure 7. Induced drag on lifting blade with small gap. *Full curve*: minimum induced drag from lifting-line theory; *broken curve*: estimate of Betz; *small circles*: measurements of Hürlimann (1963). C_w = drag coefficient, s = gap width, l = blade chord.

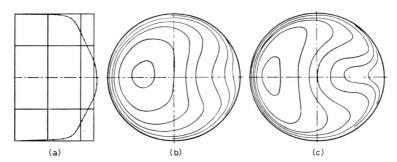

Figure 8. Measured contours of constant axial velocity at the exit of a circular bend resulting from the velocity distribution of a straight inlet pipe (a); bend angle 21 degr. (b); 42 degr. after Detra (1953) (c).

Another secondary flow problem arises in connection with curved tubes, figure 8. If the axial velocity at the beginning of the curve is a function of the radius, stemming for instance from a length of straight tube upstream of the bend, the different particles of the fluid are under different centrifugal force. The high-speed central masses are driven to the concave part of the tube wall and produce a complicated secondary movement. The figure shows the contours of constant axial velocity at the end of the bend for two different bend angles (21 and 42 degrees).

Detra (1953) attempted a theoretical explanation on the simplified assumption that the bending angles are quite small and that a centrifugal force field exists whose intensity depends on the square of the velocity. Viscosity was afterwards neglected. Though such a procedure looks rather rough it gave results which were qualitatively in accordance with observations for small angles. It is interesting to calculate the total exit kinetic energy of this so-to-speak "internal induced" flow and its corresponding loss. Calculations of this sort for elliptic as well as circular tube sections are shown in figure 9. The results which can naturally be meaningful only for small bend angles show clearly that "broad edge" tubes are much better in this respect than "high edge" tubes; the latter have, to speak in terms of induced drag, a bad aspect ratio. Similar effects in curved diffusors will be shown later in this paper. It is quite clear that a much more sophisticated approach should be made, which

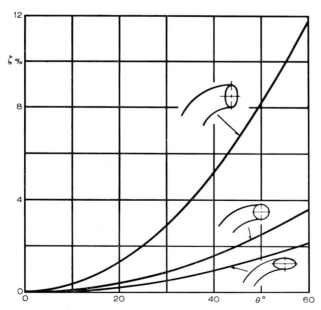

Figure 9. Calculated secondary-flow losses for different angles of bend with circular section and elliptical sections, "broad edge" and "high edge" (Detra 1953).

includes turbulence and exchange of energy between the streamlines; however, I
fear that computational difficulties will be formidable.

As I mentioned before, strong curvature in ducted flow is not rare. The resultant
effects of centrifugal force are important in boundary layers as well as in secondary
flow effects. One knows that the turbulent exchange of momentum or vorticity must
be different on convex and concave surfaces. Preliminary results of some direct
measurements of the total frictional torque on quarter cylinders are shown in
figure 10. These measurements of Fauconnet were made a long time ago but unfortunately had to be stopped prematurely and therefore were never published.
Care was taken to suppress secondary flow (high aspect ratio) and very good surface finish was attained. We can see in comparison to Schlichting's formula
(smooth flat plate) a considerable increase of the total friction coefficient on the

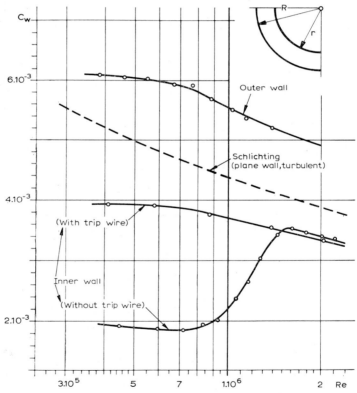

Figure 10. Measured torque on quarter-circle convex and concave cylindrical walls (Fauconnet)
The outer wall shows a larger friction force than the inner one. For the latter, laminarity persists
up to relatively high Reynolds numbers. However, a trip wire can produce early transition to
turbulence. Schlichting's curve for flat-plate friction is inserted for comparison.

concave wall, and a corresponding decrease on the convex wall. On the convex wall we have the interesting feature that laminar flow remains established up to a considerable Reynolds number. The addition of a turbulence-producing wire to the wall gave accordingly stronger friction.

IV. SEPARATION AND REATTACHMENT

Even in the Leonardo sketch, figure 1, one could observe separation and reattachment. Figure 11 shows another example, the well known Borda–Carnot case. In a yet to be published investigation by Sprenger, the diameter of a circular tube is doubled abruptly, a jet is formed and mixing follows. After some distance, one sees the formation of a flow with nearly constant velocity. The apparent fluctuations of dynamic pressure that are indicated were made visible by slowly drawing a pitot tube across the flow. Though not too much can be drawn from such registrations they show in a simple and quick way where turbulence does appear and give hints of its intensity. Perhaps I might mention from personal remembrance that Prandtl

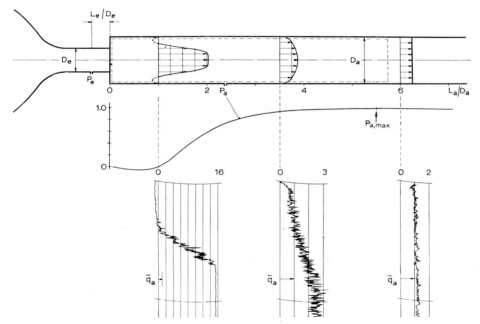

Figure 11. Borda–Carnot pressure rise from sudden doubling of the diameter of a circular tube. *Top*: velocity-distributions (mean values); *middle*: pressure distribution on tube wall; *bottom*: response of a pitot tube when moved slowly across the diameter.

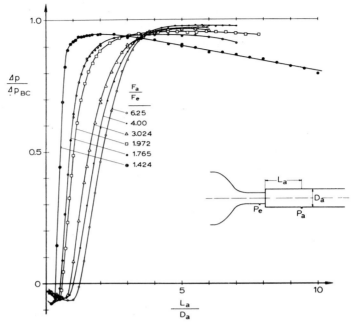

Figure 12. Borda–Carnot pressure rise along the wall of the larger tube for different area ratios.

Figure 13. Voith turbo-fan, electrically driven, for ventilation of automobile tunnels.

used such rather incomplete data at the time he developed his famous mixing-length theory of turbulence.

Figure 12 shows the pressure rise along the walls of the downstream duct for increasing ratios of area enlargement. The data is normalized with respect to the Borda–Carnot pressure rise. In nearly every case, up to 95 to 97 percent of the Borda–Carnot value is attained. The maximum of pressure lies downstream, very near to the section of approximately uniform velocity. It would be interesting to make an exact measurement of turbulence at this location; according to the rough determination of figure 11 one should expect something like isotropy. Downstream of the maximum pressure point wall friction acts strongly and produces a pressure drop. Similar measurements have shown that the effects of misaligning the center lines of

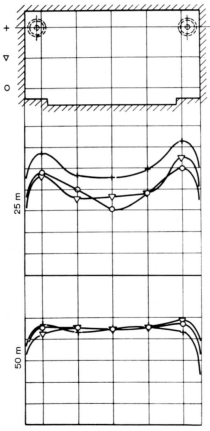

Figure 14. Velocity distribution in automobile tunnel similar to that of figure 13 at different heights and distances (25 and 50 m from nozzle plane).

References p. 24

the two tubes are quickly washed out, the velocity distribution at downstream stages being remarkably constant. I think that this sudden-expansion flow process deserves more experimental work, as it seems to be typical for internal mixing.

In figure 13 is shown another interesting example of internal mixing. In several one-way automobile tunnels the German firm of Voith has successfully installed electrically driven jet mechanisms for ventilation purposes. They naturally have to be placed in corners to avoid obstruction of the tunnel area, and sometimes they are even mounted partially in niches. The interesting fact (figure 14) is that in some distance downstream, for instance 50 meters, the whole tunnel cross-section has a nearly uniform velocity distribution even though the mean velocity of the tunnel stream is 7 to 8 times smaller than the jet velocity at the nozzle. For tunnels up to perhaps 800 yards in length, this system seems to be a cheap and effective solution to the ventilation problem. The jets are built with contra-rotating axial fans and are symmetric in the direction of the axis, so that jet flow can be reversed in case of a change of traffic direction in the tunnel.

V. ELBOWS

Flow in an elbow of rectangular section is shown in figure 15. The pressure loss occurs in the following way: Up to the inner corner the flow is regular. Then separation occurs with a kind of free stream-surface with contraction. A calculation can be made in this plane case. The contraction is found by simple application of the inviscid conformal theory. Now if we make a Borda–Carnot estimation of the pressure rise downstream of the minimum cross-section (using figure 12), we get a recovery which differs only by a few percent from that actually observed.

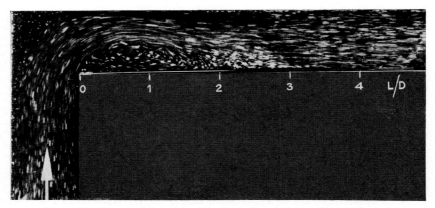

Figure 15. Flow in 90° rectangular elbow. Separation and reattachment.

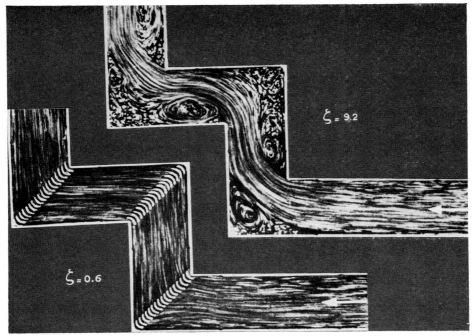

Figure 16. Flow through double elbows without and with corner vanes. Upper figure: formation of a flow-band; $\zeta = 9.2$, *not* $3 \times 1.3 = 3.9$. Lower figure: $\zeta = 0.6$, *not* $3 \times 0.23 = 0.7$.

The problem gets more complicated if we have multiple corners as shown in figure 16. This data of Sprenger is also not yet published. Two features of the flow in the channel without turning vanes should be specially mentioned:

1. As separation occurs in the concave corners, there is a *band* of rather regular flow twisting through the channel;
2. The pressure drops of the individual corners making up the configuration are not additive (i.e., the measured overall loss of 9.2 is greater than 3×1.3).

The channel with cascades of turning vanes in the corners, such as are used in wind tunnels and gas-turbine ducts, is naturally much better; here the sum of the individual losses is nearer to the observed total loss and, interestingly, the overall loss is now less than the summation of individual losses.

Sprenger has made measurements on a large number of other elbow configurations, figure 17. Here the Reynolds-number effect is sometimes quite large, especially in cases where the inner corner is not sharp but has a small radius. At higher Reynolds numbers there is a peculiar decrease in loss, followed by a strong rise. One should take a closer look at the reasons for the seemingly erratic behaviour of some arrangements.

References p. 24

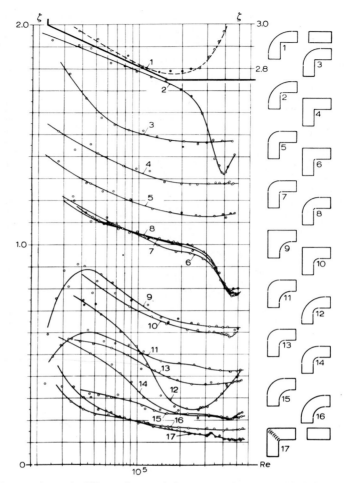

Figure 17. Pressure losses in different forms of elbow. Note the remarkable influence of the inner radius (Sprenger, to be published).

The phenomenon of band flow can also be seen in other configurations. Figure 18 shows (a similar case can be seen in an old Göttingen film) how a band of flow can be formed inside a wide circular volume. The fluid enters the cavity at the right and leaves at the bottom, the small chambers extending from the top and left side being closed-ended. It would be interesting to also study this type of flow at higher Reynolds numbers and to explain in simple terms why this band or jet is stable.

A similar effect can be observed in the so-called cross-flow fans, figure 19, which after a long interruption were developed from the old Mortier fan used in French

Figure 18. Band formation within a circular box.

mines (Coester 1959). Air twice passes radially through a wheel of cylindrical blades. In the inner volume of the wheel some guiding surfaces were formerly used. Now one does better without them. The picture again shows the band of flow. The problem is of some importance as fans of this type have found many applications; for instance, they can be considered for combined boundary layer suction and blowing on wings of airplanes.

VI. DIFFUSORS

Diffusors are important elements in turbomachinery. For a long time it has been known that the angle of divergence should be relatively small (8 to 12° total). Otherwise the efficiency of pressure recuperation is bad and the flow rather pulsating since separation occurs.

A simple application of boundary-layer theory can work reliably only if continuity of the whole flow is taken into account, and the thickness of the layer is not

References p. 24

Figure 19. Band formation through the wheel of a cross-flow fan (Dätwyler).

so large that the potential-flow core disappears (Ackeret 1958). I will first outline a very simple case—the plane diffusor with straight walls and relatively small boundary layer thickness (figure 20).

We introduce the usual symbols:

U = velocity in the core (potential flow)
θ = momentum thickness
δ^* = displacement thickness
$H = \delta^*/\theta$ parameter
τ_0 = shear stress at the walls
$h(x)$ = geometrical width of the diffusor.

Now, continuity demands:

$$U(h - 2\delta^*) = \text{const.} = Q \tag{1}$$

For the boundary layer we use the general momentum integral equation:

$$\frac{\mathrm{d}\theta}{\mathrm{d}x} + \frac{\theta}{U}\frac{\mathrm{d}U}{\mathrm{d}x}(H + 2) = \frac{\tau_0}{\rho U^2}$$

and inserting continuity we get:

$$\frac{d\theta}{dx} = \frac{\frac{\tau_0}{\rho Q^2}(h-2H\theta)^3 + \theta(H+2)\left(\frac{dh}{dx} - 2\theta\frac{dH}{dx}\right)}{h+2H\theta(H+1)} \tag{2}$$

where the velocity U does not enter explicitly.

Now there are a number of different methods for calculating turbulent boundary layers in adverse pressure gradients. I have used the old Gruschwitz method which employs a form parameter

$$\eta = 1 - \frac{u_\theta^2}{U^2}$$

which is related in an empirical way with H; for instance, after Pretsch

$$\eta = 1 - \left(\frac{H-1}{H(H+1)}\right)^{H-1}$$

which follows from the integration of a separate differential equation:

$$\theta\frac{d(U^2\eta)}{dx} + A(U^2\eta) = BU^2 \tag{3}$$

where A and B are empirical constants.

For $\tau_0/\rho U^2$ we use the Blasius law:

$$\frac{\tau_0}{\rho U^2} = \frac{\zeta}{\left[\frac{U\theta}{\nu}\right]^{\frac{1}{4}}}$$

Equations (2) and (3) can be solved simultaneously step by step.

The case of rotational symmetry was treated later by Schlichting & Gersten (1961) who used the boundary layer method of Truckenbrodt and who generalized the calculations for relatively thick boundary layers, obtaining some interesting results.

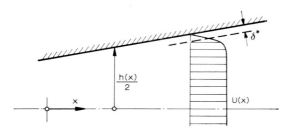

Figure 20. Boundary layer in a plane, straight diffusor.

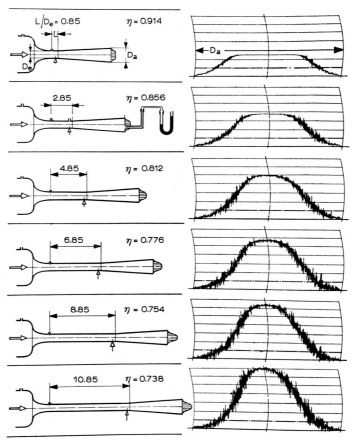

Figure 21. "Plateau" formation at the exit of a straight conical diffusor for different entrance
conditions produced by entrance ducts of various length. Turbulence is also visible in a qualitative
way. Area ratio = 4.0 and total divergence angle = 8°.

A first important fact is the large influence of the entry conditions, as expressed
for example by the thickness

$$\delta_1^* \quad \text{or} \quad \theta_1$$

The pressure-rise efficiency η_d which can be defined by:

$$\eta_d = \frac{Q(p_2 - p_1)}{\dfrac{\rho}{2}\displaystyle\int_{(1)} u^3\,\mathrm{d}y - \dfrac{\rho}{2}Q\bar{u}_2^2}$$

or alternatively:

$$\eta_d = \frac{p_2 - p_1}{\frac{\rho}{2}(\bar{u}_1^2 - \bar{u}_2^2)}$$

goes down rapidly with increasing θ_1.

In figure 21 we see the change in the velocity distribution at the exit of a circular diffusor for different lengths of the entrance tube. For small lengths there is a "plateau" or core of uniform velocity at the exit; for longer lengths the boundary layer reaches nearly to the center of the exit plane (Sprenger 1959).

Calculations were made for a circular diffusor with a total divergence angle of 8°, figure 22. The measured efficiencies show some scatter but are, in the whole, in agreement with calculations.

The influence of long entrance tubes was known even at the time of the Romans. There is an amusing story mentioned in the book of Sextus Julius Frontinus (100 A.D.), translated by the eminent and enthusiastic American hydraulician Clemens Herschel (1899). The inhabitants of Rome got their water from reservoirs and the amount delivered to each home was metered by a gauged orifice. Some people took advantage of the arrangement by setting some sort of diffusor near the opening,

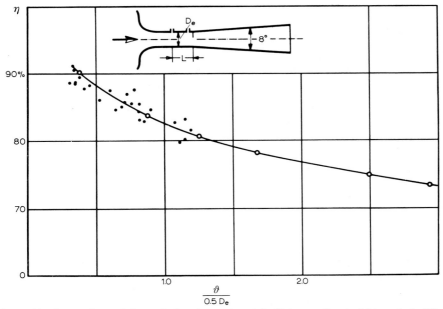

Figure 22. Comparison of theoretical and experimental efficiency of a straight conical diffusor with varied momentum thickness at entrance. Area ratio = 4.0 and total divergence angle = 8°.

References p. 24

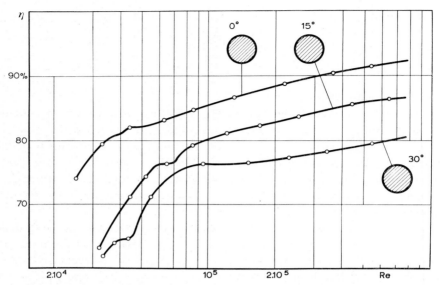

Figure 23. Pressure-rise efficiency of straight and bent conical diffusors. The parameter is the bend angle of the diffusor. Area ratio = 4.0 and total divergence angle = 8°.

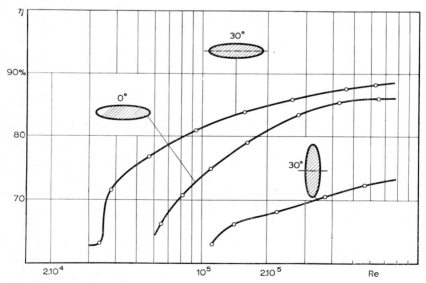

Figure 24. Pressure-rise efficiency for diffusors of circular entrance and elliptical outlet sections. 0° = straight, and 30° bent with "broad edge" (good) and "high edge" (bad) position of the major axis. Area ratio = 4.0 and equivalent total divergence angle = 8°.

thereby increasing the flow rate of their system. The authorities were forced to stop this fraudulence by ordering that enlargements of the tube section could be made only after at least 50 feet of horizontal length of constant-diameter pipe.

Bent diffusors are often used in hydraulic machinery. In such configurations secondary flow appears and Reynolds number has a marked influence. The detrimental effect of curvature on diffusor performance is shown in figure 23 for units with circular cross-sections. Quite serious losses can also occur if the diffusor cross-section gradually changes from circular to elliptic between inlet and outlet. This can be seen by comparing the zero-curvature performance curves of figures 23 and 24. Figure 24 also shows the performance of the changing-cross-section diffusor when it is bent. It is interesting to note the improvement that can be obtained by laying the major axis of the ellipse normal to the plane of the diffusor axis, and the bad influence of the "high" position. The latter situation prevails in most radial fans or pumps and deserves an extended study. I can only mention here the different experiments with *vortex generators* made by Sprenger (1959) which gave astonishing improvements in the "high" case. These are described fully in his dissertation.

Boundary layer suction has also been tried in diffusors. I might perhaps mention an old experiment done at Göttingen, where suction was applied to a diffusor of large divergence angle, figure 25. One can see the complete separation that occurs

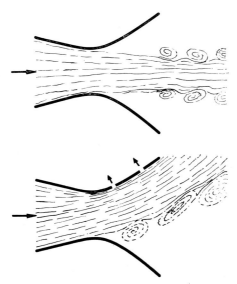

Figure 25. Plane diffusor with large divergence angle; *top*, without suction (complete separation); *bottom*, with two suction slots in operation (one-sided attachment). This shows the possibilities of flow control by suction.

without suction, and the bistable flow that exists when suction is applied to one side. You are probably all aware of the work that is presently going on for developing very small diffusors with bistability for amplyfying purposes and logical elements; this shows anew that even bad things (I mean separation) can be turned round to the good, if fancy is combined with ingenuity.

REFERENCES

As it is practically impossible to give a complete list of references, only those books and papers which are directly concerned with the content of this paper are listed.

Ackeret, J. (1958) *Grenzschichten in geraden und gekrümmten Diffusoren*. Grenzschichtforschung (Boundary Layer Research), IUTAM Symposium 1957. Springer-Verlag, Berlin, pp. 22–40.

Ackeret, J. & Rott, N. (1949) *Über die Strömung von Gasen durch ungestaffelte Profilgitter*. Schweiz. Bauzeitung (SBZ), 67. Jahrgang, pp. 40–1 and 58–61. Zürich.

d'Alembert, J. R. (1744) *Traité de l'équilibre et du Mouvement des fluides*. Paris.

Bernoulli, D. (1738) *Hydrodynamica*. Argentorati.

Coester, R. (1959) *Theoretische und experimentelle Untersuchungen an Querstrom-Gebläsen*. Mitt. Inst. Aerodynamik, E.T.H. Zürich, No. 28.

Detra, R. W. (1953) *The Secondary Flow in Curved Pipes*. Mitt. Inst. Aerodynamik, E.T.H. Zürich, No. 20.

Euler, L. (1754) *Opera omnia*, II–15. Introduction by J. Ackeret. Zürich 1957.

Euler, L. (1766–1788) *Opera omnia*, II–13. Edited by C. Truesdell with a very valuable introduction. Zürich 1956.

Herschel, C. (1899) *The two books on water supply of the City of Rome of Sextus Julius Frontinus*. Boston 1899, p. 205.

Hürlimann, R. (1963) *Untersuchungen über Strömungsvorgänge an Schaufelenden in der Nähe von Wänden*. Mitt. Inst. Aerodynamik, E.T.H. Zürich, No. 31.

Rouse, H. & Ince, S. (1957) *History of Hydraulics*. Iowa Institute of Hydraulics Research, State University of Iowa.

Schlichting, H. (1961) *Three-dimensional Boundary Layer Flow*. Association international de recherches hydrauliques 9me Assemblée générale Dubrovnik, Yougoslavie, pp. 1262–90.

Schlichting, H. & Gersten, K. (1961) *Berechnung der Strömung in rotationssymmetrischen Diffusoren mit Hilfe der Grenzschicht-Theorie*. Zeitschrift für Flugwissenschaften (ZfW), Heft 4/5, pp. 135–40. Verlag Vieweg, Braunschweig, Germany.

Sprenger, H. (1959) *Experimentelle Untersuchungen an geraden und gekrümmten Diffusoren*. Mitt. Inst. Aerodynamik, E.T.H. Zürich, No. 27.

Weisbach J. (1855) *Die experimentelle Hydraulik*. Freiberg 1855.

Discussion

F. H. CLAUSER (*University of California, Santa Cruz, California*)

Prof. Ackeret, we are grateful to you for presenting a fascinating panorama of the phenomena that occur in real internal flows. The theory of potential flows has great beauty and I think many of us are impressed with the usefulness of the analogy between perfect fluids and electric and magnetic fields. And yet there is a wealth of variety and sophistication in real flows for which there is no counterpart in electric or magnetic fields. Electric fields do not become turbulent or experience shock waves or form wakes and jets. As you have shown, these and many other phenomena are not uncommon in real flows. And when real flows take place internally in the presence of walls, the contrast with potential flows becomes even greater. We have you to thank for reminding us that our analyses should maintain a watch upon nature lest theory lead us into unreality.

M. V. MORKOVIN (*The Martin Company, Baltimore, Maryland*)

I would like to ask Prof. Ackeret if he could crystallize the central message of his talk for us, especially the directions in which he thinks some of these internal flow problems that he gave such a kaleidoscopic picture of should lead us. With all your experience, where should we look, in what direction should we be going, what is important?

J. ACKERET

It is important to *observe*. For instance if you are studying turbulence you need to have more *observations*. It is important to know more about the phenomenon, and this increased knowledge can only be achieved by means of observations and measurements with instruments such as hot wires. In physics, for example, the theorists and the experimentalists work absolutely in parallel. I think that this is the most important thing even for turbulence research. We have a few theories but they are not at all certain. We need to know the phenomenon better.

Without observing we can't imagine what actually happens in some fluid flows. But if you have observations and then try to explain the observations—what happens, what forces are working?—then you can find the theory. I remember Prandtl; he always carried his famous sheets of paper with him. On these he would postulate what *might* be happening in a particular fluid flow situation, but only *after* observations had been made. Consider the curious experiment of G. I. Taylor in rotating fluids. You could never predict what happens. The behavior is not complicated, but one could never conceive it. When a submerged cylinder is drawn through a rotating volume of water, there is a cylinder of water over the submerged cylinder which moves exactly as the cylinder itself; this liquid volume has a movement of flow around it that is the same as that around a solid cylinder. G. I. Taylor is the man who does things with the simplest experimental configurations. It's really wonderful. His laboratory and staff are quite small, the rigs are simple, but he *thinks* about his problems. A marvelous example was his ability to calculate the strength of an atomic bomb by only using photographs of the explosion and nothing else!

M. V. MORKOVIN

It's still special case by special case?

J. ACKERET

Yes, naturally. Most configurations are so complicated once you have computation in mind. Even if you have a simple configuration it is complicated. Take the Borda–Carnot flow for example; it is a simple thing and you can calculate the efficiency and the pressure rise. But in general, I think it is necessary to have measurements because things happen which you can't imagine. Theories applicable for many cases? it's impossible. Only the very simplest cases can be handled. I think the physicists now have the same difficulty.

M. V. MORKOVIN

If, among other things, this is to be a plea for visualization techniques, suppose one has the basic topography of a given special flow; is there then an extra step that has hope? For instance, is the use of modified concepts of eddy viscosity and so forth a reasonable approach?

J. ACKERET

I think so. For example, the equations I showed for calculating the flow in diffusers also transmit the wonderful and deep influence of diffuser entrance conditions on performance; they force out characteristics that might exist. In general, I think that observation plus subsequent thinking about a particular real flow will permit you to later calculate many additional effects of that flow.

S. J. KLINE (*Stanford University, Stanford, California*)

I certainly agree with your remarks, and I am going to show some pictures of turbulence in my own presentation. I would, however, like to make one comment on Dr. Morkovin's remarks. The calculations that we have done at Stanford indicate that unstalled diffuser performance can be predicted exceptionally well using the equations that Prof. Ackeret has written on the board which account for the continuity linking in internal flows. However, this isn't the case for stalled flows, even in what we call the transitory stall regime. We don't know how to compute such flows adequately. If you want a place where there is almost no data of any utility, it's in internal flow situations with a large separated eddy. The flow apparently is stable and you can reproduce the profiles, but we don't really know what the controlling parameters are, much less the basic flow situation. Here is a case aside from the basic turbulence problem where we really need more data. In answer to Dr. Morkovin's question, my own feeling is that we need more measurements of these flow fields. A few people are doing this but not very many.

F. H. CLAUSER

Prof. Ackeret, I am sure that I speak for the entire audience in thanking you for presenting a most fascinating address, and I am very grateful to you.

Observed Structure Features in Turbulent and Transitional Boundary Layers

S. J. KLINE

Stanford University, Stanford, California

SUMMARY

A survey is presented of a number of boundary layer phenomena which have been observed but not fully explored or correlated. It is found that all these phenomena relate to turbulence or to some type of transition region. The survey suggests that some degree of additional understanding of turbulent boundary layers can be achieved by focusing attention on turbulence production processes. It also suggests that in regions of high production these processes are associated with zones of intense mean shear, usually not immediately at a solid boundary. A threshold value of mean strain and fluctuations appears to be necessary to maintain the production processes. Possible relations of the production processes with certain types of instability are discussed. It is concluded that the results are incomplete, but the concepts are consistent with known data and useful in suggesting avenues for further research.

I. INTRODUCTION

This paper discusses a number of boundary layer phenomena about which our knowledge is "rudimentary". The term rudimentary is used to indicate observed phenomena about which we cannot yet make accurate mathematical analyses or predictions. In this way, a display is provided of some things we must learn more about before we can reach satisfactory design capability in internal flow.

In problems where knowledge remains rudimentary, it is to be expected that experiments will lead the way. Moreover, experiments at this stage are often qualitative in nature and intended only to gain a preliminary, general understanding. Very frequently in fluid mechanics such a preliminary understanding is useful to designers, and it is often also necessary before more definitive investigations, either analytic or experimental, can be envisaged.

References p. 66–68

All the phenomena considered here occur in boundary layers at high Reynolds numbers, and with at most small local separations. Despite this, such a variety of phenomena exist that it is not possible to be exhaustive. An attempt is made to describe the salient features, to indicate the general state of knowledge, and to provide more detailed references.

The term transitional is used in this discussion not only to indicate boundary layers that are changing from a laminar to a turbulent condition, but also layers that are changing from turbulent to laminar or layers that are adjusting to abrupt changes in the external flow conditions.

To organize the phenomena and indicate when each may occur, it is convenient to visualize a hypothetical flow situation in which nearly all the phenomena could occur on a single wall. A sketch of this situation is shown in figure 1. Since many of the phenomena are transient and/or three-dimensional in nature, they are better displayed by motion pictures than by the still photos shown herein. Reference to available motion pictures is therefore given whenever possible. It must also be remembered that the available photographs were taken in various apparati for various purposes with the then-available techniques for visualization, and some have been enlarged from small motion picture frames. They are not in reality part of a single flow; considerable variation in photo quality and resolution of detail consequently occurs.

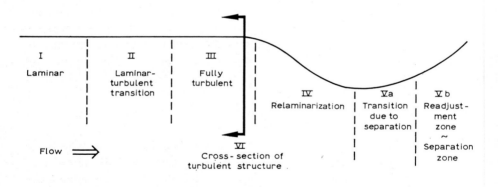

Figure 1. Hypothetical flow constructed to illustrate many observed structure features.

Seven kinds of phenomena are discussed. The first six follow in order down the wall of the hypothetical flow situation, as shown on figure 1. The seventh shows the flow structure on a cross section through the flow in the third region (fully turbulent flow); it illustrates the relation between the structures observed and the well-known regions of the mean-velocity profile.

In a final section a discussion of some of the implications of the phenomena is given. Although clearly still incomplete, the viewpoint presented does seem to give a more organized view of certain phenomena than has previously been available.

II. LAMINAR-TURBULENT TRANSITION IN ZERO PRESSURE GRADIENT WITHOUT LOCAL TRIPS

Laminar-turbulent transition has been studied experimentally and theoretically for a longer period of time and probably by more investigators than any other phenomenon to be described. Despite this, it is only in the past two decades that the general features of the sequence of events leading to natural* transition have been determined for the flat plate with zero pressure gradient. Even in this case, many details are still not fully known.

The typical natural transition seems to involve six stages. The first and last are, respectively, wholly laminar and fully turbulent flow; hence, four recognizable stages occur in between. Moving downstream with the flow these four stages are: (i) *two-dimensional unstable waves* arising from a viscous instability in the laminar layer (these are often called Tollmien–Schlichting waves); (ii) the formation of *peaks and valleys*; that is, longitudinal streaks in the mean-velocity profiles; (iii) the *breakdown* of one or more low-speed streaks leading to the formation of "spots" of turbulence; (iv) the *growth of spots* by cross-contamination to cover the entire cross-section, leading to a fully turbulent flow. The transition process, if occurring by itself without trips or stimulators, does not usually occur abruptly; typically it involves a total distance in the flow direction roughly equal to the extent of the preceding laminar zone. Brief general descriptions of each zone are now given. Motion Pictures showing most of these phenomena are available (Emmons 1952; Meyer & Kline 1961b; NCFMF 1965a).

The Tollmien–Schlichting instability arises from the viscous instability in the laminar layer. It is a two-dimensional wave motion that selectively amplifies disturbances over a band of unstable frequencies. Even though the theory describes amplification in time and the observed growth is in space, truly remarkable agreement exists between the classic measurements of Schubauer & Skramstad (1948) and the improved calculations of the unstable range of frequencies from linear

---

* The term "natural" is here used synonymously with "absence of local trips". A natural transition is one in which a disturbance emanating from upstream is amplified and causes transition; whether the disturbance is inherent "noise" in the flow system or is purposely introduced is not considered. A forced transition, on the other hand, occurs when a disturbance is so large that the flow becomes turbulent at or very near the disturbance causing transition rather than farther downstream.

References p. 66–68

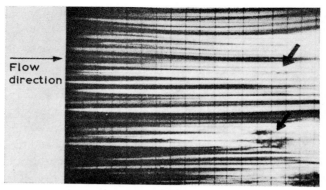

Figure 2. Photo of "peak-valley" region; visualization by dye injected at wall. Arrows point to start of a "breakdown" process.

theory due primarily to C. C. Lin (1945, 1955). Photos of the two-dimensional Tollmien–Schlichting instability are not shown*.

In exceptionally careful and thorough experiments, Klebanoff & Tidstrom (1959) have traced the growth of unstable waves into the non-linear region. They report that when the velocity perturbation due to the wave exceeds approximately 10 percent of mean speed, non-linear effects become important; the mean flow becomes three-dimensional. A series of "peaks and valleys" form consisting of variations in mean-speed transverse to the flow. These longitudinal peaks and valleys are clearly visible in the motion pictures of Meyer & Kline (1961b); see figure 2. Both the hot-wire data of Klebanoff & Tidstrom, and the pictures of Meyer & Kline indicate that the observed peak-and-valley structure involves a secondary vorticity in the streamwise direction of small magnitude but large cumulative effect. The pattern is sketched in figure 3. The level of fluctuations in the regions of low mean-speed is always found to be higher than in the neighboring zones of high mean-speed. (It is for this reason that Klebanoff refers to the zones of low mean-speed as peaks and those of high mean-speed as valleys.) The increasing fluctuations in the regions of low mean-speed subsequently participate in the very sudden "breakdown" process which is the third stage of transition.

* Photos purporting to show Tollmien–Schlichting waves are available, but a controversy exists concerning their validity. In the only well-verified experiment, Klebanoff & Tidstrom (see below) found that the two-dimensional waves persist only in the linear range, up to about 10 percent wave amplitude. Since dye and smoke-marking methods do not show 10 percent fluctuations but follow the mean flow, there is serious doubt that the waves observed by some experimenters with smoke are in fact Tollmien–Schlichting waves. It is possible that larger wave amplitudes are reached in the presence of favorable pressure gradients or with initial conditions that are more exactly two-dimensional, but the question remains open. For this reason photos are omitted. In any event, the existence of the unstable waves is very well verified by hot-wire data.

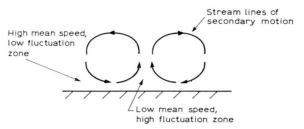

Figure 3. Sketch of "peak-valley" structure in third stage of laminar-turbulent transition. End view. Flow is out of paper. Not to scale.

The breakdown process has been studied in considerable detail by several observers, including Klebanoff and co-workers (1959), Hama *et al.* (1961), Kovasznay *et al.* (1962). Motion pictures are also available; Meyer & Kline (1961b), NCFMF (1965a). In the breakdown process, a layer of intensified mean-strain rate forms away from the wall in the low-mean-speed or peak region. The level of fluctuations in this region increases until a burst or breakdown occurs; the time scales of breakdown are small compared to the previous processes of transition. At and subsequent to breakdown a new flow structure is observed in both the hot-wire and the dye pictures; this structure consists of a "spot" of turbulence. Hence breakdown and "turbulent spot formation" are essentially the same stage in the transition process. Controversy still exists regarding the exact details and causation of breakdown and initial spot formation; an excellent summary of the various viewpoints and questions is given in the recent discussion of Stuart (1965a); see also Stuart (1965b).

Essentially, a "spot" is an isolated patch of turbulent flow in an otherwise laminar flow field; see figure 4a. It is now well established that the flow within a spot has the same essential character as the flow in a fully turbulent region, and that the process of spot formation is common to transition in at least several kinds

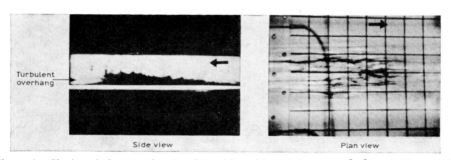

Figure 4a. Single turbulent spot in natural transition, side and plan views. $\partial p/\partial x = 0$, $U_\infty = 0.75$ ft/sec. Arrows show flow direction.

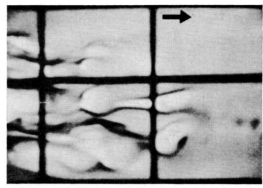

Figure 4b. Close-up photo, front end of turbulent spot on a flat plate. $\partial p/\partial x = 0$, $U_\infty = 0.75$ ft/sec. Arrow shows flow direction.

of geometries. The existence of these isolated "spots" or patches of turbulent flow was first reported by Emmons (1952) and further studied by Emmons & Bryson (1951) and Emmons & Mitchner (1952). Motion pictures of the phenomenon are available (Emmons 1952; Meyer & Kline 1961b; NCFMF 1965a). Particularly good still photos can be found in the article by Elder (1960). Excellent and very detailed studies of the shape of spots and their flow characteristics have been carried out by Klebanoff, Schubauer and co-workers (1956). These studies verify that the flow within a given spot is essentially turbulent in nature, and that an individual spot propagates through the surrounding flow field while maintaining its turbulent character. They also show that the size of the spot increases, as it moves downstream, by the production of new areas of turbulent flow along the edge of the spot; this process is usually called cross-contamination. Spot growth or cross-contamination is the next stage of transition. The motion pictures of this process (Meyer & Kline 1961b; NCFMF 1965a), the still photos (Elder 1960) and the hot-wire studies (Klebanoff, Schubauer and co-workers 1956, 1959) all show that the cross-contamination process is "local" in nature; it exists only at the front and edge of a spot; see figure 4b. Close-up motion pictures of the edge of the spot (Meyer & Kline 1961b) show that an intense wave-like action occurs which apparently creates new turbulent motion causing the spread of the spot at a reproducible angle*. But this process affects adjacent fluid only; action at a distance to create

---

* Both the angle of cross-contamination in plate flow and the spot shape were initially subject to some question due to differences in the measurements of Emmons and co-workers and those of Klebanoff and co-workers (*op. cit.*); these differences were found to be due only to the use of shallow water by Emmons and co-workers which truncates the normal spot shape and causes excessive rate of spread due to increased interference with the surrounding flow. Careful measurements are available only for the plate with zero pressure gradient.

new turbulence does not seem to be observed in the spot growth process. Detailed quantitative study of the cross-contamination process at the edge of a spot seems to be lacking.

The distribution of *spots* in time and space is Gaussian in a natural transition. This fact can be used to construct predictive methods for friction and heat transfer coefficients. One assumes the flow is turbulent in the spots and laminar everywhere else. If the extent of the transition region is known, this assumption leads to quite accurate predictions of heat transfer (Reynolds *et al.* 1958) and of friction coefficients (Dhawan & Narashima 1957–8).

A characteristic streaky structure is visible in the dye studies of "spots" very near the wall (Meyer & Kline 1961b; Elder 1960; NCFMF 1965a); see figure 4a. This streaky structure has some features in common with the "peak and valley" structure reported by Klebanoff & Tidstrom (see above), but some differences also exist. The similarities are: (i) alternate regions of high and low mean-speed transverse to the flow; (ii) the "breakup" of the regions of low mean-speed with measurable mean frequency but random time distribution in a process that is very rapid compared to the other time scales of the flow field. The differences include: (i) an order-of-magnitude-larger transverse wave number for the spacing of the low- and high-speed regions in the spots; (ii) a much more unsteady flow in the streaks beneath the spots.

The transition process is completed by either or both the transverse growth of spots by cross-contamination and the "birth" of new spots at additional transverse locations. When the entire transverse direction at some section is covered by a turbulent flow structure the boundary layer is said to be fully turbulent. The tests suggest that the "new" spots observed are due to other disturbances in the flow and not to the presence of previous spots. One can, for example, generate spots at will by introducing new disturbances of appropriate size either locally or upstream. Increasing the Reynolds number and/or the magnitude of fluctuations in the upstream flow increases the frequency of spot formation and the fraction of flow covered by spots in the transverse direction at a given location (Emmons 1951; Meyer & Kline 1961b). Quantitative correlations for the effects of disturbances of various sizes and their effects on the number of spots formed are not well-established.

III. WALL LAYERS OF THE FULLY TURBULENT FLOW

The third major region in the hypothetical flow of figure 1 is the inner portions, very near a smooth wall, of a fully turbulent layer with zero pressure gradient.

The obvious dominant feature seen in visual studies of the inner layers is the longitudinal streaks. The streaks are seen in both dye and bubble pictures, as shown

References p. 66–68

in figures 5, 11f, and 11g. A comparison of the inner layers of a laminar boundary layer viewed with comparable flow conditions and visual technique is given in figure 5. The photo of figure 5 was obtained by Meyer & Kline (1961a); it shows a flow which if untripped would be laminar everywhere, but which contains a trip in the form of a single $\frac{1}{4}''$ circular cylinder normal to the plate at one transverse location. The cylinder causes a "wedge" of turbulent flow in its downstream wake; the remainder of the flow is laminar. The contrast between the truly "glassy" appearance of the laminar region and the "streaky" structure of the turbulent wedge is evident. The same effect can be obtained in other ways; the trip is merely a convenient way of fixing location for purposes of photography.

As seen in figure 11g, the streaks of the inner layers tend to have a certain preferred spacing although the pattern is not entirely regular. It must be emphasized also that the streaky pattern is *not* stationary in space; more details on this are given in section VI and in the motion pictures by Runstadler *et al.* (1963b; excerpts available in NCFMF 1965b). The structure is thus both three-dimensional and time-dependent in its major features.

When viewed from the side, the dye or bubble streaks are seen to "breakup" suddenly from time to time. The streaks first move slowly downstream very near the wall; after some distance, an oscillation of the streak is visible in plan view; this is followed quickly by a "breakup" in which the streak, or a portion of it, moves rapidly away from the wall. The streaks are most obvious in the innermost layer, $0 \leqq y^+ \leqq 7$; the side views show most breakups occurring in the buffer layer, $7 \leqq y^+ \leqq 40$. The rapid outward movements following a breakup carry marked particles into the outer portions of the boundary layer, $y^+ \geqq 40$. Side views of such trajectories from dye studies (Rundstadler *et al.* 1963a) are shown in figure 6.

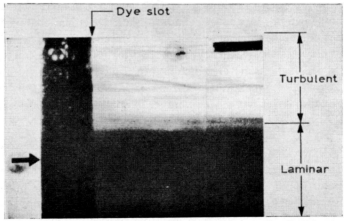

Figure 5. Contrast between laminar and turbulent wall structure visualized by dye slot. Upper part of flow is tripped.

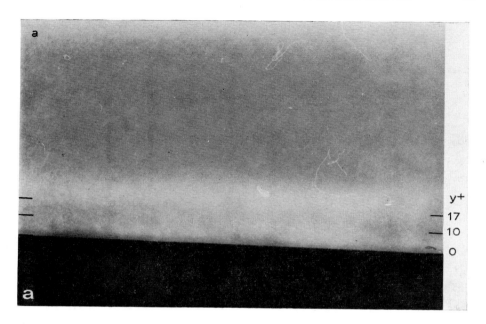

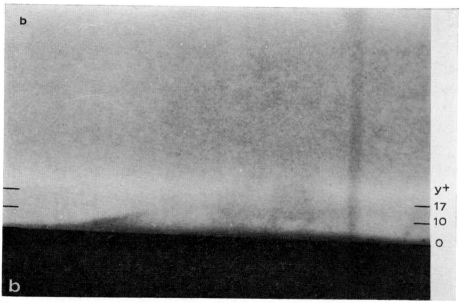

Figure 6. Side views of trajectories from break-up of low-speed streak shown by dye injected at the wall. Figs. 6a through 6f form a sequence in time for one "burst" and subsequent "quiescence".
$$y^+ = yv^*/v, \ U_\infty = 0.197 \ \text{ft/sec.}$$

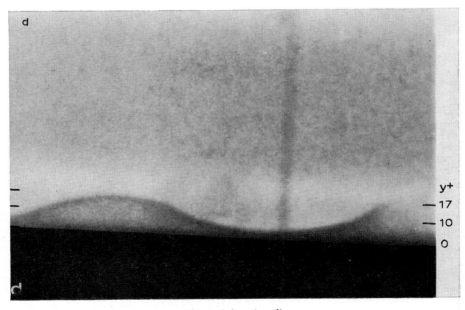

Figure 6 *(continued)*.

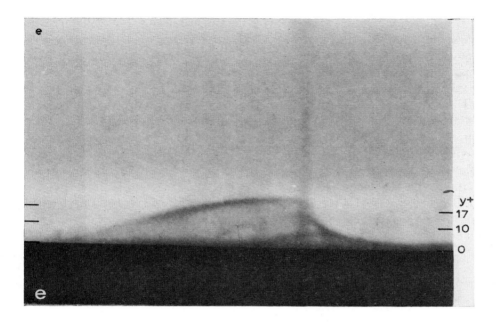

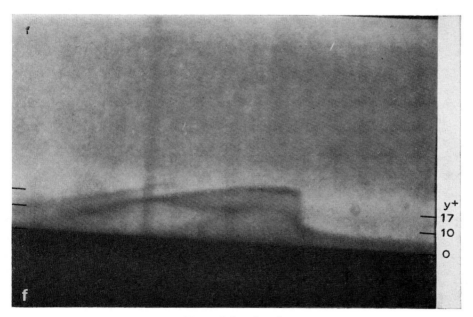

Figure 6 *(continued)*.

References p. 66–68

The streaks under spots seem to be the same phenomenon. The motion pictures reveal the same patterns, and Meyer & Kline (1961a) found the same average transverse spacing of streaks under isolated spots as in the fully turbulent layer; this includes the same variation with free-stream speed over a range of nearly 4 to 1 in velocity.

Using the combined-time-streak marker method it is possible to obtain a series of instantaneous velocity profiles normal to the flow and parallel to the wall at various distances from the wall, and to associate such profiles with the structure picture. The technique is described in detail by Schraub et al. (1965b). An example of photos obtained by using such markers, and the associated mean-velocity profile normal to the wall from the work of Schraub & Kline (1965a) are shown in figure 11. It can be seen from figure 11g that the "streaks" are regions of low mean-speed, and the regions in between are regions of higher mean-speed. This relation is uniformly found in the flows thus far observed. These observations encompass

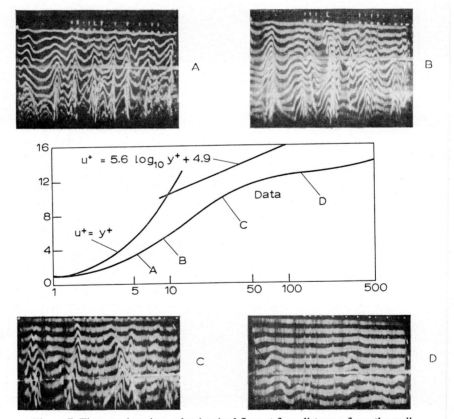

Figure 7. Time markers in a relaminarized flow at four distances from the wall.

several hundred different flows and six different apparati in two laboratories; however, they have all involved the author in some way; observations by others would be useful.

A number of more quantitative observations are now available on this streaky wall-layer structure; but these are postponed to section VI in order to give a single discussion which includes pressure-gradient flows.

IV. RELAMINARIZATION

Relaminarization is the term usually applied to the return of a flow from a turbulent to a laminar state. Relaminarization can be achieved in at least three ways: (i) by strong acceleration of the flow; (ii) by application of body forces in a direction such that the layers closest to the wall are held on the wall; (iii) by decelerating the flow through a critical value of the Reynolds number. All of these methods have been demonstrated by experiment: others may exist.

The earliest verified cases of relaminarization are apparently due to Senoo (1957), Sternberg (1954) and Sergienko & Gretsov (1959). All of these investigators studied accelerating flows and confirmed that relaminarization occurred. None of them obtained detailed measurements of the process, nor did any of them correlate the phenomenon.

More recently Moretti & Kays (1965) have measured local values of Stanton Number (heat transfer coefficient) in a channel with a controllable area program; the observed values of Stanton number are in agreement with laminar predictions for values of the parameter $K = (v/U^2)(\partial U/\partial x) \geq 4 \times 10^{-6}$.* Launder (1963) finds similar results using a hot-wire. Schraub & Kline (1965a) find cessation of the appearance of the streaks in the inner layers of the boundary layer and of the "eddies" emanating from low-speed breakup at the same value of K.

A few stills from motion pictures due to Schraub & Kline (1965a) are shown in figure 7; the mean-velocity profile is shown on the figure. Two somewhat surprising results were found by Schraub & Kline, but unfortunately neither can be seen adequately in still photos. First, when relaminarization occurs the entire flow becomes more laminar-like quite rapidly. Not only does one observe cessation of eddy formation due to bursts from the inner layers, but also that the outer layers of the flow, although still unsteady, in a quite short distance become distinctly more coherent than is typical of similar pictures of structure in turbulent flows.

---

* The parameter $- K/C_f^{3/2} = (v/u_\tau^3)(\partial p/\partial x)$ expresses the ratio of pressure to viscous forces in the wall layers, and is perhaps preferable from the theoretical viewpoint. However, C_f is only a very slowly varying quantity, and it is much more convenient to work with K which contains only external flow quantities.

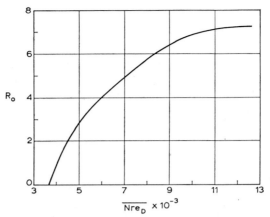

Figure 8. The effect of rotation on suppression of turbulence in a tube. R_0 = tangential speed/ mass-through-flow velocity. $\overline{N_{ReD}}$ = diameter Reynolds Number. Curve shows value of $\overline{N_{ReD}}$ for first observation of turbulent bursts.

Second, it appears that it is possible to obtain states that are still turbulent but in which the level of turbulence is reduced due to dimunition of turbulence production.* Such intermediate states might be called "laminarescent".

Body forces have been used for relaminarization by Cannon (1965). In Cannon's experiment, a fully established turbulent pipe flow was passed into a lucite tube; the lucite tube could be rotated on its axis at variable speed. Cannon's apparatus included not only a pump but also commercial tees, short elbows and so on; no attempt whatsoever was made to provide "clean" internal aerodynamics in the flow circuit. Moreover, the rotating tube was not balanced, and it vibrated visibly when running at any speed above a few r.p.m. Despite this, a very strong relaminarizing effect was observed, as shown on figure 8. Further discussion of this experiment also appears in section VII.

Finally, relaminarization can occur due to deceleration of the flow if the initial flow Reynolds number just exceeds the lower critical for pipe flow; such an experiment has been carried out by Laufer (1955). Visual observations of structure in this case do not seem to have been made. Discussion of the interpretation and possible implications of these results is also contained in section VII.

VA. TRANSITION REGIONS IN POSITIVE PRESSURE GRADIENTS

Transition from laminar to turbulent flow in a positive pressure gradient usually does not follow the sequence of events summarized in section II. When more than

* See section VII for further description.

a very mild pressure gradient is applied to a laminar boundary layer, it very quickly separates. The free shear layer formed around the dividing streamline of the separation is several orders of magnitude more unstable than the laminar boundary layer before separation. Consequently, transition often occurs in the portion of the free shear layer near the dividing streamline, and very shortly after the separation point. When such a transition occurs, the mixing in the layers near the wall is greatly increased, and this leads to reattachment in a short distance. This type of transition is normally observed in positive pressure gradients, except at very low Reynolds numbers or high Mach numbers where laminar reattachment sometimes occurs and is followed by transition still farther downstream. The sequence of events is sketched in figure 9. The main feature of transition in adverse

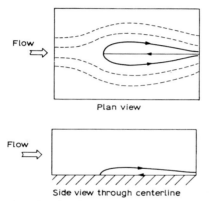

Plan view

Side view through centerline

Figure 9a. Schematic plan view showing limiting streamlines of separation bubble at the wall (solid) and outer streamlines (dotted); not to scale. Schematic side view of separation bubble through centerline; not to scale.

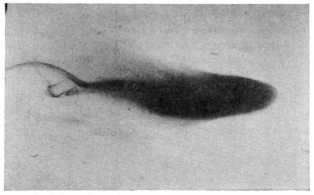

Figure 9b. Photograph of three-dimensional separation bubble visualized by dye injected at the wall. The flow direction is from right to left.

References p. 66–68

pressure gradients is thus a very thin and often relatively short separation "bubble". Such "bubbles" are observed in both internal and external flows.

Tani (1964) has recently compiled an extensive and illuminating summary of the various kinds of bubbles and their correlation for the case of airfoils; Tani includes an extensive bibliography that is not repeated here. Kline & Runstadler (1959a) have observed one case in internal flow and have recorded motion pictures of it (1959b).

An unsettled question apparently remains regarding the two- and three-dimensional nature of separation bubbles in the transverse direction. The short transition bubbles observed by Kline & Runstadler were in every case three-dimensional. These bubbles have the general form indicated in the sketch and photo of figure 9. Some two-dimensional separation bubbles have also been observed in curved diffusers in the writer's laboratory, but were not studied in detail; these two-dimensional bubbles were considerably longer in streamwise extent than the three-dimensional ones.

Tani (1964) also reports two types of bubbles, long and short, with distinguishable characteristic pressure distributions on airfoils. This led the writer, in a recent private communication, to ask Prof. Tani if it is possible that the short bubbles on airfoils are three-dimensional while the long ones are two-dimensional. Tani's reply indicated that he believes both types to be two-dimensional, but that complete data are lacking. Hence the conditions under which a three-dimensional, as opposed to a two-dimensional, bubble is to be expected remain unclear.

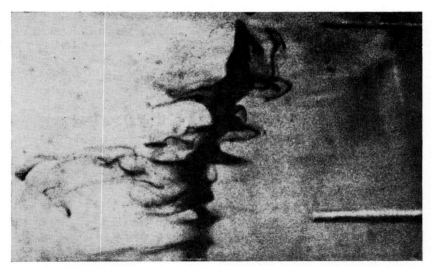

Figure 10. Streaks of backflow in a readjusting zone; visualization by dye initially located in a single transverse line at the wall. $U_{\infty} = 0.4$ ft/sec. The flow direction is from right to left.

In nozzles and venturis, transition bubbles can have significant effects. Even though the oncoming flow is turbulent, relaminarization often occurs in the converging section of nozzles and venturis due to the very high accelerations; this is particularly true at low velocities because of the U^2 term in the denominator of the parameter $K=(v/U^2)(\partial U/\partial x)$. When relaminarization of the boundary layer occurs in the converging section, a local separation bubble probably occurs in the local adverse pressure gradient near the wall just past the throat. (This adverse gradient occurs in nozzles as well as venturis; the effect can be seen from an examination of the potential flow field near the throat.) Transition to turbulent flow then occurs in the bubbles. All data indicate that such bubbles are very thin, and they may also be three-dimensional in form. Extremely careful and detailed measurements of the flow field would be necessary to observe such bubbles; such detailed measurements in nozzles or venturis do not seem to have been made. However, Hall (1959) provides an explanation for long-observed peculiarities in discharge-coefficient measurements by assuming the existence of transition bubbles in the flow situations where such behavior would be expected.

VB. READJUSTING ZONES, SEPARATION ZONES AND STREAKS OF BACKFLOW

Under certain circumstances, dye studies of the inner layers reveal what Kline & Runstadler (1959a) called "streaks of backflow". These consist of short upstream motions of streaks of fluid; they are observed when the layers very near the wall are marked in a line transverse to the flow. The upstream motions are followed by motions away from the wall and a subsequent downstream motion. An example is shown in the photograph of figure 10. Figure 10 shows the streaks to be relatively regular in transverse size and spacing.

Such streaks of backflow are observed only in adverse pressure-gradients; in no case have they been observed in favorable or zero pressure-gradients. Runstadler et al. (1963a) suggest that these streaks are the effect of the pressure forces on the streaks of low mean-speed observed in the inner layers, that is, on the low-speed portion of the inner-layer structure described in sections III and VI. Upstream motion of the streaks has been observed in two situations: readjusting zones and incipient separation zones. A readjusting zone is a region in which the boundary layer passes from a negative or mild adverse pressure gradient rapidly into a region of strong adverse pressure gradient. An incipient separation zone is a region that is approaching, but has not reached, full separation. Readjusting zones are described by Kline & Runstadler (1959a, 1959b). Incipient separation is discussed in some detail by Kline (1959) and by Sandborn & Kline (1961). The incipient separation region has also been studied experimentally by Stratford (1958)

and by Robertson & Calehuff (1957); both of these investigations revealed extremely high turbulence intensities consistent with local backflows near the wall.

However, the observations on both incipient separation and readjusting zones
remain fragmentary; few studies have been made, and no direct observations of the
streaks of backflow seem to have been reported except those of the writer's
laboratory. Study of both incipient separation and readjusting zones offers an
opportunity for increased understanding. Study of readjusting zones should aid in
determining the adjustment times of the inner layers of the turbulent boundary
layer to new external flow conditions. It is generally accepted that the readjustment
of the inner layers is rapid compared with that of the outer layers, but quantitative
data are lacking. Study of incipient separation zones should aid in understanding
separation processes in turbulent boundary layers and also the relative importance
of pressure forces and inertia forces in the wall layer structures. Studies of incipient
separation are understood to be in progress at both the U.S. National Bureau of
Standards and the National Physical Laboratory in England; current studies of
readjusting zones are not known to the writer.

VI. STRUCTURE PROFILE OF A FULLY TURBULENT BOUNDARY LAYER

Figure 11, and the equivalent motion pictures (Runstadler *et al.* 1963b), show the
structure of the fully turbulent boundary layer at various distances from the wall.
The photos of figure 11 were obtained* with the combined-time-streak marker
method using a 0.001″ platinum wire parallel to the wall, but normal to the flow,
at various distances from the wall.

Runstadler *et al.* (1963a) established a relation between the observed structure
features and the well-known regions of the turbulent mean-velocity profile for the
flat plate. Schraub & Kline (1965a) showed that the same association could be
interpreted to also include flows with favorable and unfavorable pressure gradients
provided relaminarization did not occur. The plan views of figure 11 do not of
course give all information about the fluctuating velocity field, but they do show
many features of interest, and considerable information can be obtained from them.
The photos are reproducible in their primary features.** The writer believes the
pictures of figure 11 can be taken as exemplary of the structure features observed in
fully turbulent boundary layers on smooth walls and of their association to the

---

* Thanks are due to Mr. C. K. Liu, Res. Asst., Thermosciences Laboratory, Mechanical Engineering Department, for these photos. Runstadler's original photos employed only time-lines. The
present set were retaken since much more information is obtained from combined-time-streak
markers.
** In a statistical sense, not in instantaneous detail.

regions of the mean-velocity profile for all values of pressure gradient in the absence of separation or relaminarization. A brief discussion of the principal features follows.

Outside the boundary layer, the flow has no large eddies or secondary motion, and the combined-time-streak markers proceed with little distortion, as can be seen in figure 11b. This is characteristic of the flow beyond a wall distance of about $1.2\delta_{0.99}$.*

Inside $1.2\delta_{0.99}$, isolated regions of turbulent flow are observed. In these turbulent regions, the markers are strongly convoluted and distorted; see figures 11c, d. The remainder of the flow contains undistorted markers, indicating much smaller eddy size and turbulence intensity; that is, laminar flow. If observations are made with a fixed probe, turbulent and laminar regions alternately move past the probe giving rise to the phenomenon called intermittency (Klebanoff 1956). The fraction of time the layer is turbulent increases from zero at $1.2\delta_{0.99}$ to unity at the inflexion point in the wake region of the profile. The inflexion point occurs at different values of y/δ for different pressure gradients and different R_e, but in the data so far available the association of 100% turbulent flow with the inflexion point is uniformly observed to the accuracy of the observations. When a count of the fraction of the time** which shows distorted elements in the photos is plotted as a function of y/δ, it gives Gaussian statistics for the zone between $y/\delta_{0.99} = 1.2$ and the inflexion point in the wake region. Klebanoff (1956) found Gaussian statistics for the intermittency in this region using hot-wire probes. Thus the interpretation of the regions of distorted markers on the photos as "turbulent" and the remainder of the flow as laminar appears consistent with prior measurements and nomenclature.

In the log zone of the mean-velocity profile the gross features of the observed flow structure are as one would expect from hot-wire data. The flow is everywhere turbulent, and the intensity appears to increase and the scale decrease as the wall is approached; see figure 11.

At the junction of the log and "buffer" zones of the mean-velocity profile, $y^+ \approx 40$, a new and surprising feature begins to be discernible. This is a longitudinal or "streaky" structure in the flow, already described in part in section III. At $y^+ = 40$, the structure would probably go unnoticed, but as the wall is approached the persistence and regularity of the streaks both increase until the streaks become the dominant macroscopic feature in the visual data; see figure 11. If one examines

---

* Since the value $u/U_\infty = 0.99$ is arbitrarily selected, there is no reason why $\delta_{0.99}$ should necessarily correspond to the change in structure; $1.2\delta_{0.99}$ appears a better choice in so far as structure is concerned.

** One measures area on the film and makes a small correction for the difference in convection velocity between the turbulent regions and the mean speed.

References p. 66–68

photos for stations farther and farther from the wall looking for the streaky pattern, it is seen to be visible in the photos to a y^+ of about 40.

The layers between the wall and $y^+ = 40$ can be considered as either one or two regions. Here they are discussed as two. The region $7 \leq y^+ \leq 40$ is called the "buffer layer" and the region $0 \leq y^+ \leq 7$, the "innermost layer"; collectively, the two layers together are called the inner layers. (The term laminar sublayer is purposefully avoided to prevent prejudicing the interpretation and creating fruitless controversy based on purely semantic causes.)

Since the longitudinal streaks in the inner layers are the dominant macroscopic feature observed in the structure photos and are unexpected in a two-dimensional boundary layer, some effort has been expended in the writer's laboratory to measure their characteristics and to comprehend their significance.

These studies show that the longitudinal streaks are the result of high- and low-speed flow side by side. This was established by Runstadler et al. (1963a), and confirmed by instantaneous mean-velocity measurements in the span direction which were reduced from combined-time-streak marker data (Schraub & Kline 1965a) as noted in section III; see figure 14. The data show that the low-speed streaks are wider near the wall ($y^+ = 2$), but the high-speed streaks become wider near the inner edge of the buffer region ($y^+ = 8$–12).

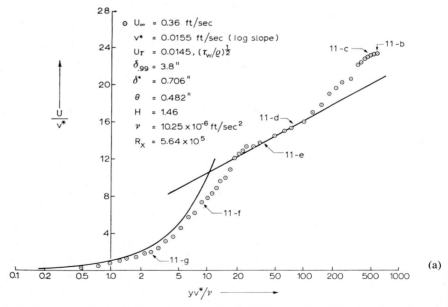

Figure 11. Structure of turbulent boundary layer illustrated by combined-time-streak markers at various distances from the wall. $y^+ = yv^*/\nu$, $v^* = \sqrt{\tau_w/\varrho}$. (a) Mean-velocity profile.

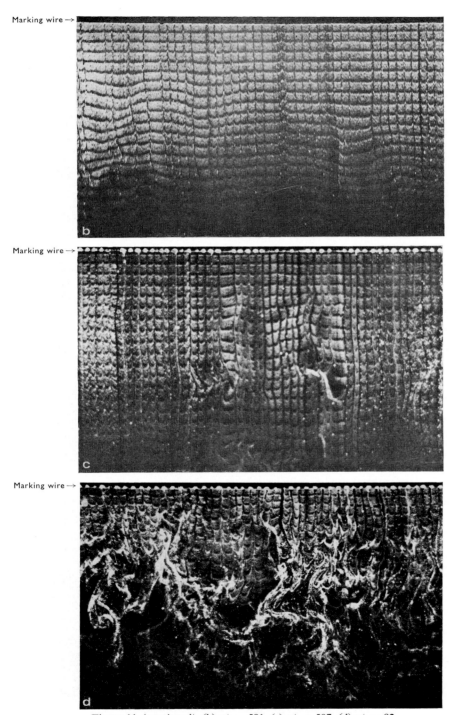

Figure 11 *(continued)*. (b) $y^+ = 581$, (c) $y^+ = 507$, (d) $y^+ = 82$.

References p. 66–68

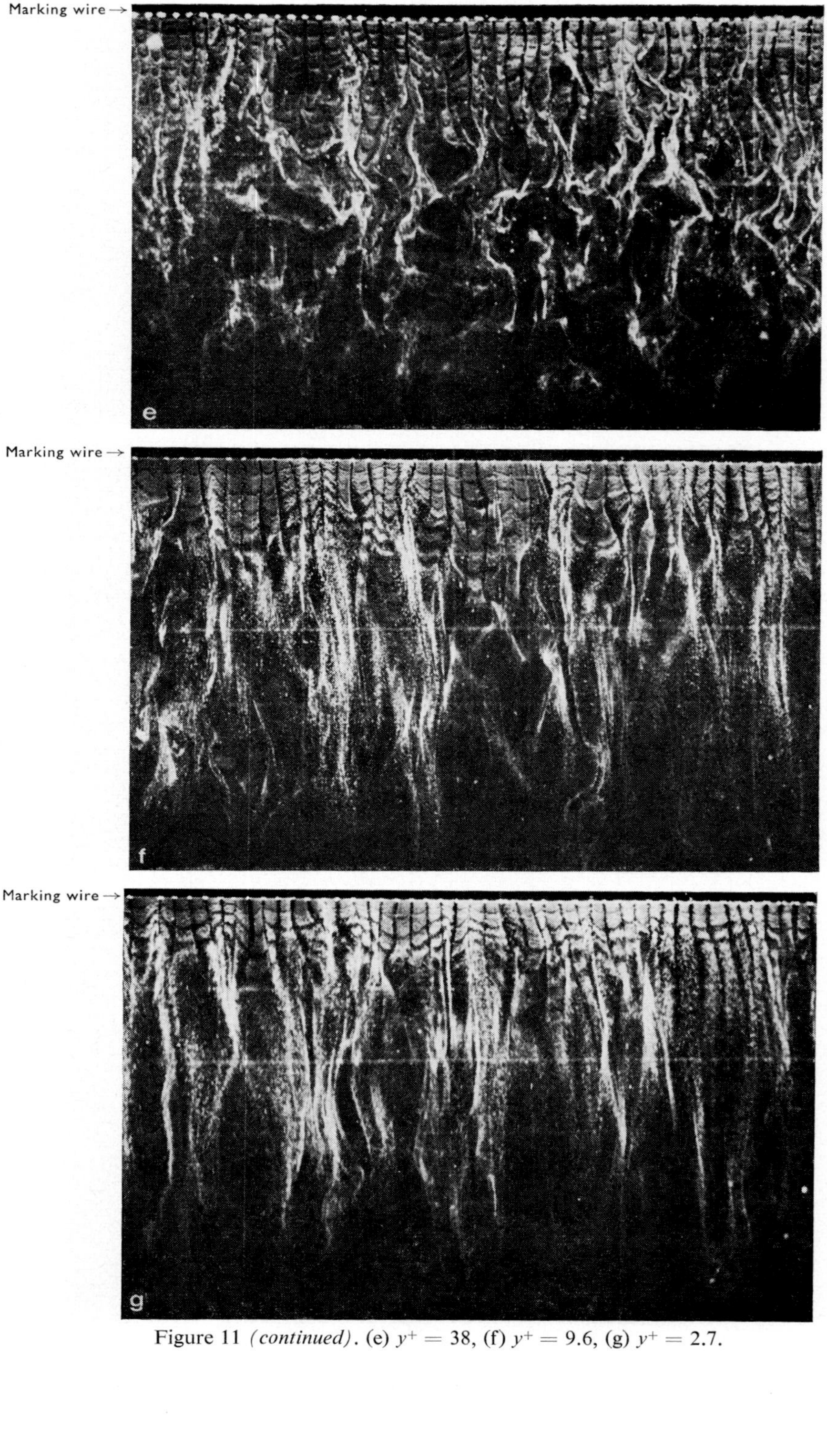
Marking wire →
e
Marking wire →
f
Marking wire →
g

Figure 11 *(continued)*. (e) $y^+ = 38$, (f) $y^+ = 9.6$, (g) $y^+ = 2.7$.

A study of end and side views, separately and together with simultaneous plan views, suggests the flow structure indicated in the sketch of figure 12. The observations indicate secondary longitudinal vorticity with concomitant flow toward the wall in the high-speed regions and away from the wall in the low-speed streaks; this would account for the accumulation of bubbles or dye injected very near the wall into the low-speed streaks, making them visible. It should be noted that the longitudinal vorticity in the inner layers is weak, but of apparently large cumulative effect. One does not observe repeated rotation about a longitudinal axis; rather, a gradual gathering of the dye or bubble markers occurs over a relatively long distance compared to transverse scales. The gathering occurs mostly in the innermost layer; the low-speed streaks move from the wall with downstream motion. The transverse oscillations observed in plan view are then seen, and finally the process is terminated by a relatively sudden "breakup" of the streak with rapid outward motion of marked particles from the wall as noted in section III; see figure 6. In the breakup process considerable longitudinal vorticity appears; most often this is of alternate sign, with paired breakups occurring or one breakup occurring just after another of opposite sign. The wavy motions and breakups are most often observed in the buffer layer. One should not obtain the impression that the streaks move steadily from the wall at some fixed angle or that a regular cyclic breakup process occurs. On the contrary, the streaks move very close to the wall for some distance, and then an outward motion and breakup occurs over a shorter distance and smaller time. The occurrence of breakups is not cyclic. Often, several occur

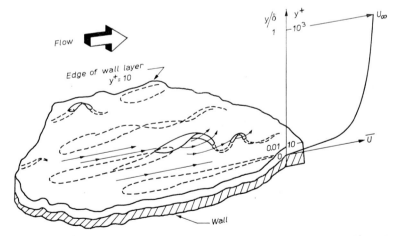

Figure 12. Sketch of wall-layer flow. Figure illustrates the projection of a low-velocity streak through a plane bounding the wall layers and located at $y^+ = 10$. The loops of the streak external to the wall layers represent the configuration of an element of the wall layer structure at the start of the ejection process. The scale of the layers near the wall has been exaggerated.

References p. 66–68

very quickly in a given physical region; the breakups are usually followed by a longer time of relative quiescence in the flow.

All attempts to examine the flow closer and closer to a smooth wall have so far lead only to reinforcement of the result that a time-dependent, three-dimensional structure (streaks) exists essentially to the wall. One set of observations has been made at $y^+ = 1/10$, and several inside $y^+ = 1/2$. The expected linear mean-velocity profile is found inward from at least $y^+ = 7$. The observations thus extend well into the inner 1/50 of the innermost layer. There is no present reason to expect important changes in structure still closer to the wall. At $y^+ = 5$ the flow does appear to be more quiescent than farther from the wall, and inside $y^+ = 2$ it appears markedly more quiescent; however, the dominant feature of the flow pictures remains the time-dependent, three-dimensional, streaky structure as close to the wall as observations have been made. Moreover, the apparently more quiescent motion at $y^+ = 2$ must be interpreted with care. The framing speed of the camera was set to picture eddies in the outer flow. Since the framing speed is kept constant, for comparison, part of the more quiescent appearance of the inner layers arises solely from the fact that the time scales of transient motions are longer on the average than in the outer regions. The excursions of instantaneous velocity about the mean value in the span direction remain of the order of 40 to 50 % as close to the wall as measurements have been made.

Schraub & Kline (1965a) were able to obtain quantitative data on several of the apparently more important features of the structure of the inner layers; this includes the average spacing of the transverse streaks, and the frequency with which

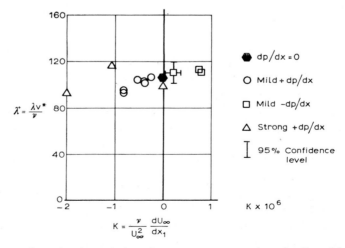

Figure 13. Non-dimensional correlation of mean transverse spacing of wall model. $\lambda^+ = \lambda v^*/v$, $K = (v/U_\infty^2)(dU_\infty/dx_1)$.

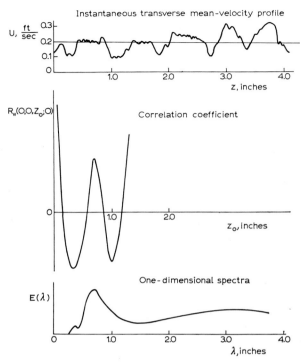

Figure 14. Typical transverse mean-velocity profile, two-point space correlation, and spectra for inner layers. Case shown is $y^+ = 12$, $U_\infty = 0.5$ ft/sec, $\bar{u} = 0.20$ ft/sec, $\partial p/\partial x_1 = 0$.

the low-speed streaks "breakup" and move along outward trajectories from the wall. Considerable data on the subsequent trajectories followed by the outgoing particles have also been obtained. Only the most salient features are described here.

The most complete data are for streak spacing. Figure 13 shows an apparently universal correlation for the streak spacing. The data were obtained by applying statistical correlation procedures to the instantaneous, transverse mean-velocity profiles obtained from photos of combined-time-streak markers. One takes first the two-point space correlation, $R(0,0,z_0; 0)$. Its Fourier transform is then calculated using a computer. The first peak of the correlation (other than zero) is taken as the wave length. Since the data procedures give a sample of only about five wave lengths for each picture, a number of pictures are analysed as separate realizations from a population. Typical results are shown in figure 14. Using information in both the individual and the summed transforms, one again confirms that the flow structure contains a preferred mean wave number, with a large variance of individual wave number about this mean. This confirms a definite *spatial* structure with a preferred *band* of wave numbers.

The time data (that is, the record obtained by observing velocity as a function of time at a single point) are consistent, but less informative. Well out in the layer Gaussian values of skewness and flatness are observed, but in the inner layers the skewness first becomes negative and then strongly positive very close to the wall. These results agree with the recent measurements of Comte-Bellot (1963). The results of both investigations are shown in figure 15. The high positive skewness near the wall, and the negative skewness slightly farther out in the flow, are consistent with wide low-speed streaks near the wall ($y^+ < 5$) and narrow low-speed streaks just a little farther out ($12 < y^+ < 20$) if one assumes that the location of streaks in the transverse direction is random in time. As will be seen, this is in fact the case. However, the spatial structure is not derivable from the first four moments of the time data since many different velocity distributions could give the same result.

The mean spacing correlates on inner layer parameters in the form $\lambda v^*/v = 100$, where $\lambda =$ mean streak spacing. Since the thickness of the innermost layer is given by $\delta_L v^*/v = 7$, the transverse width of the characteristic flow structure is about 14 times the thickness of the innermost layer. Observations of the characteristic length of the flow structure in the direction of the flow are not adequate to give numerical results at this time, but the observations do suggest it is one order of magnitude larger than the transverse spacing. Thus the inner layer structure is very long, wide in the transverse direction, but thin normal to the wall. These

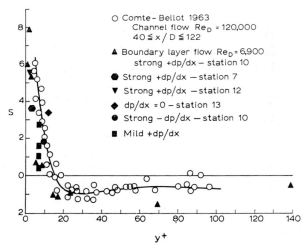

Figure 15. Skewness of velocity fluctuations in turbulent boundary layer versus distance from the wall. $S =$ skewness factor, $y^+ = yv^*/v$.

results are in agreement with the remarkable deductions of Townsend (1956) based on less complete data.

The data on F, the frequency of "breakup" (that is, the sudden outward motion of the low-speed streaks), are now also reasonably good. Schraub & Kline (1965a) have obtained an apparently adequate correlation of burst frequency versus v^* for the flat plate. When this correlation is expressed in mean-velocity form, it can be used to remove at least most of the effect of free-stream velocity, and thus make clear the effect of the pressure gradient in accelerating and decelerating flows.

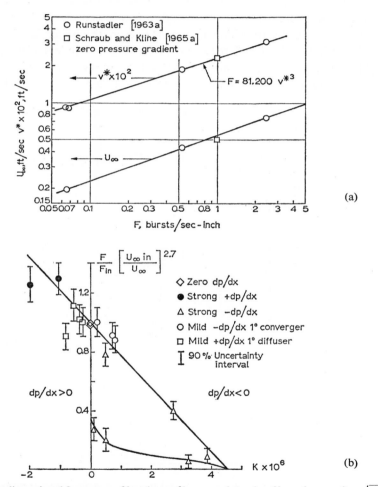

Figure 16. Non-dimensional frequency of break-up of low-speed streaks of inner layers. $v^* = \sqrt{\tau_w/\varrho}$, $F =$ bursts/sec-in., $(\ )_{in} =$ initial value, $K = (\nu/U_\infty^2)(dU_\infty/dx)$. (a) Correlation for $\partial p/\partial x = 0$; (b) Effect of $\partial p/\partial x$.

References p. 66–68

Such a plot is shown in figure 16 which has already been discussed in connection
with relaminarization due to acceleration of the flow. It must be noted that some
residual uncertainty concerning the reproducibility of these F data remain since it
was necessary to normalize the plot of figure 16 on $F_{initial}$ to obtain consistent
results. This suggests some lack of reproducibility in the dye techniques employed.

A question that inevitably arises concerns the effect of the geometric factors in a
given flow system on the streak spacing and breakup frequency. To investigate this
point, several different apparati in two laboratories have been used, with many
variations on each. The results on streak spacing appear uniform to within the
accuracy of measurement whenever the flow is turbulent, including the wall layers
under "spots" in the transition region. However, the writer has been involved,
directly or indirectly, in all these measurements, and independent observations
would be useful. Another confirmation that the streaky structure is not associated
with geometric factors in the flow system can be seen in figure 17. It shows that

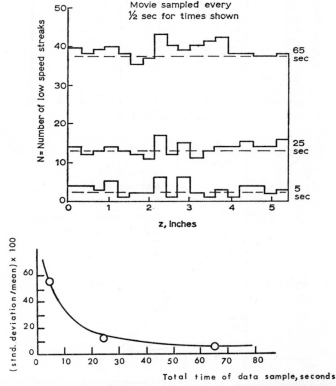

Figure 17. Histogram of transverse location of low-speed streaks for several different times, and
standard deviation of spatial distribution of low-fluid-velocity streaks versus sample time.

the location of the streaks in space is random if one observes for *sufficiently long times*. The figure is a histogram prepared by dividing the transverse direction into cells about $\lambda/5$ in width. One then locates the low-speed streaks, within the cells, on a motion-picture frame at an arbitrary starting time. The process is then repeated on frames of the same motion-picture sequence at later times. One observes a steadily more uniform distribution as time proceeds; this is verified by the rapid drop in the standard deviation of the individual count in cells from the mean value, which is also shown in figure 17. The visual data associated with these statistics are instructive. If one observes the streaky structure casually it appears fixed in space in the motion pictures; but more careful observation, for longer times against a fixed background reference grid, shows that the streaks move in at least two ways. First, the entire pattern migrates downstream—apparently with the local convective velocity. Second, when a breakup occurs, the pattern is often shifted laterally in the neighborhood of the breakup.

The fact that the mean transverse spacing of the streaks changes in a regular way with free-stream velocity also strongly suggests it is a characteristic of the flow and not of apparatus geometry. Figure 18 shows a definite "most preferred trajectory" near the wall (that is, for a finite distance in the flow direction), but a wide spread of distribution about this mode. If followed sufficiently far, the eddy loses coherence (as is to be expected in a turbulent process). The distribution becomes flatter and flatter. The data of figure 18 are for the flat-plate case. Comparable order in the trajectory data has not yet been achieved for non-equilibrium flows.

In summary, one observes reproducible structure features associated with each portion of the known mean-velocity profile. The observations in the wake and log regions are in accord with much known data and, while perhaps instructive, do not suggest new results. The observations in the inner layers, on the contrary, show a

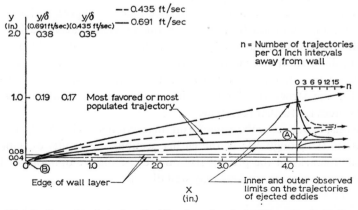

Figure 18. Distribution of trajectories of eddies from breakup of low-speed streaks; $\partial p/\partial x = 0$.

References p. 66–68

three-dimensional, time-dependent streaky structure. This structure is apparently universal for the inner layers in turbulent flow on smooth walls. The streaky structure is composed of regions of low- and high-speed flow side by side. The *mean* transverse spacing of these regions correlates for all pressure gradients on a wall-layer Reynolds number; considerable variance in individual spacing is found, indicating a band of preferred wave numbers. The slow-speed streaks are observed to move down the wall and then rather suddenly move rapidly outward following statistically measurable trajectories for considerable distances. The streaky structure is observed to move in space; streak location is random over long times.

Thus while many details of the flow structure are still not known, at least the most obvious macroscopic features of the inner layers seem to be established with some degree of assurance. The implications of these observations are considered in the next section.

VII. DISCUSSION AND CONCLUSIONS

The observed structure features summarized in sections II through VI deal almost entirely with turbulence; its onset in various ways, its cessation due to differing effects, and its structure in a given situation. This is not surprising since it is common experience that laminar flows in the free stream or the boundary layer are computable to almost any desired degree of design accuracy, but knowledge of turbulence in all its manifestations is still in a rudimentary stage.

Probably because not-entirely-intractable theories have been developed* for turbulence decay, most current discussions of turbulent processes give a central role to the decay processes. Here, however, we concern ourselves with the class of observations we cannot describe analytically. We take the opposing view, and center the discussion on the production processes. Such a view is also clearly incomplete because the turbulence field at any point is determined by the balance between production, dissipation and net transport. However, as we will see, concentration on turbulence production does provide some coherence and qualitative understanding for the structures described in sections II–VI. It also suggests some possible avenues for further researches.

Despite this, in one sense the remarks on this section must be clearly distinguished from sections II through VI: in the earlier sections the results of data were described; the remarks of the present section are speculative opinions of the writer with which many current workers may well disagree.

---

* Most notably by Batchelor (1953).

Converting the Navier–Stokes equations to the Reynolds form (time averages of mean plus fluctuating quantities) and comparing with the viscous, differential energy equation in a comparable form leads to the turbulence production term, **Pr**. Cartesian tensor notation including the repeated index sum convention is used.

$$\mathbf{Pr} = -\overline{u_i u_j}\, \frac{\partial U_i}{\partial x_j}$$

The derivation can be found in any standard work on turbulence; e.g. Hinze (1959), Lumley & Panofsky (1964), Townsend (1956). The quantity **Pr** gives the average value of the rate at which mechanical energies of the mean flow are converted to fluctuations (turbulence). The turbulence production tensor shows that turbulence can be increased, decreased and started and stopped in at least two distinct ways: (i) by a change in mean strain, $\partial U_i/\partial x_j$; (ii) by a change in the fluctuations and their correlations, $\overline{u_i u_j}$. Since the production tensor contains nine scalar terms, a number of subcases including combinations of effects are possible.

At this point it is helpful also to introduce the idea of stability of a given flow; we will later distinguish types of stability in at least one sense. We will have occasion to refer to the well-established fact that free shear-layers are far less stable than bound shear-layers. We will also need to recognize that even though viscosity does in *some* circumstances amplify disturbances, it *always* acts to dissipate the energy of fluctuations, and hence to cause the decay of turbulence. The two effects of viscosity do occur simultaneously in some situations.

Given that decay of the turbulent fluctuations is always occurring, it is not a long step to the idea that a minimum level of production must occur locally if the turbulent processes are not to die away. This idea provides a clear basis for a distinction between decaying turbulence fields (now at least partially understood via homogeneous turbulence theory, and the extensions of its ideas to shear flows) and the boundary layer processes described in sections II–VI. In the decaying turbulent field, such as in the wake of a grid, turbulence is produced at a high rate in a narrow zone close behind the grid, but the rate of production per unit volume decreases rapidly and continuously farther downstream. In the boundary layer flows, on the other hand, turbulence production is maintained at high rates to downstream infinity; there is a layer at every x_1 station where production considerably exceeds dissipation. This is seen very clearly in the data of Klebanoff (1956), figure 19, and is confirmed by the independent measurements of Townsend (1956). One does not usually see turbulence production data presented on a single linear scale because the plot is then almost impossible to read with good accuracy. In figure 19 the data are purposefully shown on a linear scale so that one obtains a visual image of the rate of turbulence production per unit volume. In this plot the truly striking concentration of production into a narrow region of high mean-strain near the wall

58   S. J. KLINE

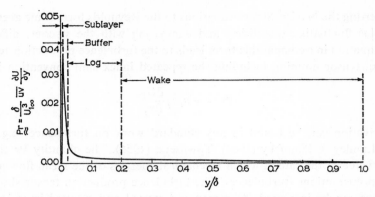

Figure 19. Non-dimensional rate of turbulence production per unit volume versus distance from
the wall (from Klebanoff 1956).

is very evident. Indeed the region is so narrow, that difficulty is encountered in
constructing the figure. It would seem clear that some explicit input regarding
turbulence production is required to give an adequate description of at least the
inner portions of boundary layer flows.

Consider, as an example, the turbulent boundary layer on a semi-infinite flat
plate; $dp/dx = 0$. We ask how the turbulence is produced? An answer frequently
given is, "by the working of turbulence stresses against the mean strain". But this
does not tell us much. It merely says in words that $-\overline{u_i u_j}(\partial U_i/\partial x_j)$ is the *average*
rate of production. It does not tell us how the fluctuations arise, what sustains them,
nor how they can be stopped, started or controlled in level. A deeper understanding
is clearly needed.

Historically, two extreme points of view exist; each is now set in its most extreme
form for purposes of contrast, but probably very few, if any, current workers
actually believe these extreme statements are entirely accurate. The older view
states that turbulence exists in the outer portions of the boundary layer; it acts
through the Reynolds stresses to drag along a very thin but passive layer near the
wall. In this view, no explanations of how the fluctuations in the outer layers arise
or how they are maintained are normally offered. This view is found in most of the
older elementary fluid mechanics texts. In the second view, the turbulence is
assumed to be produced by an "instability" of the layers very near the wall.
Various models have been proposed; the earliest appear to be due to Einstein & Li
(1956) and apparently independently at about the same time by Hanratty (1956).
Both these papers suggest that the innermost layer is two-dimensional but repeatedly grows in thickness and then collapses. Runstadler *et al.* (1963a) suggest
that the observed breakup and outward trajectory of the slow-speed streaks (see
sections III and VI) are the primary source of turbulence production in the bound-

ary layer on smooth walls. The discussion given in that work sifts the available evidence in some detail. Runstadler *et al.* conclude that this hypothesis is not only consistent with known data but also makes possible the explanation of many effects that are otherwise at least very difficult to rationalize.

In a notable synthesis, Townsend (1956) has taken what may be considered an intermediate view between these extremes. Townsend analyzes shear flows primarily in terms of the behavior of certain simple "large eddy structures". The form of the large eddies is taken to be such that they are not inconsistent with two-point space correlation measurements and that they could arise from random fluctuations reasonably often. Reynolds number similarity and the concept of energy equilibrium are then applied to the large eddies. The analysis contains a minimum of free parameters, and it leads to a description of the downstream limiting behavior of free shear layers, jets, wakes and the outer portions of the turbulent boundary layer in terms of a constant eddy viscosity. This result is in agreement with the suggestion of Clauser (1956) for the outer portion of equilibrium boundary layers, and Prandtl's long-employed hypothesis for wakes and jets. These theories do provide workable approximations (which are about as accurate as most measurements in turbulent flow) for the far downstream regions of wakes and jets and for the outer portion of equilibrium turbulent boundary layers. Doubt still exists whether the central results will provide even reasonable approximations for the outer part of non-equilibrium turbulent boundary layers, and it is clear that the description does not fit the starting zone of jets or wakes nor the inner portions of the turbulent boundary layer. This is equivalent to stating that the formulation works well in regions of low turbulence production per unit volume, and in cases where a very particular kind of structural balance exists between the production of turbulence and dissipation; they do not in general give appropriate descriptions for regions of high turbulence production per unit volume. This remark should not be construed as criticism of the theories; they are based on assumptions of similarity or, alternately, employ the concepts of decay of large eddies as a physical basis, and it is not to be expected that they would also describe regions of large turbulence production per unit volume such as the wall layers of the turbulent boundary layer. On the other hand, one does see more clearly the need to study the processes of turbulence production per se.

Currently, the writer and several colleagues are resummarizing the evidence; we reach several conclusions. First, the purely passive view of the wall layers is no longer tenable in view of the present totality of evidence. Second, the term "instability" as used in connection with the inner layers of the boundary layer must be used with some caution. The meaning of instability, in this sense, differs in at least two ways from its use in connection with "classical" instabilities associated with names such as Tollmien-Schlichting, Taylor, Kelvin-Helmholtz, etc. The "classical" instabilities involve amplification of disturbances, and they can be set in motion by infinitely small fluctuations. For the maintenance of turbulence in a boundary layer, however, a very high level of disturbance seems necessary. Thus the classical instabilities are describable by linear mathematics; turbulence is apparently inherently non-linear. The classical instabilities all involve a shift in the entire nature of the flow. For example, the Taylor instability causes a change from one-dimensional annular flow to cellular flow. The turbulent boundary layer, on the other hand, is very persistent in nature; in a gross sense it is statistically very stable; small disturbances do not cause a shift to a new statistical steady state, nor do large ones. Experimentally this is very well known; theoretically it has been shown to be true for small disturbances by Tiederman (1965). Thus what is described by Runstadler *et al.* (1963a) is not an instability of the entire flow field, but rather the "breakup" of a certain flow structure that forms repeatedly near the wall; the process occurs locally and only in a narrow layer. In this sense one might consider it to be a "local" instability in contrast to the classical cases which might be called "global". Because of these differences, some workers prefer not to use the term instability at all in describing the turbulent boundary layer. One can instead use terms like "interaction" or "amplified response". The important thing of course is not the terminology but rather that the physical processes be clearly understood and described. In this sense, the important thing is the existence of a non-linear interaction between the outer and the wall layers of the turbulent boundary layer. In this interaction, the inner layers apparently respond to the pre-existing fluctuation field, over a band of wave numbers, creating the streaky wall structure and subsequent breakups of the low-speed streaks. The fluctuations resulting from these "breakups" create a larger r.m.s. turbulence intensity than existed in the impressed fluctuations; amplification clearly occurs. (This amplification effect is particularly evident in the data of Uzkan & Reynolds (1965) to be described below.) The export of the large fluctuations so created into the outer layers of the flow (net transport of turbulence) then completes the interaction and maintains the turbulent processes. These interactions seem central in the critical turbulence production that controls the structure of the boundary layer. Since they form a loop, it is probably irrelevant for the steady state process where one begins in describing them.

Several features of this process appear common to all the observed structures summarized in sections II through VI. First, a minimum or threshold level of fluctuations and mean strain seems to be needed to maintain the processes. How these threshold levels are reached does not seem to be important. Second, turbulence production seems to occur primarily in narrow regions of intense mean-strain, usually along some kind of free shear layer. This narrow layer acts as a "local instability" or "amplifier" in its response to pre-existing fluctuations thereby creating large fluctuations. In the boundary layer the large fluctuations appear to act both to maintain the concentration of mean strain (through the Reynolds stresses) and to supply the threshold level of disturbances needed to create further turbulence production. Apparently it is in this way that the processes become self-sustaining. It is probably significant that, in both the natural transition in zero pressure gradient and in the fully turbulent layer, three-dimensional structures involving free shear layers are observed as important parts of the breakdown processes even when such three-dimensionality is not indicated by the symmetry of boundary or initial conditions.

The concept of threshold values suggests that the ultimate description of turbulence production must be non-linear; it must treat finite not merely infinitesimal disturbances. In a current investigation, Reynolds (1965) employs this idea to provide an estimate of the mean transverse streak spacing observed by Schraub & Kline (1965a) in the inner-layer structure. Reynolds finds the profile of the inner layers stable to small disturbances, but unstable to large ones. He finds moreover that the most unstable wave number for large transverse spacing agrees to 1% with the measured value for the mean spacing of low-speed streaks due to Schraub & Kline (1965a). The accuracy is probably fortuitous,* but the result is very encouraging regarding the concepts suggested above.

In another current work, Black (1966) has developed a theory based on a primary instability in the boundary layer. Black's model is two-dimensional; he considers an instability of the Kelvin–Helmholtz type occurring near the wall and then propagating outward. In a sense, the work can be considered an extension and generalization of the results of Einstein & Li (1956) and Hanratty (1956). Black obtains excellent estimates of the mean profile, including the entire region from the wall through the log zone, and good estimates of quantities involving derivatives of the mean profiles. Black also obtains a value for a combination of mean measured values of both streak spacing of the inner layers and the frequency of breakup which is in agreement to about 20% with the measured values due to Schraub & Kline (1965a). He also obtains the same analytic form of breakup frequency as a function of u_τ as that found experimentally by Schraub & Kline. Black does employ two empirical constants—the well-established values for the constants in the log portion of the profile, but one can in principle see how these values might be calculated within the framework of Black's theory. It is possible that some of this information may come from the work of Reynolds, but an attempt to do this has not been made. Black's theory omits the effect of some terms in the differential equation.

Thus the theories based on instability models for the inner layers are currently

---

* The theory is second-order not exact, and an appreciable uncertainty exists in the measurements.

References p. 66–68

quite incomplete; they employ oversimplified models, neglect terms, and make use of some empirical information. Despite these existing shortcomings, the approach appears quite promising. It comes closer to providing a theory based on fundamental descriptions, and it gives (even in the present incomplete state) more detailed information in better agreement with the experiments than any other known approach. Indeed, the surprising thing is that even in the still simpler theories of Hanratty and of Einstein & Li, one finds, very easily, a much more complete and better estimate of the observed mean velocity of the inner layers ($0 \leqq y^+ \leqq 50$) than by any other method. It would appear that the concept of a "local, non-linear" instability is at least generally correct and provides a promising avenue for further analytic work.

We now report additional somewhat-more-detailed evidence on the consistency of these concepts and try to relate them to the observed structures reported in sections II through VII.

The concept of threshold values for mean strain and fluctuations is in agreement with many observations. Elder (1960) reports that transition to turbulence occurs at a certain level of fluctuation regardless of whether the fluctuation arises from amplification of small disturbances or from a large local disturbance. Many observers have noted that the flow under turbulent spots remains turbulent even though the spot may be convecting through the mean flow field and the surrounding areas of flow are laminar. The remarkable transition studies of Klebanoff et al. (1959), Kovasznay et al. (1962), and Hama et al. (1961) on the breakdown process tend to support the local-free-shear-layer and the threshold concepts. They show breakdown to turbulence away from the wall in three-dimensional layers of intense shear concentration, followed by a sudden shift in local regions to a new self-sustaining type of process. The movie of Meyer & Kline (1961b) shows that cross-contamination, the lateral spread of turbulent processes, at the edge of a spot in the transition region proceeds by an intense "wave-like" disturbance and is highly localized. The wave appears to create new streaks, new breakups and hence new large disturbances, but only by direct contact along the edge of the spot, not at a distance.

A comment regarding future researches seems appropriate here. If it is true that a change in processes occurs beyond certain threshold values of disturbance and mean strain, then it would seem unlikely that experimental or theoretical investigation of the flow *below* this threshold value will yield much insight into turbulence production. If, as also suggested here, insight into production is essential to understanding boundary layers, then it must follow that more study is needed on the fully turbulent processes; in recent years the most detailed investigations have been done on the earlier stages of transition. In this same vein, a good place to investigate the threshold values and the details of turbulence onset and production unobscured by prior turbulent history would seem to be along the front and side edges of a turbulent spot during transition; no study of this seems to have been done other than the qualitative photos by Meyer & Kline (1961b).

Indications of both the importance of threshold values and of the "amplification" of disturbances by the inner layers appear in the work of Uzkan & Reynolds (1965). They performed an experiment in which grid turbulence was introduced into a channel; one wall of the channel was made of a sliding belt so that the speed of the wall could be controlled. Measurements of turbulence intensity near the wall and in the free stream were made. Typical results are indicated on figure 20; they show that when the wall is stationary the intensity of turbulent fluctuations near the wall is much higher than at the same x location in the free stream; on the other hand, when the wall is moved at free-stream speed the fluctuation intensity near the wall is much lower than at the same x location in the free stream. Not only is this result indicative of the need for finite values of mean strain, but also it seems in direct conflict with the concept of "passive" wall layers. It is at least very difficult to see how one can view the inner layers as "passive" when they amplify fluctuations; that is, the inner layers create fluctuations much larger than those impressed from the outside. Indeed, when the mean strain is removed and the inner layers are truly passive, the opposite effect is observed; the inner layers then damp fluctuations from the free stream.

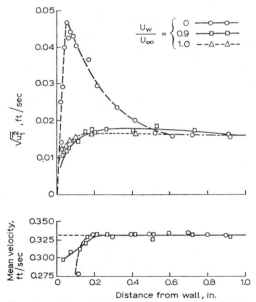

Figure 20. The effect of wall speed on the mean velocity and longitudinal turbulence intensity profiles.

References p. 66–68

The results of figure 20 lead naturally to another concept which is useful in organizing our thinking. The curve marked $U_w/U_\infty = 0.9$, shows a much reduced level of turbulence from the curve where $U_w/U_\infty = 0$. Turbulence production occurs, but at a much reduced level.* We observe that turbulence is not a single state, but at least a succession of states strongly influenced by the amount of production occurring. One suspects that *at the very least* a "magnitude factor" describing the amount of turbulence production will be necessary for an adequate description of turbulent shear flows.

In this context, relaminarization is also understandable as a dimunition of either fluctuations or mean strain below the necessary threshold values. Indeed, one observes that relaminarization is merely the end state of a series of states in which the level of production is successively reduced below, say, the equivalent value for a zero-pressure-gradient flow on a flat plate at the same Reynolds number. There are a number of ways in which such a dimunition can be made to occur. One is flow acceleration as studied by Launder (1963), Moretti & Kays (1965) and Schraub & Kline (1965a). Another is reduction of mean strain by alteration of boundary conditions along the wall (Uzkan & Reynolds 1965). A third is the imposition of body forces which tend to stabilize the critical layers where the bulk of the production occurs. Cannon (1965) accomplished such stabilization within a rotating tube; Eskinazi & Yeh (1956) and Margolis (1963) studied similar effects in curved flows. Several studies, including those of Daily & Bugliarello (1961a, b), have investigated the effects of long fibres and long chain molecules on reduction of turbulence, presumably by damping fluctuations. The concepts developed above suggest that more effective results will be achieved if the fibres (or long molecules) are injected primarily into the critical layers; current studies under the direction of J. L. Lumley are investigating this avenue, but have not been reported at present. Heiser (1964) has reported the effect of magneto-hydrodynamic body forces on turbulence suppression.

Several comments seem appropriate. First, in the accelerating flows studied by Launder (1963), Moretti & Kays (1965) and Schraub & Kline (1965a) it should be noted that the dimunition in turbulence production apparently arises from the term $-\overline{u_1^2}(\partial U_1/\partial x_1)$. When $\partial U_1/\partial x_1$ is positive, the term is negative. Hence if the acceleration is sufficiently large and the mean speed sufficiently low, the term $-\overline{u_1^2}(\partial U_1/\partial x_1)$ can offset the term $-\overline{u_1 u_2}(\partial U_1/\partial x_2)$, and production ceases. For smaller acceleration, production is merely reduced. Indeed, the parameter $K = (\nu/U_1^2)(\partial U_1/\partial x_1)$, which was shown to correlate relaminarization in section IV, is readily found by combining an equation for a fixed ratio of the two terms $-\overline{u_1^2}(\partial U_1/\partial x_1)$ and

---

* This result suggests that very small values of $\partial U_i/\partial x_j$ are sufficient to produce turbulence if $\overline{u_i u_j}$ is large. However, it is not yet clear whether separate thresholds for $\overline{u_i u_j}$ and $\partial U_i/\partial x_j$ exist or whether only the product is important.

$-\overline{u_1 u_2}\,(\partial U_1/\partial x_2)$ with the usual similarity arguments for inner layers. A somewhat more detailed but essentially similar argument is given by Back, Massier & Gier (1964) who reach similar conclusions concerning relaminarization processes.

The very large effect of body forces found by Cannon (1965) suggests that further work is needed on the common situation of turbulent flows over curved walls where the turbulence production may be either augmented or decreased according to the direction of the centrifugal field. Such effects probably also play an important role in Coriolis fields, as for example in centrifugal impellers, but no explicit studies on this effect seem to have been published.*

The effects observed in transition bubbles in adverse pressure gradients, in readjusting zones and on rough walls, although far from complete, so far also seem consistent with the concepts suggested above. In separation bubbles and behind most trips, breakdown is usually found to occur in the free shear layer. In adverse pressure gradients, turbulence production appears to rise, and the measurements of Schraub & Kline (1965a) indicate an increased frequency of low-speed-streak "breakup". The effects appear similar in readjusting zones, but quantitative measurements are lacking. On rough walls, the observations of Tani and co-workers (1962) indicate increased generation of free shear layers; the concomitant increase in turbulence level and drag has been measured by many workers.

It is specifically noted that an alteration in conditions at the wall alone, from smooth to fully rough, affects not just the wall region, but sufficiently far downstream it alters the character of the entire layer; in particular the thickness of the layer, the effective turbulent viscosity, and the turbulence intensity are all markedly increased.

An important avenue for continued research would thus seem to be more detailed investigations of the amplification of disturbances of many sorts in both two- and three-dimensional free shear layers. Such studies would need to control the input disturbances and measure response.

In summary, it is not surprising that most of the boundary layer phenomena about which our knowledge remains in a rudimentary stage are concerned with turbulence. On the other hand, the large number of new phenomena related to turbulent processes that have been disclosed only in the last two decades is surprising in view of the long history of research in this area. Given this history, it would seem unlikely that we are yet even aware of all the phenomena that exist. This implies the need for continued qualitative as well as additional detailed quantitative observations.

---

* Since preparation of this manuscript, turbulence suppression owing to Coriolis forces has been demonstrated experimentally by R. A. Halleen and J. P. Johnston in the writer's laboratory.

References p. 66–68

In the present discussion an attempt has been made to show that some degree of additional coherence and qualitative understanding of known turbulent structures can be achieved by focusing attention on the production processes. In regions where production is very high, such as in the inner portion of turbulent boundary layers and the early region of wakes and jets, the production processes appear to arise from interactions between the fluctuations and a region of concentrated mean strain, usually along two or three-dimensional free shear layers. A threshold value of mean strain and fluctuations seems needed to maintain this type of process. These views seem consistent with existing evidence, and promising; they lead to a number of interesting avenues for further research. On the other hand, they are clearly incomplete, and only in due time can they be judged fully. In the meantime they may be of some value as a physical rationale of turbulent boundary layer processes.

REFERENCES

Back, L. H., Massier, P. F. & Gier, H. L. (1964) *Convective Heat-Transfer in a Convergent-Divergent Nozzle*. Int. J. Heat and Mass Transfer **7**, 5, pp. 549–68.

Batchelor, G. K. (1953) *Homogeneous Turbulence*. Cambridge Univ. Press, London.

Black, T. J. (1966) *Some Practical Applications of a New Theory of Wall Turbulence*. Proceedings Heat Transfer and Fluid Mech. Inst. Stanford Univ. Press.

Cannon, J. C. (1965) *Heat Transfer from a Fluid Flowing Inside a Rotating Cylinder*. Ph.D. thesis, Mech. Engrg. Dept., Stanford Univ.

Clauser, F. H. (1954) *Turbulent Boundary Layer in Adverse Pressure Gradients*. J. Aero. Sci. **21**, pp. 91–108.

Clauser, F. H. (1956) *The Turbulent Boundary Layer*. Advances in Applied Mechanics, Vol. IV. Academic Press, New York.

Comte-Bellot, G. (1963) *Coefficients de dissymétrie et d'applatissement, spectres et corrélations en turbulence de conduite*. Journal de Mécanique, Vol. II, No. 2, pp. 105–28.

Daily, J. W. & Bugliarello, G. A. (1961a) *Basic Data for Dilute Fiber Suspensions in Uniform Flow with Shear*. TAPPI Magazine **44**, No. 7, July.

Daily, J. W. & Bugliarello, G. A. (1961b) *Rheological Models and Laminar Shear Flow of Fiber Suspensions*. TAPPI Magazine **44**, No. 12, December.

Dhawan, S. & Narashima, R. (1957–8) *Some Properties of Boundary Layer Flow during the Transition from Laminar to Turbulent Motion*. J. Fluid Mech. **3**, pp. 418–36.

Einstein, H. A. & Li, H. (1956) *The Viscous Sublayer along a Smooth Boundary*. Am. Soc. Civil Engrs. Proc. **82**, pp. 945-1 to 945-27.

Elder, J. W. (1960) *An Experimental Investigation of Turbulent Spots and Breakdown to Turbulence*. J. Fluid Mech. **9**, Pt. 2, pp. 235–46.

Emmons, H. W. (1951) *The Laminar-Turbulent Transition in a Boundary Layer*, Part I. J. Aero. Sci. **18**, No. 7, pp. 490–8.

Emmons, H. W. & Bryson, A. E. (1951) *The Laminar-Turbulent Transition in a Boundary Layer*, Part II. Proceedings of 1st U.S. National Congress of Theoretical and Applied Mechanics, pp. 859–68.

Emmons, H. W. & Mitchner, M. (1952) *Transition from Laminar to Turbulent Flow in a Thin Film of Water Flowing Down an Inclined Glass Plate*. Motion picture, available as item E-2 from Engineering Societies Library, 345 East 47th Street, New York City, New York.

Eskinazi, S. & Yeh, H. (1956) *An Investigation on Fully Developed Turbulent Flows in a Curved Channel*. J. Aero. Sci. **23**, 1, pp. 23–34 and 75.

Hall, G. W. (1959) *Application of Boundary Layer Theory to Explain Some Nozzle and Venturi Flow Peculiarities*. Institution of Mech. Engrs. **173**, No. 36, pp. 837–70. (Bri.)

Hama, F. R. (1961) *Boundary-Layer Transition Induced by a Vibrating Ribbon on a Flat Plate*. Proceedings 1960 Heat Transfer and Fluid Mech. Inst. Stanford Univ. Press, pp. 92–101.

Hanratty, T. J. (1956) *Turbulent Exchange of Mass and Momentum with a Boundary*. J. Am. Inst. Chem. Engrs. **2**, No. 3, pp. 359–62.

Heiser, W. (1964) *Mechanical Engineering Projects*. Mech. Engrg. Dept., Massachusetts Institute of Technology.

Hinze, J. O. (1959) *Turbulence*. McGraw-Hill Book Co., New York.

Klebanoff, P. S. (1956) *Characteristics of Turbulence in a Boundary Layer with Zero Pressure Gradient*. NACA Report 1247.

Klebanoff, P. S., Tidstrom, K. D. & Sargent, L. M. (1962) *The Three-Dimensional Nature of Boundary-Layer Instability*. J. Fluid Mech. **12**, Pt. 1, pp. 1–34.

Klebanoff, P. S. & Schubauer, G. B. (1956) *Contributions on the Mechanics of Boundary-Layer Transition*. NACA Report 1289.

Klebanoff, P. S. & Tidstrom, K. D. (1959) *Evolution of Amplified Waves Leading to Transition in a Boundary Layer with Zero Pressure Gradient*. NASA TN-D-195.

Kline, S. J. (1959) *On the Nature of Stall*. J. Basic Engrg., TASME **81**, Series D, pp. 305–20.

Kline, S. J. (1963) *Flow Visualization*. 30 min. teaching motion picture, available from Educational Services Incorporated, Watertown, Mass. (USA).

Kline, S. J. & Runstadler, P. W. (1959a) *Some Preliminary Results of Visual Studies of the Flow Model of the Wall Layers of the Turbulent Boundary Layer*. J. Appl. Mech., TASME, pp. 166–70.

Kline, S. J. & Runstadler, P. W. (1959b) *Some Preliminary Results of Visual Studies of the Flow Model of the Wall Layers of the Turbulent Boundary Layer*. Motion picture, available as item K-1 from Engineering Societies Library, 345 E 47th St., NYC, USA.

Kovasznay, L. S. G., Komoda, H. & Vasudeva, B. R. (1962) *Detailed Flow Field in Transition*. Proceedings 1962 Heat Transfer and Fluid Mech. Inst. Stanford Univ. Press, pp. 1–26.

Laufer, J. (1955) *The Structure of Turbulence in Fully Developed Pipe Flow*. NACA Report 1174.

Launder, B. E. (1963) *The Turbulent Boundary Layer in a Strongly Negative Pressure Gradient*. M.I.T. Gas Turbine Lab. Report No. 71.

Lin, C. C. (1945) *On the Stability of Two-Dimensional Parallel Flows*, Parts I, II, III. Quart. Appl. Math. **3**, pp. 117–42; 218–34; 277–301.

Lin, C. C. (1955) *Theory of Hydrodynamic Stability*. Cambridge Univ. Press, London.

Lumley, J. L. & Panofsky, H. A. (1964) *The Structure of Atmospheric Turbulence*. John Wiley and Sons, New York.

Margolis, D. P., (1963) *An Investigation of a Curved Mixing Layer*. Final Report, Contract No. DA-ARO(D)-31-124-G196, Project No. 3227-E.

Meyer, K. A. & Kline, S. J. (1961a) *A Visual Study of the Flow Model in the Later Stages of Laminar-Turbulent Transition on a Flat Plate*. Report MD-7, Thermosciences Div., Mech. Engrg. Dept., Stanford Univ.

Meyer, K. A. & Kline, S. J. (1961b) *A Visual Study of the Flow Model in the Later Stages of Laminar-Turbulent Transition on a Flat Plate*. Motion picture, available as item M-3 from Engineering Societies Library, 345 E 47th St., NYC, USA.

Moretti, P. M. & Kays, W. M. (1965) *Heat Transfer through an Incompressible Turbulent Boundary Layer with Varying Free-Stream Velocity and Varying Surface Temperature*. Report PG-1, Thermosciences Div., Mech. Engrg. Dept., Stanford Univ.

National Committee for Fluid Mech. Films (1965a), Loop FM-1, 8 mm film, available from Educational Services Incorporated, 47 Galen St., Watertown 72, Mass. (USA).

National Committee for Fluid Mech. Films (1965b), Loop FM-2, 8 mm film, available from Educational Services Incorporated, Watertown, Mass. (USA).

Reynolds, W. C., Kays, W. M. & Kline, S. J. (1958) *Heat Transfer in the Turbulent Incompressible Boundary Layer*, Part IV: *Effect of Location of Transition and Prediction of Heat Transfer in a Known Transition Region*. NASA memo 12-4-58w.

Reynolds, W. C. (1965), unpublished.

Robertson, J. M. & Calehuff, G. (1957) *Turbulence in a Diffuser Boundary Layer*. J. of Hydraulics Div., Proc. Am. Soc. Civil Engrs., Proc. Paper 1393.

Runstadler, P. W., Kline, S. J. & Reynolds, W. C. (1963a) *An Investigation of the Flow Structure of the Turbulent Boundary Layer*. Report MD-8, Thermosciences Div., Mech. Engrg. Dept., Stanford Univ.

Runstadler, P. W., Kline, S. J. & Reynolds, W. C. (1963b) *A Visual Study of the Flow Structure in the Fully Developed Turbulent Boundary Layer on a Flat Plate*. Motion picture, available as item R-7 from Engineering Societies Library, 345 E 47th St., NYC, USA.

Sandborn, V. A. & Kline, S. J. (1961) *Flow Models in Boundary-Layer Stall Inception*. J. Basic Engrg., TASME **83**, Series D, No. 3, pp. 317–27.

Schraub, F. A. & Kline, S. J. (1965a) *A Study of the Structure of the Turbulent Boundary Layer with and without Longitudinal Pressure Gradients*. Report MD-12, Thermosciences Div., Mech. Engrg. Dept., Stanford Univ.

Schraub, F. A., Kline, S. J., Henry, J., Runstadler, P. W. & Littell, A. (1965b) *Use of Hydrogen Bubbles for Quantitative Determination of Time-Dependent Velocity Fields in Low-Speed Water Flows*. J. Basic Engrg., TASME, pp. 429–44.

Schubauer, G. B. & Skramstad, H. K. (1948) *Laminar Boundary Layer Oscillations and Transition on a Flat Plate*. NACA Report 909.

Senoo, Y. (1957) *The Boundary Layer on the End Wall of a Turbine Nozzle Cascade*. M.I.T. Gas Turbine Lab. Report No. 35; also TASME **80**, p. 1711; also ASME Paper A-172.

Sergienko, A. A. & Gretsov, V. K. (1959) *Transition from a Turbulent into a Laminar Boundary Layer*. Soviet Physics "Doklady", Vol. 4, No. 1. (A translation of the "Physics Section" of the Proceedings of the Academy of Sciences of the USSR, Russian Original Vol. 124, Nos. 1–6, published by the Am. Institute of Physics., Inc.)

Sternberg, J. (1954) *The Transition from a Turbulent to a Laminar Boundary Layer*. U.S. Army Bal. Res. Lab. Rept. 906, Aberdeen, Maryland.

Stratford, B. S. (1958) *An Experimental Flow with Zero Skin Friction Throughout its Region of Pressure Rise*. J. Fluid Mech. **5**, Pt. 2, pp. 17–35.

Stuart, J. T. (1965a) *Hydrodynamic Stability*. Appl. Mech. Rev. **18**, No. 7, pp. 523–31.

Stuart, J. T. (1965b) *The Production of Intense Shear Layers by Vortex Stretching and Convection*. NPL Aero Report 1147. (Bri.)

Tani, I. (1964) *Low-Speed Flows Involving Bubble Separations*. Progress in Aero. Sciences **5**. Pergamon Press, Oxford.

Tani, I., Komoda, H., Komatzu, Y., & Iuchi, M. (1962) *Boundary Layer Transition by Isolated Roughness*. Report No. 375, Aeronautical Research Institute, Univ. of Tokyo.

Tiederman, W. G. (1965) *Stability of Turbulent Poiseuille Flow with Application to the Malkus Theory of Turbulence*. Report FM-2, Thermosciences Div., Mech. Engrg. Dept., Stanford Univ.

Townsend, A. A. (1956) *The Structure of Turbulent Shear Flow*. Cambridge Univ. Press, London.

Uzkan, T. & Reynolds, W. C. (1965) *A Turbulent Boundary Layer on a Wall Moving at Free-Stream Velocity*. Report MD-14, Thermosciences Div., Mech. Engrg. Dept., Stanford Univ.

Discussion

G. B. SCHUBAUER (*National Bureau of Standards, Washington, D.C.*)

I want to compliment Dr. Kline for throwing considerable light on the sublayer. Concerning the name, my only defense of the term "laminar sublayer" would be the evidence that the mean flow there behaves as though it were in effect laminar, depending of course on where we place the outer limit. I realize, however, that the term is not descriptive of the actual structure of this layer. Whatever we should call it, and I prefer to remain neutral on this point, I believe that work of the kind Dr. Kline is doing is very definitely shedding light on the structure of this layer and the flow processes taking place there.

S. J. KLINE

I certainly agree with Dr. Schubauer that in the inner layer one does get a linear profile, and all the evidence is that molecular viscosity dominates the shear processes there. Although I didn't show it here today, we have measured sublayer velocity profiles using a hot wire in a water flow. What the data suggest is that you don't have a nice, steady two-dimensional laminar flow as in the classical picture. It is a three-dimensional time-dependent kind of laminar flow. We have also obtained velocity traces from the bubble pictures, and these show the high- and low-speed regions very clearly. This is $\bar{u} = f(z)$ (z being the transverse dimension). The excursions from mean speed in time or space are by no means small. Near the wall they are from 30 to 40 % of the mean speed itself. It is clearly a three-dimensional structure, and the data you saw showed that the structure moves randomly in time. Despite all this, I agree with you that it is dominated by molecular viscosity.

T. J. BLACK (*Illinois Institute of Technology, Chicago, Illinois*)

I'd like to bring up the point of the turbulent structure which Prof. Kline has pointed out clearly as one of the key factors, if not *the* key factor, in this mystery. It seems to me that we can now see two possible and quite distinct mechanisms for turbulence production and, by the same token, for turbulent momentum transfer. One of these is what we might term the classical mechanism; it depends upon the assumption that random turbulence in the presence of a mean rate of strain is capable of transferring momentum. We accordingly interpret the Reynolds equation as an energy equation which says that when you have momentum transfer or correlated $u'v'$ in the presence of a mean rate of strain you will have turbulent-energy production. The alternative mechanism is an instability mechanism. If there is a breakdown of flow in the sublayer due to a dramatic instability in that layer, such as Prof. Kline is proposing, then you have by definition a transfer of energy from the basic flow to some other mode (i.e., to the turbulent motion). We must now interpret the Reynolds equation in the reversed sense; that is to say, if we have turbulent-energy production due to an instability, then correlated $u'v'$ (i.e., turbulent momentum transfer) automatically follows. At the risk of being controversial, it seems to me quite important to put the cart before the horse. Effectively (not in time, but in terms of cause and effect) which comes first, turbulent-energy production or turbulent momentum transfer? Is it all due to random turbulent transport of momentum or is it all due to instability, or is it a combination of both? There is one very rough and crude little experiment which I did and which I would like to mention since it gives some indication as to where the truth may lie. If the classical model is right, we would expect the production of turbulence to be more or less continuous because of the continuous presence of random turbulence in the flow. Therefore, if we measure $u'v'$ as an instantaneous property and plot it against time (measuring it, say, just outside the sublayer) we would expect it to fluctuate, but to do so about a definite negative mean. On the other hand, if the stability mechanism is solely responsible for momentum transfer, then since it is a periodic mechanism we would expect the instantaneous $u'v'$ to exhibit quite distinct peaks and to otherwise fluctuate about zero mean. What I did was to put a crossed hot-wire in the sublayer at the maximum-energy-production point. The resulting $u'v'$ time history exhibited quite definite and fairly regular peaks, in comparison with which the intervening fluctuations were very small indeed. These preliminary results suggest that the basic turbulence mechanism is that of periodic instability, aided perhaps by a small degree of momentum transfer due to random turbulence. If we throw out the classical mechanism completely and say that all, or effectively all, of the momentum transfer is effected through the instability, then we have a situation in which the basic flow is determined entirely by viscous stresses and by the stability-governed energy exchange. We then see turbulent flow simply as a developing time-dependent laminar flow that is repeatedly "chopped" by this instability. I would like to have Prof. Kline's comments on this approach.

S. J. KLINE

That's a question we can't answer. It is certainly a basic question. We see certain things going on. As Dr. Clauser has pointed out, the things we are least certain about are the relations between them and the kind of mathematics that one wants to do in order to perform a decent calculation. It is a very subtle subject and I don't think you can ignore what Prof. Coles has pointed out—that the outer region looks like a wake. There is a spectral transfer between whatever production mechanism exists and the ultimate outer flow; this is certainly part of it, as I said in the very beginning in talking about production. We have a qualitative feel for certain things which look like they are going to give us some understanding, and which already have some engineering utility, but it's an incomplete story. It's just part of the story that I'm talking about. You certainly have a cascade mechanism also operating; it's inevitable as you ultimately go to higher frequencies, i.e. to dissipation. However, I think you have to put in the other element; otherwise, you are only emphasizing one side of the problem.

C. I. H. NICHOLL (*Laval University, Quebec, Canada*)

I would like to make one comment in support of Prof. Kline. I think that these billowing movements that he has shown us in such elegant pictures must be absolutely fundamental, because if you apply a relatively small buoyancy gradient (for example, a density gradient which makes the turbulence work against gravity at a rate which is a small fraction of the production or dissipation) it will kill the turbulence. This sort of motion must be there, a motion which is very, very dependent upon the buoyancy gradient.

S. J. KLINE

There are several experiments on body forces that have been reported. People have generated body forces by magnetohydrodynamic means, by flow in curved channels and with flow in rotating systems. When you apply a body force that stabilizes the crucial layers, then you do get laminar flow again; this is rather strong evidence that something particularly important is going on in the layers very close to the wall. The Klebanoff production data, of course, also show this.

R. E. KRONAUER (*Harvard University, Cambridge, Massachusetts*)

I would like to offer some further experimental support for these "streaks". This is data taken with hot wires in a 5-inch-diameter pipe having a centerline velocity of 9.6 ft/sec. Looking upstream, we've located a fixed and a movable hot wire in the same transverse plane (figure 21). We form the correlation between the velocity components u' for various transverse spacings, z^+. This was motivated by Prof. Kline's photographs. If you consider a plot of the correlation function vs. z^+ obtained using a broad-band u' signal, there is no evidence of the transverse periodicity shown by the photographs (figure 22). However, if you use a notch filter with a fairly broad band (20 to 40 cps in this case) you get a correlation with definite periodicity (figure 22).

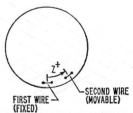

Figure 21. Hot wires in the same transverse plane of a turbulent pipe flow; pipe diameter = 5 in.

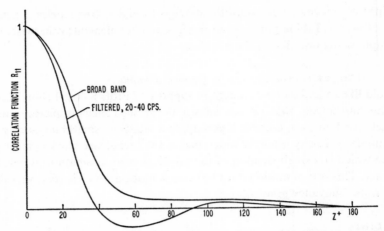

Figure 22. Correlation between the velocity components u' for various transverse spacings in the pipe flow of figure 21.

This is to say, if you single out the right frequency band, which means that you essentially single out a certain band of longitudinal wavelengths, you get a definite transverse wavelength. This wavelength checks well with the results Prof. Kline has calculated—about 105 on the z^+ scale. These measurements were made at $y^+ \cong 2.3$, way down in the sublayer, and the length of the wires was about 15 on the z^+ scale.

By estimating the convective velocity and knowing the frequency, we can estimate the longitudinal wavelength. This turns out to be about 380 on the z^+ scale. Seen from above (looking toward the wall), these waves are inclined to the flow in either one of two ways (figure 23) at a slope of about 1/4. What this suggests is that the streaks in the photographs are in fact two sets of waves, propagating as indicated by the arrows, and producing a standing-wave pattern which is modulated in the streamwise direction with a wavelength about 4 times the transverse wavelength. Careful examination of the streak photographs show definite evidence of streamwise modulation.

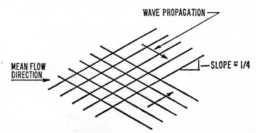

Figure 23. Possible standing-wave patterns in the sublayer of a turbulent boundary layer (plan view).

We now can go a step further. We can estimate that the center of the eddy must be somewhere around $y^+ = 15$ or 20 by studying the streak photographs at different y^+. From the known angle of the eddy we can now calculate the parameters which enter the linearized stability analysis (Tollmien–Schlichting analysis), in particular the characteristic-length parameter defining the thickness of the critical layer:

$$l = \left(\frac{du}{dy}\bigg|_{crit} \alpha/\nu\right)^{-\frac{1}{3}}$$

where α is the wave number. This parameter has the same ratio to y_{crit} as it does for unstable Tollmien–Schlichting waves, about 0.28. Another parameter, the Reynolds number based on the mean velocity at the eddy center and the distance from the wall, is somewhat lower than would be expected for unstable Tollmien–Schlichting waves, by a factor of about 4.

I think it may reasonably be conjectured that these waves in the sublayer are extracting energy from the mean motion by the same viscous processes which are known to work in the linearized stability analysis of two-dimensional waves.

S. J. KLINE

Our statistical measurements give us a value of 100 on the z^+ scale for the most frequently occurring wavelength. Prof. Kronauer is one step ahead of us because we have just begun to realize why some other people who have done hot-wire studies did not get this type of correlation. The reason is exactly as he has stated. In obtaining $u(z)$ data from the bubble pictures we can only get 4 or 5 streaks in one film frame. Since we need at least 20 to get an adequate mean, we have to consider these as samples from a population and treat a series of them in order to get an appropriate average. In doing this, an interesting thing happens. Indicated in

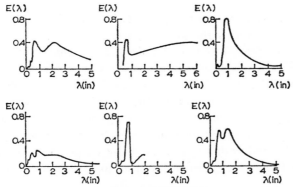

Figure 24. Typical samples of spectrum from individual frames. $y^+ = 1.62$, turbulent boundary layer. Data of Schraub & Kline (1965a).

figure 24 are 6 different energy spectra, the one-dimensional spectrum vs. λ. These are chosen from a much larger population and represent the principal types of spectra that are found. Typically, out of a sample of six spectra one is flat, one is extremely peaked and four have a definite peak. If you accumulate a histogram of these you get something like what is indicated in figure 25. There is a definite band of preference and a secondary peak which raises the maximum wavelength in the energy spectrum of the population from 100 to about 120. However, if I take the spectrum of the average, figure 26, it's much flatter, suggesting that the white

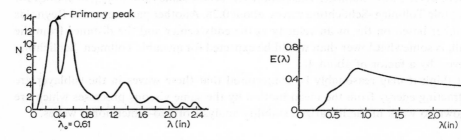

Figure 25 (left). Distribution of peaks from 31 individual spectra like those of figure 24.

Figure 26 (right). Ensemble spectrum from the 31 frames also used in figure 25, $y^+ = 1.62$.

noise in the turbulence field swamps the entire correlation—which is exactly what you have observed. So, as I have suspected for a few months now, it is possible that you will not be able to pick the correlation out in the usual way. The streaks move randomly over time so that, in combination with the other mechanism and the high background white noise, it is apparently very easy to swamp the result unless you carefully filter. These are very difficult measurements to make.

M. V. MORKOVIN (*The Martin Company, Baltimore, Maryland*)

I think that one can view the same phenomena in very many different ways. There has been a tendency here to emphasize the mathematical viewpoint, both in Prof. Kline's $\overline{u'v'}\, du/dy$ production term and in the instability approach. I think we all probably agree that there is a basic physical fundamental mechanism which contributes a tremendous amount to the turbulence production, namely the stretching of vortices along vortex lines or along axes somewhat inclined to them. This, before we get into the exclusiveness of stability or instability phenomena, I think needs to be understood a little bit more deeply. For instance, the latest calculations* of Prof. J. T. Stuart with respect to these laminar instabilities show

---

* *The Production of Intense Shear Layers by Vortex Stretching and Convection*, Nat. Phys. Lab. Report 1147, May 1965.

that there is indeed this mechanism again, leading to the necessary strong concentration of vorticity even in the second stage of the Tollmien–Schlichting process, which must be non-linear and three-dimensional. I would suggest that we keep our eyes on the physics first before we put mathematics into the problem. One way of looking at this would be, and this is my question to Prof. Kline, to try to demonstrate the exclusiveness or less-exclusiveness of the stability process through other related cases. Is there an equivalent set of data for free shear layers? We know that we have turbulence production in such layers but we don't have the strongly laminarized flow along a wall which exists in bound layers and this would probably make it rather difficult for the particular instability mechanism described here to be present. Are you working on something like this?

S. J. KLINE

No, we are not. It is quite clear that if you have a rough wall, completely hydraulically rough, or a free shear layer then you don't see the streaky structure. In fact we are just now doing some work on rough walls. If you have a "half-rough" wall you see some of the streaky structure, but if it is totally rough the streaks disappear entirely. You apparently then get turbulence production from the wakes of obstacles sticking out from the wall. At least one would suspect this. In the free-shear-layer case, there are some people here who are much better qualified to comment on this than I am. From what we have looked at, it does not seem to be the same; you don't see the streaky structure. I think the streaks have something to do with the wall. There seems to be more than one way in which turbulence can be produced.

H. W. LIEPMANN (*California Institute of Technology, Pasadena, California*)

I would just like to make a statement of ignorance. I do not understand the difference between the instability and the other mechanism. I don't see any contradiction and I don't see any definition of the terms; I also do not see what else you can expect from measuring the correlation in the first place. Of course you get these wavy phenomena! Therefore, I think these terms should be better defined before we speak about exclusiveness. Maybe I just missed the point.

F. H. CLAUSER (*University of California, Santa Cruz, California*)

In order to bring a little order, I think we ought to discuss the definitions of the two concepts.

S. J. KLINE

I am not sure I understood Prof. Liepmann. Are you referring to my remarks on instability?

H. W. LIEPMANN

No, it was Dr. Black's statement that there was some mechanism involving the $u'v'$ correlation and the $\partial u/\partial y$ distribution that is different from the instability. I can't see the difference. I also do not see what it means to say that you have a non-stationary laminar flow. What else is it? It is always laminar. So these terms will have to be better defined before we can discuss them.

T. J. BLACK

I think we can make a clear distinction between the two mechanisms. In the classical momentum-exchange mechanism the necessary prerequisite is the prior presence of turbulence in the shear layer. In the alternative model which I am proposing, instability and breakdown of the flow leads to energy transfer which in turn results in the production of turbulence. Turbulence does not precipitate this mechanism but occurs as a by-product of it. I think that there is quite a clear distinction between these two mechanisms. It is a difference between cause and effect, in my mind.

Let me put it in another way; in the classical model, the role of random turbulence is to transport momentum. In the stability model the role of turbulence is to excite a three-dimensional instability which then gives rise to further turbulence production. The role of turbulence in each case is quite different.

S. J. KLINE

I think there is some evidence on the point that Prof. Liepmann is making. Once you come to the breakdown process there is quite a catastrophic change in the fluid phenomena. The results of K. A. Meyer (1961a) show that, within the scatter of the data, you get the same correlation for the streaks in the visual data underneath the spot, so that some new mechanism does enter in. There is a distinct change along the edge of the spot that you can see in the transition pictures. You see streaks moving along and kicking off new ones. When you look back at the spots you can see the streaks in the dye; Elder's pictures show the same thing. Elder also concluded that you have to get up to a certain fluctuation level, and it doesn't matter how you get up to this level, but once you do the process is then somehow self-maintained. I think that $\int \mathbf{Pr} dy$ shows quite clearly that something has to go on happening. You have to keep on producing turbulence; this doesn't occur in a grid flow, but it does in a boundary layer. There is a distinction between the two cases.

F. H. CLAUSER

I think we still have one point hanging about the use of the filter.

R. E. KRONAUER

When you use a filter you select a frequency. Whether this frequency corresponds to a single wave number or not depends on whether the waves of that frequency have a single speed. In fact the longitudinal correlations show the wave number to be quite highly selected. Now, what I am reporting is transverse correlations. If these correlations have well-defined peaks and valleys, then the transverse wave number is also quite highly selected. This says that the waves of the selected frequency not only possess a relatively constant speed but also a well-defined inclination.

S. J. KLINE

If you change the frequency of the filter to another value, do you find this kind of correlation or does it flatten?

R. E. KRONAUER

Near the wall you don't find much at other frequencies. If you look further out, say at a y^+ of 200, you find a whole broad band. For any particular frequency in that band there is a strongly selected longitudinal wave number, and a rather-well-defined transverse wave number. If you are interested, I can show you additional data there which includes waves whose longitudinal extent is of the order of 10,000 on the y^+ scale and transversely are on the order of 1000.

T. B. BENJAMIN (*Cambridge University, Cambridge, England*)

I don't wish to take issue specifically on anything that Prof. Kline or Dr. Black has said, but I feel I must inject a note of warning as regards the basic interpretation of some of the matters that have been discussed. It seems to me that the usual argument applied to the energy budget is potentially very misleading. That this is so is proved in the one physical example available whereby these general ideas about the energy budget can be tested definitely; I refer to the classical case of Tollmien–Schlichting waves, under conditions neighbouring on the upper branch of the neutral-stability curve. This is, I believe, the only realistic example where the mechanisms of dissipation and of energy-production from the mean flow are independent. By the usual argument, it might seem that if one increased the dissipation and did nothing else, then the disturbance would tend to die away. In fact, exactly the opposite is true. One has the paradoxical situation that any new influence tending to increase the rate of production (such as a favourable pressure gradient, which is well known to enhance the development of Reynolds stress at the critical layer) tends to wipe out the disturbance, whereas dissipation tends to augment it. This paradox is easily resolved, however, and the principles involved seem likely to apply to boundary-layer turbulence just as well as to Tollmien–Schlichting waves.* I don't think this is a suitable time to take up these theoretical questions but, recognizing their intricacy, I do think it is timely to plead for some caution about energy-balance arguments.

B. G. NEWMAN (*McGill University, Montreal, Canada*)

I would like to make two very mundane comments. In the outer part of boundary layers, wakes, free jets and what not the mechanism obviously isn't very important since the flows are well known to be viscous independent. Secondly, I think the inner part of the flow, the layer next to the wall, is very satisfactorily described as a viscous sublayer.

J. M. ROBERTSON (*University of Illinois, Urbana, Illinois*)

I would also like to raise a point. I think that in your study the pressure gradients, particularly the adverse ones, were rather mild. When you get stronger gradients you get a larger production term, expressed by $\overline{u'v'}$ (du/dy), in the outer region; there must be some other mechanism for this.

M. R. HEAD (*Cambridge University, Cambridge, England*)

I just wanted to ask whether the parameter $(\nu/\rho u_\tau^3)(dp/dx)$ wouldn't be a more satisfactory parameter for correlating the results in the wall region?

S. J. KLINE

I think you are right. If you actually go through the arguments to get the parameter (which has been done, for example, by Back, Massier & Gier (1964)), you get the K-value that I showed divided by $C_f^{\frac{3}{2}}$; this is in fact the parameter you just mentioned. However, since C_f is a slowly varying function, and the data scatters over $\pm$ 50 %, it is a lot more convenient not to worry about C_f and to plot K since it contains only external parameters, and does not have a wall shear in it. If you really had accurate enough data, it would probably be better to use the parameter you just described.

I would like to make a comment about the things that Dr. Benjamin said but I can discuss it with him later.

Finally, I think we have to be a little cautious here. After all, we have been studying this problem for 50 years; we all have a skewed attitude towards it based on history. We have to be a little bit careful in applying these old ideas and in criticizing new ones. The old ones if not wrong are at least insufficient; they really don't work, and we know this.

---

* For a discussion see: T. B. Benjamin, *Fluid Flow with Flexible Boundaries*, Proc. 11th Internat. Congr. Appl. Mech. (1964), to be published by Springer, Berlin.

M. R. HEAD

I wonder if I might just mention this parameter $(v/\rho u_\tau^3)\,(dp/dx)$, which we call $\varDelta$. We have been doing experiments on relaminarization and the thing that we have found is that the breakdown of the inner layer, which presumably is the beginning of relaminarization, appears to occur at a fairly well-defined value of $\varDelta$ quite independently, and this is the surprising thing, of boundary layer thickness and Reynolds number.

S. J. KLINE

I think that is consistent with our findings. I would like to discuss it with you later.

F. H. CLAUSER

I think this leaves only one question unanswered. The second transition, is it properly called de-re-laminarization?

Critical Review of Existing Methods for Calculating the Development of Turbulent Boundary Layers

J. C. ROTTA

Aerodynamische Versuchsanstalt, Göttingen, Germany

SUMMARY

A brief survey of representations of the velocity profiles and skin-friction formulae is followed by a review of recently proposed methods to predict the development of turbulent boundary layers on impermeable walls in two-dimensional flow of constant fluid properties. The shortcomings of the presently used methods are pointed out. The effect of the upstream history on the turbulent motion is demonstrated for some different boundary layers, and methods which take this effect into account are discussed. Finally, the conception of eddy-viscosity as a basis for turbulent boundary layer calculation is treated.

NOTATION

B	wake factor, equation (2.6)
C	constant of the law of the wall, equation (2.10)
$c_D = \dfrac{2}{\rho U^3} \displaystyle\int_0^\infty \tau \dfrac{\partial u}{\partial y}\, \mathrm{d}y$	dissipation coefficient
$c_f = 2\tau_w/\rho U^2$	local skin-friction coefficient
F_D	function defined by equation (4.3)
$F(H_1)$	entrainment function, equation (4.6)
$\left.\begin{aligned} H_1 &= (\delta - \delta_1)/\delta_2 \\ H_{12} &= \delta_1/\delta_2 \\ H_{32} &= \delta_3/\delta_2 \end{aligned}\right\}$	velocity-profile shape parameters
I	velocity-profile shape parameter, defined by equation (2.4)
K	constant of the velocity-defect law, equation (2.10)
p	pressure

Q	volume flux in the boundary layer, equation (4.6)
Q_t	volume flux of turbulent fluid, equation (4.7)
U	velocity at the edge of the boundary layer
u	local velocity component in x-direction
$u_\tau = \sqrt{\tau_w/\rho}$	skin-friction velocity
w	wake function
x	coordinate parallel to the surface and in the flow direction
y	distance from the surface
$\left.\begin{array}{l}\alpha\\\beta\\\lambda\end{array}\right\}$	constants, equation (5.1)
γ	intermittency factor
δ	boundary layer thickness
$\delta_1 = \displaystyle\int_0^\infty \left(1 - \frac{u}{U}\right)\mathrm{d}y$	displacement thickness
$\delta_2 = \displaystyle\int_0^\infty \frac{u}{U}\left(1 - \frac{u}{U}\right)\mathrm{d}y$	momentum thickness
$\delta_3 = \displaystyle\int_0^\infty \frac{u}{U}\left[1 - \left(\frac{u}{U}\right)^2\right]\mathrm{d}y$	kinetic-energy thickness
ε	eddy-viscosity
$\eta = y/\delta$	
$\kappa (= 0.4)$	universal constant
ν	viscosity
ν_e	effective viscosity, equation (6.2)
$\Pi = \dfrac{\delta_1}{\tau_w}\dfrac{\mathrm{d}p}{\mathrm{d}x}$	pressure-gradient parameter
τ	shear stress
τ_w	shear stress at the surface
τ_t	turbulent shear stress

1. INTRODUCTION

From the viewpoint of the engineering application of fluid mechanics, there is a great need for computational methods which predict accurately the skin friction, the growth, and the location of separation of turbulent boundary layers. The theoretical background and the methods mostly in use now are described in text-books, e.g. Schlichting (1965), and in some survey articles by Clauser (1956) and Rotta (1962).

References p. 101–102

The problem is far from being solved and an increasing research activity in this field is observed in recent times. Interesting ideas have been advanced within the last few years, and tests have also been performed. It is the main purpose of this paper to discuss the new developments from a critical point of view.

The subject is restricted to turbulent boundary layers on impermeable walls in two-dimensional flow with constant fluid properties.

2. VELOCITY PROFILES AND SKIN FRICTION

The usual way of calculating turbulent boundary layers is by using the von Kármán momentum integral equation,

$$\frac{d\delta_2}{dx} + (H_{12}+2)\frac{\delta_2}{U}\frac{dU}{dx} = \frac{c_f}{2} \tag{2.1}$$

If the velocity at the edge of the layer, U, is given along x, then this equation contains three unknowns: the momentum thickness δ_2, the shape parameter $H_{12} = \delta_1/\delta_2$, and the local skin-friction coefficient c_f. These unknowns must be interrelated with each other and with known flow parameters.

Some of the required relationships can be established if the velocity profiles are defined. The simplest possibility, to assume the velocity profiles as a one-parameter family which may be approximated by a power law, gives to some extent satisfactory results, but fails in that no skin-friction law can be derived. A more refined representation is based on the two-layer model: The layer near the surface is represented by the universal law of the wall,

$$\frac{u}{u_\tau} = f\left(\frac{yu_\tau}{\nu}\right) \tag{2.2}$$

and the outer part is represented by the velocity-defect law,

$$\frac{U-u}{u_\tau} = F\left(\frac{yu_\tau}{\delta_1 U}\right) \tag{2.3}$$

where the function F is assumed as a one-parameter family of curves. A characteristic parameter of the defect law is defined by

$$I = \int_0^\infty \left(\frac{U-u}{u_\tau}\right)^2 d\left(\frac{yu_\tau}{\delta_1 U}\right) \approx \left(1 - \frac{1}{H_{12}}\right)\sqrt{2/c_f} \tag{2.4}$$

where $u_\tau = \sqrt{\tau_w/\rho} = \sqrt{c_f/2}U$. Both laws overlap in the logarithmic part of the profile,

$$u = \frac{1}{\kappa}\ln y + \text{const.} \tag{2.5}$$

where κ is a universal constant ($= 0.4$).

The defect law may be well approximated with the aid of the wake function $w(y/\delta)$,

$$\frac{U-u}{u_\tau} = -\frac{1}{\kappa}\ln\frac{y}{\delta} + \frac{B}{\kappa}[2-w(y/\delta)] \quad \text{for } 40\frac{v}{u_\tau} < y \leq \delta \qquad (2.6)$$

where the wake factor B is a free parameter, such that there exists a unique relationship between B and the shape parameter I, defined by (2.4). Numerical values of the wake function have been given by Coles (1956). Analytical approximations have been proposed by Moses (1964),

$$w(y/\delta) = 2(3\eta^2 - 2\eta^3) \qquad (2.7)$$

by Spalding (1965),

$$w(y/\delta) = 1 - \cos(\pi\eta) \qquad (2.8)$$

and by Rotta (1964),

$$w(y/\delta) = 39\eta^3 - 125\eta^4 + 183\eta^5 - 133\eta^6 + 38\eta^7 \qquad (2.9)$$

All velocity-profile parameters, including the local skin-friction coefficient, can be computed from these relations. The velocity profiles depend on two parameters, viz. the wake factor B and the Reynolds number $u_\tau\delta/v$, which can be converted, for instance, into the shape parameter H_{12} and the Reynolds number $U\delta_2/v$.

On figure 1 the ratio of kinetic-energy thickness to momentum thickness, $H_{32} = \delta_3/\delta_2$, is shown as a function of H_{12} and $U\delta_1/v$. The effect of the Reynolds number is small. The agreement with the experimental results of a boundary layer with increasing pressure gradient (Schubauer & Klebanoff 1951) and of a boundary layer with decreasing pressure gradient (Bradshaw & Ferriss 1965) is good. It is in fact this part of the turbulent boundary layer theory which is most satisfactorily established.

The skin-friction law, derived from the two-layer model reads

$$\sqrt{2/c_f} = \frac{1}{\kappa}\ln\left(\frac{U\delta_1}{v}\right) + C + K \qquad (2.10)$$

where C is the constant ($= 5.2$) appearing in the usual formulation of the law of the wall, and K can be calculated as a function of the wake factor B. The widely used Ludwieg–Tillmann (1949) skin-friction law,

$$c_f = 0.246\left(\frac{U\delta_2}{v}\right)^{-0.268} \times 10^{-0.678H_{12}} \qquad (2.11)$$

is very convenient, but it is based on experiments covering only a limited range of Reynolds numbers, and in addition it overestimates the value of c_f at large values of H_{12}. Equation (2.10) will give better results for high Reynolds numbers as well

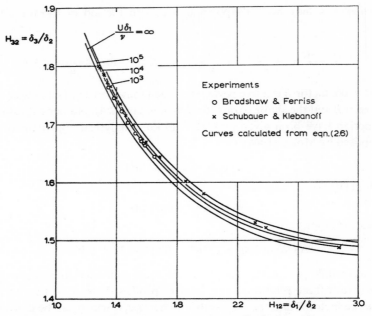

Figure 1. Relationship between velocity-profile shape parameters.

as for large values of H_{12}. The results of the two laws are compared on figure 2, where $c_f \times (U\delta_2/v)^{0.268}$ is plotted on a logarithmic scale versus H_{12}. The Ludwieg–Tillmann formula represents a single straight line in this diagram.

A modified expression for the value of K in (2.10) has recently been suggested by Nash (1964), which gives $c_f \to 0$ for $H_{12}=3$.

Another important advantage of the two-layer model is that it can easily be extended to rough surfaces. This has been confirmed by tests performed by Perry & Joubert (1963).

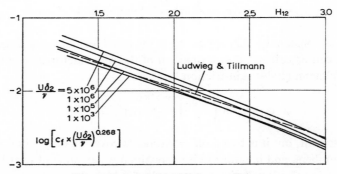

Figure 2. Local skin-friction coefficient.

3. EQUILIBRIUM BOUNDARY LAYERS

In order to obtain a determinate system of equations, an additional relation is needed for the variation of the shape parameter H_{12} or I. The first approach was made by Buri (1931), who postulated the shape parameter to be a function of pressure gradient and Reynolds number. This method, which is a direct analogue of Pohlhausen's method for the laminar layers, is applicable only under certain circumstances, namely if the pressure gradient parameter $\Pi = (\delta_1/\tau_w)(\mathrm{d}p/\mathrm{d}x)$ is kept constant in the flow direction. If this condition is fulfilled, the shape parameter I settles to an (almost) constant value. For this group of boundary layers, which are called equilibrium boundary layers or self-preserving layers, there exists a functional relationship

$$I = f(\Pi) \tag{3.1}$$

On the basis of available experimental results and theoretical considerations, Nash (1965) has deduced the relation

$$I = 6.1\sqrt{\Pi + 1.81} - 1.7 \tag{3.2}$$

which will be considered as a reasonable approximation for further discussions. The relation is plotted on figure 3 and is found to be in good agreement with the experimental results of equilibrium layers by Clauser (1954), Bradshaw & Ferriss (1965), Herring & Norbury (1963), and includes the flat plate case for which $\Pi = 0$. In addition the results of some non-equilibrium boundary layers are shown on figure 3. In some cases considerable deviations from the equilibrium curve are

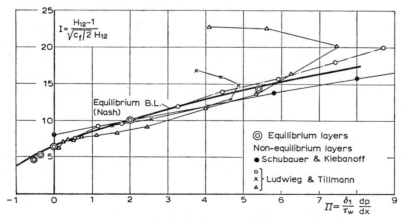

Figure 3. Variation of shape parameter I with pressure gradient.
Equilibrium boundary layers: $I = 6.1\sqrt{\Pi + 1.81} - 1.7$.

References p. 101–102

observed and it becomes clear that the shape of the velocity profile cannot be expressed merely as a function of the local value of Π in general cases.

4. THE SHAPE-PARAMETER EQUATION

The majority of the calculation methods nowadays in use are based on a first order differential equation for the shape parameter. Since the influencing magnitudes, viz. the pressure gradient and the shear stress, appear linearly as two additive terms in the boundary layer equation, an auxiliary equation of the type

$$\delta_2 \frac{dH_{12}}{dx} = - \frac{\delta_2}{U} \frac{dU}{dx} M - N \tag{4.1}$$

is in agreement with the actual behaviour of the turbulent boundary layer. In fact, almost all the shape-parameter equations given in the literature can be reduced to this form, although in some cases other shape factors, like $H_{32} = \delta_3/\delta_2$ or $H_1 = (\delta - \delta_1)/\delta_2$, are used.

Analytical expressions for the functions M and N can be derived from the boundary layer equations. When a particular family of velocity profiles is introduced, M can readily be calculated as a function of the shape parameter, whereas N depends on the shape parameter of the velocity profile and on some other quantity of the turbulent motion. This other quantity is, in most cases, the shear-stress distribution. This is the point where any analysis must rely on experimental results. Since a clear physical basis for the comparison of experimental results is missing, and since many of the available data suffer from the lack of two-dimensionality, it is the point where the most uncertainty has crept into the calculation methods. Generally, N is considered as being a function of the shape parameter and the local Reynolds number, which however turns out to be a very restrictive assumption, as will be shown later. There is an almost unlimited number of possibilities for deriving the shape-parameter equation from the boundary layer equations, as is outlined in detail by Rotta (1962). We will briefly discuss only three examples to which contributions have recently been made.

4.1. The Kinetic-Energy Equation

When the kinetic-energy integral equation is combined with the momentum equation, the following differential equation is obtained for the shape parameter H_{32}

$$\delta_2 \frac{dH_{32}}{dx} = (H_{12}-1)H_{32}\frac{\delta_2}{U}\frac{dU}{dx} + c_D - H_{32}\frac{c_f}{2} \tag{4.2}$$

where c_D is the dissipation coefficient which, on the basis of the two-layer model, can be expressed as

$$c_D = c_f(1 + \sqrt{c_f/2}\,F_D) \tag{4.3}$$

Values of F_D have been determined from experimental results of boundary layers with increasing value of H_{12} by the present writer (Rotta 1952), and have been related to the shape parameter I. Recently Fernholz (1964) and Spalding (1965) have reviewed the available information. Spalding's recommendation together with the author's relationship are shown on figure 4. In order to obtain a finite value of c_D as separation is approached, F_D is required to vary as I^3 when I goes to infinity. Spalding's relation meets this condition, whereas the author's relation gives $c_D \to 0$ at separation, which is not realistic. Also plotted on figure 4 are the values for the equilibrium boundary layers, according to (3.2). The Reynolds number has a small effect; however, the values are considerably higher than those determined from boundary layers with increasing H_{12}.

Truckenbrodt (1952) suggested, on the basis of the author's investigations, the often-used formula

$$c_D = \frac{0.0112}{\left(\dfrac{U\delta_2}{\nu}\right)^{\frac{1}{6}}} \tag{4.4}$$

and Walz (1965) derived from Clauser's (1954) equilibrium layers

$$c_D = \frac{0.00962 + 0.1644(H_{32} - 1.5)^{4.81}}{\left(\dfrac{U\delta_2}{\nu}\right)^{(0.2317H_{32} - 0.2644)}} \tag{4.5}$$

which gives higher values than those calculated from (4.4).

4.2. *The Entrainment Equation of Head*

An entirely different idea has been advanced by Head (1960), who related the shape parameter of the velocity profile to the rate at which fluid is entrained in the boundary layer. In particular, the amount of fluid entrained per unit length and unit width of the layer is assumed to be

$$\frac{dQ}{dx} = \frac{d}{dx}[U(\delta - \delta_1)] = U\,F(H_1) \tag{4.6}$$

where $Q = \displaystyle\int_0^\delta u\,dy$ is the volume flux in the boundary layer and $F(H_1)$ is a dimensionless function of the shape parameter $H_1 = (\delta - \delta_1)/\delta_2$. The relation (4.6) may be justified by physical arguments. The rate of irrotational fluid entering the region of turbulent motion depends on the intensity of the velocity fluctuations near the edge of the turbulent region. On the other hand, the turbulent shear stress which

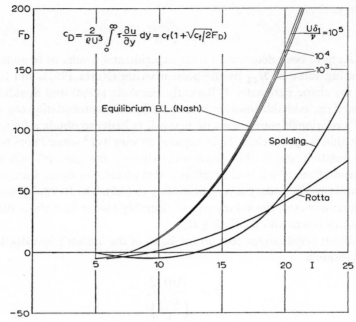

Figure 4. Dissipation integral.

controls the mean-velocity profile is also a function of the fluctuation intensity. It is thus plausible to postulate a dependence of the rate of entrainment upon the shape of the velocity profile.

There exists a relation between the two shape parameters H_1 and H_{12}; it has been determined by Head from measurements of Schubauer & Klebanoff (1951) and Newman (1951) and is shown on the left-hand part of figure 5. The curve calculated on the basis of power-law profiles is indicated by a dotted line. The

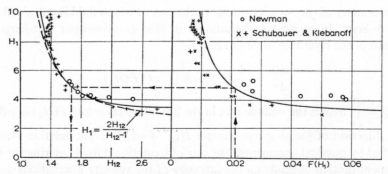

Figure 5. Head's theory of entrainment in the turbulent boundary layer.

function $F(H_1)$ has been determined from the same measurements and is given on the right-hand part of figure 5. An example of how the diagram is to be used, if $F(H_1)$ is given and H_{12} is to be determined, is indicated by dotted lines.

A new entrainment equation has been developed by Thompson (1965), who replaced the total volume flux Q by the volume flux of turbulent fluid in the boundary layer,

$$Q_t = \int_0^\infty \gamma u_t \, dy \tag{4.7}$$

where γ is the intermittency factor and u_t is the mean velocity of the turbulent fluid. Thompson also included terms to allow for the effects of cross-flow and wall curvature and found improved agreement with experiments, especially in equilibrium layers. Spalding (1965) has derived a relation between the dissipation integral and the entrainment rate.

4.3. *The Method of Moses*

Moses (1964) developed a method in which the momentum integral equation is satisfied not only for the entire boundary layer, as is expressed by (2.1), but in addition for the inner half of the layer. This gives a second differential equation:

$$u_{0.5} \frac{\partial}{\partial x}\left(\delta \int_0^{0.5} u \, d\eta\right) - \frac{\partial}{\partial x}\left(\delta \int_0^{0.5} u^2 \, d\eta\right) = -\frac{\delta}{2} U \frac{dU}{dx} + \frac{\tau_w - \tau_{0.5}}{\rho} \tag{4.8}$$

where $\eta = y/\delta$ and the suffix 0.5 indicates values at $\eta = 0.5$. The velocity profiles are assumed according to the two-layer model. The value of the shear stress $\tau_{0.5}$ is computed with the Boussinesq relation

$$\tau_{0.5}/\rho = \left(\varepsilon \frac{\partial u}{\partial y}\right)_{0.5} \tag{4.9}$$

where the eddy-viscosity, ε, is approximated from zero-pressure-gradient experiments. The following relation is given (for $U\delta/v \geq 5000$)

$$\frac{\varepsilon_{0.5}}{U\delta} = \frac{0.004}{\ln(U\delta/v) - 7.6} + 0.0013 \tag{4.10}$$

4.4. *Discussion of the Shape-Parameter Equation*

It is fully realized now that a shape-parameter equation of the form of (4.1), in which N is considered to be a function of H_{12} and $U\delta_2/v$, will not give satisfactory results for all types of pressure distributions because the upstream history affects the development of the turbulent boundary layer in a more complex manner than is expressed by this equation. For illustration, two examples from Head's paper are reproduced on figure 6. The upper diagram shows a boundary layer which approaches the point of separation very suddenly. In this case the calculated shape parameter, H_{12}, is below the experimental values. On the lower diagram, H_{12} increases more slowly in the flow direction. In this case the theory predicts values of H_{12} which are too high. These examples are typical not only for Head's method, but for all methods known. Calculations performed by Walz (1965) confirm this observation.

From the standpoint of application there are two questions:

1. Which of the existing methods can best be recommended?
2. Is there any possibility of improving the calculation on the basis that M and N are functions of local parameters?

At first glance it seems merely a matter of task as to whether the kinetic-energy equation or the entrainment equation or any other equation is used together with the momentum equation; identical results, at least with respect to the function M, are expected. In fact, some differences are observed for the different approaches and are a consequence of the approximative character of the assumed velocity profiles. For example, a 25% lower value for M is obtained from Head's entrain-

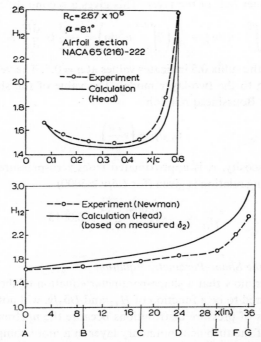

Figure 6. Development of the shape parameter in adverse pressure gradients.

ment equation than from the kinetic-energy equation at $H_{12}=1.4$, and a 40% lower value at $H_{12}=2$, if power law profiles are assumed. The magnitude of M determines the sensibility of the profile shape to changes in the pressure gradient. A smaller value of M means a slower response of H_{12} to changes in $(\delta_2/U)(dU/dx)$.

A rational way to judge the qualification of a particular shape-parameter equation is to apply it to a number of examples for which experimental data are available. Thompson (1964) has compared the results of several existing methods with a large amount of experimental data. According to these investigations, Head's entrainment equation proved generally the most satisfactory.

With regard to the second question, it can not be excluded that another combination of M and N can be found, which gives still better results for a wide variety of pressure distributions. In order to find the answer, it is necessary to perform extensive calculations with systematic variations of M and N.

5. THE EFFECT OF UPSTREAM HISTORY

The effect of upstream history on the shear-stress distribution has often been discussed. We will demonstrate this effect by a few examples. The basis of the comparisons are the equilibrium layers, for which a fixed relation between I and Π exists according to (3.2). When, in addition, the velocity-defect law of (2.6) is adopted, the shear-stress distribution can be computed by integrating the boundary layer equation. Thus a certain shear-stress distribution is associated with each pair of values I and c_f.* Such shear-stress distributions, which correspond to the local equilibrium conditions, are plotted together with the experimental distributions of the separating boundary layer of Schubauer & Klebanoff (1951) on figure 7. The value of I increases in the flow direction, and the differences between the calculated and measured shear distributions grow at the same time. The calculated distributions are too high.

Similarly, figure 8 shows the results of tests made by Sandborn & Slogar (1955) in comparison with shear-stress distributions calculated in the same way as before. The value of I also increases in the flow direction for this layer and the differences between the experimental and calculated distributions show the same tendency as in the previous case.

Figure 9 presents the test results of Bradshaw & Ferriss (1965). In this case the shape parameter I decreases in the flow direction. The shear-stress distributions calculated for local equilibrium conditions are below the measured distributions for $x > 65$ in.

---

* The effect of c_f on the dimensionless shear-stress distribution, τ/τ_w, is small.

References p. 101–102

In order to summarize these results, the maximum values of τ for each case have been plotted versus the x-coordinate on figure 10. In the first case, the experimental as well as the calculated τ_{max} increase in the downstream direction; in the case of Bradshaw's layer, both curves of τ_{max} decrease. But in all three cases the two curves diverge. It follows clearly from these comparisons that the actual values of the shear stress sometimes deviate considerably from the equilibrium distribu-

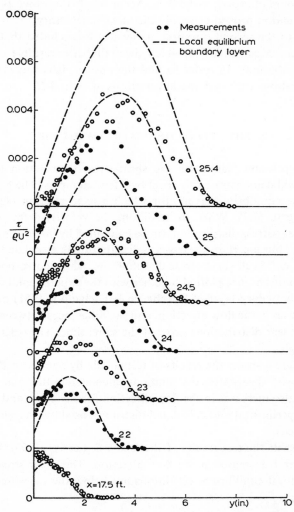

Figure 7. Shear-stress distribution of a turbulent boundary layer with increasing pressure gradient (Schubauer & Klebanoff).

tions. A relaxation time of a certain length is required for the shear stress to accommodate to the equilibrium condition. It is obvious that the neglect of this upstream effect will cause an erroneous prediction of the boundary layer development.

Two interesting attempts to overcome the inherent shortcomings of the previous methods have recently been published.

Nash (1965) studied the behaviour of various types of boundary layers and

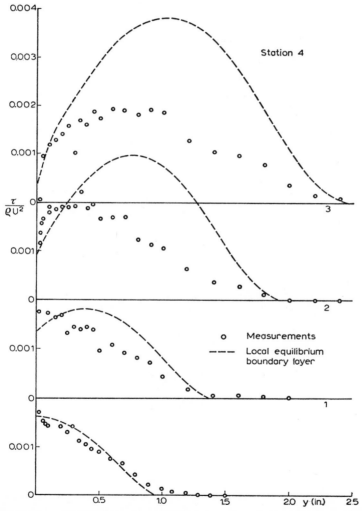

Figure 8. Shear-stress distribution of a turbulent boundary layer with increasing pressure gradient (Sandborn & Slogar).

proposed a second-order differential equation,

$$\delta_1^2 \frac{\mathrm{d}^2 I}{\mathrm{d}x^2} = \lambda \left\{ \delta_1 \frac{\mathrm{d}}{\mathrm{d}x}(I - I_e) \right\}^\alpha (I - I_e)^\beta \qquad (5.1)$$

for the variation of the shape parameter I, where I_e is the value of I if the boundary were in equilibrium at the local value of Π. Provisional values of the coefficients λ, α, and β have been assessed to give satisfactory agreement with experimental data

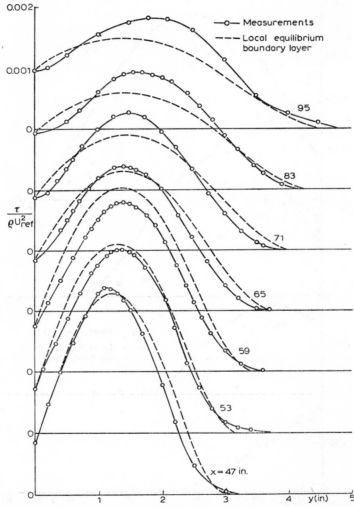

Figure 9. Shear-stress distribution in a redeveloping turbulent boundary layer (Bradshaw & Ferriss).

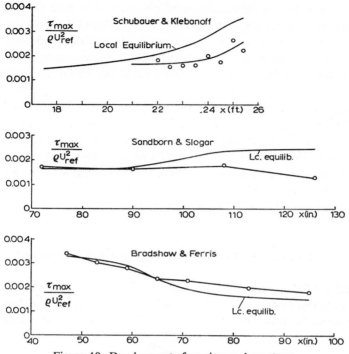

Figure 10. Development of maximum shear stress.

in some cases. Nash suggested the following values:

$$\frac{d}{dx}(I-I_e) > 0 \; : \; \lambda = -0.25; \quad \alpha = 3; \quad \beta = -2$$

$$\frac{d}{dx}(I-I_e) < 0 \; : \; \lambda = 5; \quad \alpha = 2; \quad \beta = -2$$

The difference in the values of λ and α, depending on the sign of $d(I-I_e)/dx$, is considered to be of prime importance in describing the different types of response of I. The results calculated from this shape-parameter equation have been found in good agreement with experiments if suitable initial values of I and dI/dx have been assumed.

Another approach was made by McDonald & Stoddart (1965), which is based on the von Kármán momentum equation (2.1) and the moment of momentum integral equation. The shear-stress integral, which appears in the latter equation, is not related to the velocity-profile parameters, but is approximated in terms of the skin-friction coefficient and the dimensionless distance above the surface of the maximum shear stress. The variation of this dimensionless distance is computed from a first-order differential equation, which is obtained with the use of experi-mental data. Thus a system of three first-order differential equations has to be solved. A comprehensive series of comparisons of calculated and measured boundary layers has been made which indicate, in many cases, good agreement between predicted and experimental behaviour if the initial values are suitably chosen.

The calculation methods treated in the previous section require two initial con-ditions to be specified. One further condition has to be specified when the upstream history is taken into account. The examples performed by the methods of Nash and McDonald & Stoddart show that the results are sometimes very sensitive to this third initial condition. The problem of how this initial value is to be determined when the development of a boundary layer is to be predicted for which no experi-mental data are available, requires further study.

6. APPLICATION OF THE EDDY-VISCOSITY CONCEPT

The prediction of the boundary layer based on integral relations and an assumed velocity profile will always be of an approximate nature. A more detailed calcula-tion of turbulent boundary layers is possible with the use of Boussinesq's relation,

$$\tau_t = \rho\varepsilon \frac{\partial u}{\partial y} \tag{6.1}$$

provided that reasonable assumptions with respect to the distribution of the eddy-viscosity ε can be made. This concept has successfully been applied to free-tur-bulence problems for a long time. In turbulent boundary layers, the problem of finding an adequate assumption for the distribution of ε is rendered more difficult for two major reasons:

1. The turbulent motion close to the solid wall is much affected by the presence of the wall, whereas at greater distances from the wall, the flow pattern resembles very much that of a wake.
2. Turbulent boundary layers develop in a great variety of pressure fields.

The simplest assumption of a constant value of ε in the outer region of the layer was applied to equilibrium boundary layers in constant and variable pressure by Clauser (1956) and Townsend (1956). The solutions obtained in this way were joined with the universal law of the wall to give velocity profiles for the whole boundary layer.

A more approximative treatment has been made by Libby, Baronti & Napolitano (1964) on the same basis. These authors also started from a two-layer model and computed the shear-stress distribution of the inner layer from the boundary layer equations, assuming a velocity distribution in accordance with the universal law of the wall. A polynominal representation was used for the shear stress in the outer layer. From this shear stress distribution and a constant value of ε the velocity profile was obtained by integrating (6.1). The method has been applied to equilibrium and near-equilibrium flows, and reasonable results have been obtained.

An analytically more precise approach has recently been performed by Mellor & Gibson (1963) and Mellor (1964). The basis of this work is a completely defined hypothesis for the effective viscosity,

$$v_e = v + \varepsilon \tag{6.2}$$

as is seen from figure 11. In particular, it is expressed as

$$v_e/v = \varphi\{(\kappa^2 y^2/v)|\partial u/\partial y|\} \quad \text{for small } y$$
$$\tag{6.3}$$
$$v_e/U\delta_1 = \Phi\{(\kappa^2 y^2/U\delta_1)|\partial u/\partial y|\} \quad \text{for large } y$$

Both functions apply in the overlap region, thus it follows that here $v_e \approx \varepsilon = \kappa^2 y^2|\partial u/\partial y|$, which is identical with Prandtl's mixing-length theorem. Furthermore $\varphi \to 1$ as $y \to 0$, and the complete function φ throughout the viscous sublayer is obtained from Laufer's (1954) pipe measurements. For large enough y, a constant value $\Phi = 0.016$ was chosen. The complete equations of motion have been solved numerically for the case of equilibrium layers over the whole range of values of Π.

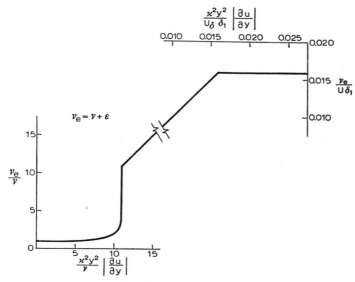

Figure 11. The effective viscosity (after Mellor).

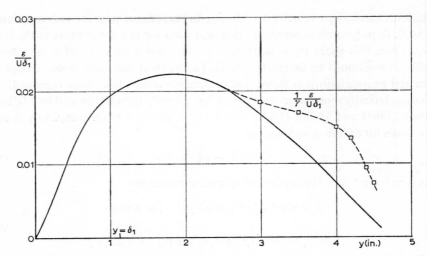

Figure 12. Eddy viscosity of an equilibrium boundary layer, $\Pi = 5.4$, $I = 14.1$ (Bradshaw & Ferriss).

Generally speaking, the results are found in satisfactory agreement with experimental data.

Let us have a look at the actual behaviour of the eddy-viscosity in order to examine the underlying assumptions of Mellor & Gibson and their applicability to more general cases. Figure 12 shows the non-dimensional eddy-viscosity cal-

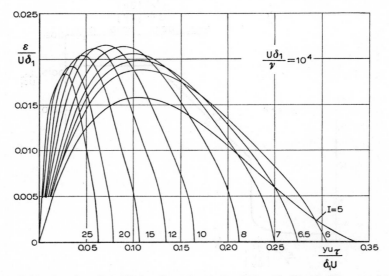

Figure 13. Eddy viscosity of equilibrium boundary layers (using Nash's relation, equation (3.2)).

culated from the experimental velocity profile of the equilibrium boundary layer investigated by Bradshaw & Ferriss (1965). It is seen that $\varepsilon/(U\delta_1)$ is not constant in the outer part, but decreases continuously to zero with growing distance from the wall. This explains why the experimental velocity approaches the free stream value more rapidly than is predicted on the basis of a constant eddy-viscosity. This caused Townsend (1956) to take the intermittency of the turbulent motion into account. But even the value of $\varepsilon/(\gamma U\delta_1)$ decreases with the distance from the surface, as is seen from the diagram.

The non-dimensional eddy-viscosity of equilibrium layers of various values of I is plotted versus the non-dimensional distance from the wall on figure 13. These results have been calculated on the basis of Nash's relation between I and Π, (3.2), and velocity profiles constructed of the logarithmic law of the wall and Coles' wake function. The value of ε increases first with y up to a maximum and then decreases again. This is in agreement with the behaviour already shown on figure 12. In addition to this, there is a considerable variation in the magnitude of ε with the parameter I. The variation of $\varepsilon/(U\delta_1)$ in a non-equilibrium boundary layer is shown on figure 14. These curves were determined from the experimental velocity profiles and shear-stress distributions measured by Bradshaw & Ferriss. In order to demonstrate the variation of $\varepsilon/(U\delta_1)$ with the shape parameter I, the maximum values from figures 13 and 14 have been replotted as functions of I on figure 15.

The figures 12 to 15 indicate that the assumption of a constant value of $\varepsilon/(U\delta_1)$ in the outer part of a turbulent boundary layer is not more than a rough approximation. Although there was no investigation made in the present study as to the

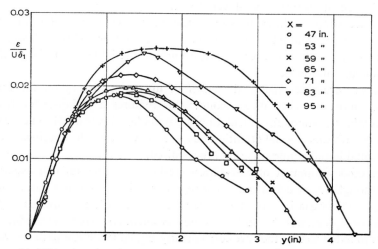

Figure 14. Eddy viscosity of a non-equilibrium boundary layer (Bradshaw & Ferriss).

References p. 101–102

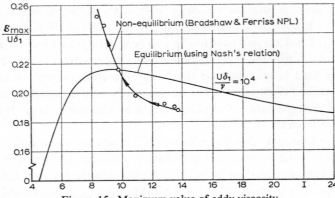

Figure 15. Maximum value of eddy viscosity.

sensitivity of the calculation results to variations in the eddy-viscosity, it can be concluded that more refined relations for ε are required if results of higher accuracy are desired. In non-equilibrium flow, the eddy-viscosity is much affected by the upstream history of the flow.

7. CONCLUDING REMARKS

The present status of turbulent-boundary-layer calculation methods may be summarized as follows:
1. The velocity profiles and the local skin-friction coefficient are represented with sufficient accuracy by the two-layer model.
2. The calculation methods mostly in use now, which are based on the von Kármán momentum integral equation and a first order differential equation for the velocity-profile shape parameter, do not give reliable results for all kinds of pressure distributions.
3. For more accurate results, the effect of upstream history on the turbulent motion must be taken into account; this requires a higher-order system of differential equations for calculating the boundary layer development. In connection with this, special attention has to be devoted to the specification of the additional initial conditions that are required.

The further development of calculation methods requires reliable experimental data. Although there exists a great quantity of experimental results, additional tests with systematic variations of the pressure distribution are desirable; any three-dimensional-flow effects should be carefully avoided. All experimental data should be fully tabulated so that they are conveniently available for comparisons with new theories.

For refinement of the calculation methods at later stages, the Reynolds normal stresses and the effect of surface curvature should be taken into account.

REFERENCES

Bradshaw, P. & Ferriss, D. H. (1965) *The Response of a Retarded Equilibrium Turbulent Boundary Layer to the Sudden Removal of Pressure Gradient.* Nat. Phys. Lab. Aero Rep. 1145.

Buri, A. (1931) *Eine Berechnungsgrundiage für die turbulente Grenzschicht bei beschleunigter und verzögerter Grundströmung.* Dissertation d. Eidgen. Techn. Hochschule Zürich.

Clauser, F. H. (1954) *Turbulent Boundary Layers in Adverse Pressure Gradients.* J. Aero. Sci. **21**, 91–108.

Clauser, F. H. (1956) *The Turbulent Boundary Layer.* Advances in Applied Mechanics, Vol. IV. Academic Press, New York.

Coles, D. (1956) *The Law of the Wake in the Turbulent Boundary Layer.* J. Fluid Mech. **1**, 191–226.

Fernholz, H. (1964) *Halbempirische Gesetze zur Berechnung turbulenter Grenzschichten nach der Methode der Integralbedingungen.* Ing. Arch. **33**, 384–95.

Head, M. R. (1960) *Entrainment in the Turbulent Boundary Layer.* Aero. Res. Counc. Rep. & Mem. 3152.

Herring, H. J. & Norbury, J. F. (1963) *Some Experiments on Equilibrium Turbulent Boundary Layers in Favorable Pressure Gradients.* Princeton Univ., Dept. Aerospace Mech. Sci. FLD No. 15.

Laufer, J. (1954) *The Structure of Turbulence in Fully Developed Pipe Flow.* NACA Rep. 1174.

Libby, P. A., Baronti, P. O. & Napolitano, L. (1964) *Study of the Incompressible Turbulent Boundary Layer with Pressure Gradient.* AIAA J. **2**, 445–52.

Ludwieg, H. & Tillmann, W. (1949) *Untersuchungen über die Wandschubspannung in turbulenten Reibungsschichten.* Ing. Arch. **17**, 288–99.

McDonald, H. & Stoddart, J. A. P. (1965) *On the Development of the Incompressible Turbulent Boundary Layer.* British Aircr. Corp. Rep. No. Ae 225.

Mellor, G. L. (1964) *The Effect of Pressure Gradients on Turbulent Flow Near a Smooth Wall.* Princeton Univ., Dept. Aerospace Mech. Sci. FLD No. 14.

Mellor, G. L. (1964) *Equilibrium Turbulent Boundary Layers.* AIAA J. **2**, 1650–1.

Mellor, G. L. & Gibson, D. M. (1963) *Equilibrium Turbulent Boundary Layers.* Princeton Univ., Dept. Aerospace Mech. Sci. FLD No. 13.

Moses, H. L. (1964) *The Behavior of Turbulent Boundary Layers in Adverse Pressure Gradients.* Gas Turbine Lab., Mass. Inst. Techn. Rep. No. 73.

Nash, J. F. (1964) *A Note on Skin-Friction Laws for the Incompressible Turbulent Boundary Layer.* Nat. Phys. Lab. Aero Rep. 1135.

Nash, J. F. (1965) *Turbulent-Boundary-Layer Behaviour and the Auxiliary Equation.* Nat. Phys. Lab. Aero Rep. 1137; AGARDograph 97, 245–79.

Newman, B. G. (1951) *Some Contributions to the Study of the Turbulent Boundary-Layer Near Separation.* Aero. Res. consult. Comm. Aero. Res. Lab. (Melbourne, Australia) Rep. ACA-53.

Perry, A. E. & Joubert, P. N. (1963) *Rough-Wall Boundary Layers in Adverse Pressure Gradients.* J. Fluid Mech. **17**, 193–211.

Rotta, J. (1952) *Schubspannungsverteilung und Energiedissipation bei turbulenten Grenzschichten.* Ing. Arch. **20**, 195–207.

Rotta, J. C. (1962) *Turbulent Boundary Layers in Incompressible Flow.* Progress in Aeronautical Sciences, Vol. 2, 1–219 (editors: A. Ferri, D. Küchemann, L. H. G. Sterne). Pergamon Press, Oxford.

Rotta, J. C. (1964) *Temperaturverteilungen in der turbulenten Grenzschicht an der ebenen Platte.* Int. J. Heat Mass Transfer **7**, 215–28.

Sandborn, V. A. & Slogar, R. J. (1955) *Study of the Momentum Distribution of Turbulent Boundary Layers in Adverse Pressure Gradients.* NACA T.N. 3264.

Schlichting, H. (1960) *Boundary Layer Theory*. 4th edition. McGraw-Hill, New York.

Schlichting, H. (1965) *Grenzschichttheorie*. Verlag Braun, Karlsruhe.

Schubauer, G. B. & Klebanoff, P. S. (1951) *Investigation of Separation of the Turbulent Boundary Layer*. NACA Rep. 1030.

Spalding, D. B. (1965) *The Kinetic-Energy-Deficit Equation of the Turbulent Boundary Layer*. AGARDograph 97, 191–244.

Thompson, B. G. J. (1964) *A Critical Review of Existing Methods of Calculating the Turbulent Boundary Layer*. Aero. Res. Counc. 26 109; AIAA J. **3**, 746–7.

Thompson, B. G. J. (1965) *The Calculation of Shape-Factor Development in Incompressible Turbulent Boundary Layers With and Without Transpiration*. AGARDograph 97, 159–90.

Townsend, A. A. (1956) *The Structure of Turbulent Shear Flow*. Cambridge University Press, London.

Truckenbrodt, E. (1952) *Ein Quadraturverfahren zur Berechnung der laminaren und turbulenten Reibungsschicht bei ebener und rotationssymmetrischer Strömung*. Ing. Arch. **20**, 211–28.

Walz, A. (1965) *Über Fortschritte in Näherungstheorie und Praxis der Berechnung laminarer und turbulenter Grenzschichten mit Wärmeübergang*. Z. Flugwiss. **13**, 89–102.

Discussion

D. Coles (*California Institute of Technology, Pasadena, California*)

We have already had several demonstrations this morning of what I might call the mystique of the turbulence business, and I'm willing to give one more. As I understand the situation that we all face, and the one Dr. Rotta tried to describe, we want to calculate the boundary layer development under arbitrary conditions. So far, these are idealized two-dimensional flows without compressibility. To an experimenter, who only believes what he sees, this means that we have solutions and are looking for equations. This is a little bit harder than the other way around. In my mind, working with an assumption about the eddy viscosity is the other face of the coin. It is an effort to complete the equations and proceed with the calculations. If this is not done, perhaps the problem can still be reduced to two stages. First we contemplate the case of equilibrium boundary layers, which were invented by Prof. Clauser; these are a special set of solutions to the unknown equations. Second, we try to use this knowledge in the general situation. I don't want to propose a method for doing this but I would like to mention what I think is a useful analogy with the Boltzmann equation. We know an equilibrium solution to this equation, and the most productive attempts to go beyond this have involved a kind of relaxation approximation. I think this is where we stand in the turbulent boundary layer business now. We need a relaxation equation. Preferably it should have some physics in it, and not be just a pure guess. My own feeling is that the physics will be found in the ideas of entrainment and turbulence production, and probably in a combination of these ideas.

G. L. MELLOR (*Princeton University, Princeton, New Jersey*)

Professor Rotta has already described my eddy-viscosity hypothesis and essentially it includes Clauser's constant-eddy-viscosity far away from the wall and Prandtl's assumption close to the wall. The main idea is that there is an overlap which slides back and forth depending on the Reynolds number. One thing about this particular approach is that it does seem to predict Stratford's data for the nearly separating flow; any hypothesis that explicitly mentions u_τ can't work in this case.

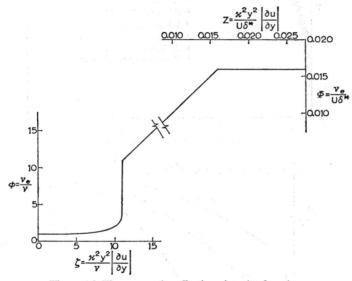

Figure 16. The composite effective-viscosity function.

Figure 16 shows the eddy-viscosity hypothesis that Dr. Rotta was talking about; whether or not you let the viscosity trail off to zero at the free-stream end makes no measurable significance in the calculations. The next figure (fig. 17) is simply the velocity profile for the constant-pressure case. What the hypothesis essentially does is incorporate this data from the zero-pressure-gradient case; in other words, the empiricism involved in the eddy-viscosity hypothesis is just this data, and nothing else. The next figure (fig. 18) shows Clauser's two cases, with the constant-pressure case repeated without the data. These are equilibrium boundary layers corresponding to $\beta = (\delta^*/\tau_0)\,(dp/dx) = 0$, 1.8, 8. The next figure (fig. 19) is Stratford's data corresponding to $\beta = \infty$ ($\tau_0 = 0$); along with it is the data for $\beta = 8$. It shows, if you plot the data on this particular kind of a defect basis which I won't take time to explain, that they are not very different except near the wall.*

---

* This work appears in the February 1966 issue of the Journal of Fluid Mechanics.

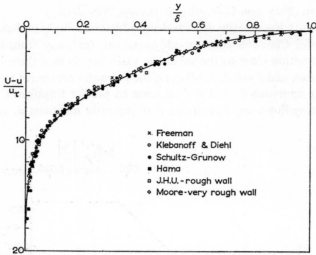

Figure 17. Equilibrium defect profiles for $\beta = 0$ (constant pressure). The data is from Clauser (1954). The solid line is calculated.

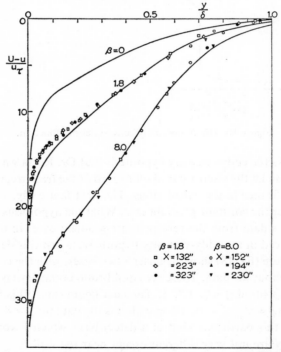

Figure 18. Equilibrium defect profiles for $\beta \geqq 0$. The data is from Clauser (1954). The solid lines are calculated.

What we have done since this investigation is to apply the same hypothesis to general pressure gradients rather than just to those which produce equilibrium profiles. We have this programmed much as A.M.O. Smith has done with laminar profiles, but we have the eddy-viscosity hypothesis in our method. The first data we looked at was from Schubauer & Spangenberg because this seems to be an experiment on a flat plate in which very little secondary flow was present. The next figure (fig. 20) shows the results of solving the complete set of partial differential equations for this case by computer. This is without any further modification of the eddy-viscosity hypothesis. The middle and lower curves show the shape factor and C_f distribution respectively.

In the outer layer we used $v_e/U\delta^* = K$, a constant. The value of K is different for pipes and channels and so forth, and expresses what we don't know about the outer part of the profile. On the other hand, the inner part of the profile seems to be reproducible for a great variety of flow conditions. For boundary layers, we have set $K = 0.016$. However, it is evident that K should be made to vary slightly if perfect agreement with the shape factor is to be achieved (for large distances downstream a K of 0.013 will give perfect agreement; I think that some type of modification to K can be justified physically, but there is not the time to go into that now). Nevertheless, C_f and separation are predicted quite well when $K = 0.016$. The

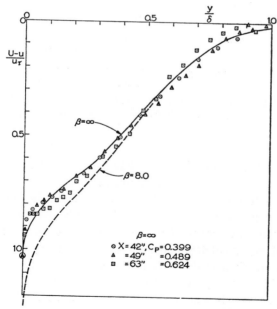

Figure 19. Equilibrium defect profile for $\beta = \infty$. The data is from Stratford (1959) and is compared with the calculated solid line. In the range $0 \leqq y/\delta \leqq 0.30$, $u \sim y^{\frac{1}{4}}$. The dashed line for $\beta = 8$ is from figure 18.

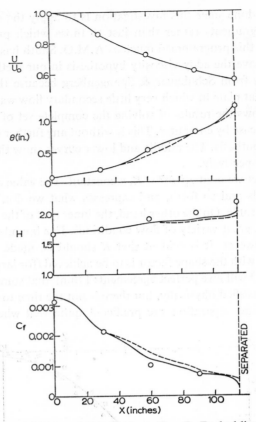

Figure 20. Data is from Schubauer & Spangenberg, Case D. Dashed line is without secondary
flow and solid line is with secondary flow.

dashed lines in the figure represent a straight-forward calculation assuming no
secondary flow. The amount of secondary flow can be determined from a momentum
balance so that θ is forced to agree with the data. The solid line is our calculation with secondary flow included. We assumed the eddy viscosity was isotropic and
computed the divergent or convergent cross flows (or secondary flows).

We also studied the data of Schubauer & Klebanoff which has stronger secondary
flow near the region of separation. We developed a method for calculating these
flows with the eddy-viscosity model and found that, although a correction for
secondary flow appears to be significant enough so that it should be included in any
theory, it doesn't account for all of the discrepancy between calculation and
measurement.

Bradshaw has produced some new data for an essentially equilibrium profile which has its pressure gradient relaxed at some point along the flow. Very few integral theories will reproduce the type of decay that was observed downstream of the relaxation point. I don't think that integral methods are going to be of much help in such cases. However, I feel that the eddy-viscosity hypothesis does offer some hope.

Another effect that has to be considered is that of streamline curvature. We have looked at the data of Eskinazi & Yeh for flow in a curved channel and have calculated the corresponding eddy viscosity. It was very much suppressed on the inside wall of the bend and very much amplified on the outer wall. This is consistent with what can be deduced by simple argument from the stability point of view. It indicates that curvature effects have an influence on the constant K (which is our ignorance factor), and probably have an effect on the data of Schubauer & Klebanoff, for example.

In conclusion, then, I would like to suggest that this eddy-viscosity hypothesis, with a little modification of the value of K along the flow and corrections for curvature and secondary flow. will reproduce most of the available data.

M. R. HEAD (*Cambridge University, Cambridge, England*)

I would like to say a few words in defense of integral methods. If one is prepared to do this sort of fiddling then they too can be made to give good agreement with experiment. I'm really not trying to be simply derogatory. What I do literally mean is that if one uses the integral methods, such as the entrainment method in the form that has been proposed by Thompson (1965), and includes the effect of things like dH/dx on the entrainment (just as it is included here in the eddy viscosity) and if one also takes account of the secondary flows and introduces a curvature term, then one does get very good agreement with experiment in almost every case.

G. L. MELLOR

It seems to me that all profiles are very nearly equilibrium profiles and that the total content of the history is almost entirely a turbulence lag; that lag, I think, is very much smaller than the lag or history built into the mean equation since everything there seems to point to an eddy viscosity which is almost instantly related to the local events.

M. H. BLOOM (*Polytechnic Institute of Brooklyn, Farmingdale, New York*)

I think that the point of view of Dr. Head is not really right. In order to solve the diffusive equations, we must incorporate a constitutive relation (say, involving a type of a diffusivity) one way or another. If you say inversely that any equivalent assumption will apply, then perhaps what we need is something that Dr. Rotta has included in his discussion; that is, a catalog which itemizes the various experimental influences and theoretical assumptions that have been used in many studies and what they imply with respect to the deduced diffusivity. On one hand we have computer technology available to us to permit accurate calculations to be made once a theoretical model has been posed. On the other hand we have a sequence of configuration-dependent viscosometers and the problem of deriving some sort of universal understanding from these viscosometer-dependent problems. That's the challenge. I think the way we may ultimately accomplish this is in terms of the shear directly, or in terms of the eddy diffusivity if we are willing to accept that sort of constitutive format.

F. H. CLAUSER (*University of California, Santa Cruz, California*)

I have great admiration for Prof. Rotta for taking on the assignment of analyzing such a divergent group of methods as this; I think he did remarkably well.

I think that if one looks back at the history of boundary layer predictions he will find it is rather dismal. It is a rare event when somebody predicted something new and found it verified. Turbulent boundary layer theory has a history of having to add a new constant or a new twist to meet each new piece of data that came along. I would agree with Prof. Rotta's belief that the field is wide open for better understanding of what is going on. The history has been one of heavy empiricism. There is very little in turbulent boundary layer theory that ties in with the more detailed and careful analyses that have been made of turbulence itself. It is almost as though we have two different branches of science, the one investigating the properties of turbulence, the other trying to predict the behavior of turbulent boundary layers. Turbulent boundary layer prediction is an important problem; it is crucial to much of the fluid-mechanical technology that is so valuable to our society. As time goes on we are challenged to meet ever wider ranges of conditions, with boundary layers being blown and sucked and twisted and turned. We are pleased with the progress that we have made, but we have a long way to go.

V. A. SANDBORN (*Colorado State University, Fort Collins, Colorado*)

We are making measurements at a fairly large dp/dx on an essentially one-dimensional boundary layer for which you usually only have to consider the x-direction of the equation of motion. We have been able to produce some rather severe separation conditions which have had significant values of dp/dy associated with them. It has become apparent that the y-direction equation of motion must also be considered. In general, as we see it, the conventional momentum-integral-equation approach is simply not adequate near separation because it does not take into account the fact that there are actually two equations of significance, and they are coupled.

F. H. CLAUSER

I am sure that we all are very grateful to Prof. Rotta for having given us a very comprehensive and critical review of the state of affairs in turbulent boundary layer theory and if he has inspired any of us to go home and work harder, his talk will have accomplished its purpose.

Measurements in a Turbulent Boundary Layer Maintained in a Nearly Separating Condition*

W. G. SPANGENBERG, W. R. ROWLAND AND N. E. MEASE

National Bureau of Standards, Washington, D.C.

SUMMARY

A turbulent boundary layer on a smooth, flat wall was investigated where the pressure was increasing with increasing distance downstream such as to maintain the boundary layer in the condition of near separation. The investigation was conducted with air flowing in a channel having the boundary-layer wall as the bottom. The width was sufficient to permit realization of two-dimensional boundary-layer flow. Venting and slope incorporated in the upper wall provided the control of pressure gradient by progressively decreasing the velocity within the duct with increasing distance downstream. The maximum free-stream velocity was always about 84 ft per sec. The depth was sufficient to realize a free stream above the boundary layer except at the farther downstream positions where the boundary-layer flow itself reached the upper wall and escaped through the vents. Measurements of turbulence as well as of mean flow were made in order to reveal more of the mechanics of such flows than hitherto known. Measurements of turbulence were made with hot-wire instrumentation, and these comprised turbulence intensity, transverse integral scale, and turbulent shearing stress. Mean velocities were measured both with the hot-wire anemometer and total-head tube. Skin friction was estimated from mean-velocity profiles. Measurements were made under two slightly different flow conditions, one yielding a closer approach to separation and vanishing skin friction than the other. The results indicated that the common simplifications of the classical boundary layer equations are not acceptable in describing the conditions in a near-separating boundary layer.

---

* Sponsored by the Office of Naval Research.

1. NOTATION

x	distance along surface measured from start of pressure rise which was 50 inches downstream from leading edge of test surface
y	distance normal to surface
z	cross-stream distance perpendicular to xy-plane
u, v, w	x-, y-, and z-components of turbulent velocity fluctuations
u', v'	root-mean-square values of u and v
$\overline{uv}$	mean value of the product of u and v
$\overline{u^2}$	mean value of u^2
U, V, W	local mean velocity in x, y, and z directions
U_1	local free-stream velocity
U_0	free-stream velocity at $x=0$ position
u^*	friction velocity, $\sqrt{\tau_w/\rho}$
ν	kinematic viscosity, μ/ρ
μ	viscosity
ρ	density
c_f	skin-friction coefficient, τ_w/q_1
τ	shear stress
τ_w	shear stress at wall
δ	boundary layer thickness
δ^*	boundary layer displacement thickness, $\displaystyle\int_0^\infty \left(1 - \frac{U}{U_1}\right)\mathrm{d}y$
δ^{**}	boundary layer energy thickness, $\displaystyle\int_0^\infty \frac{U}{U_1}\left[1 - \left(\frac{U}{U_1}\right)^2\right]\mathrm{d}y$
θ	boundary layer momentum thickness, $\displaystyle\int_0^\infty \frac{U}{U_1}\left(1 - \frac{U}{U_1}\right)\mathrm{d}y$
H	boundary layer shape parameter, δ^*/θ
p	static pressure
p_0	static pressure at $x=0$ position
G	parameter defining equilibrium boundary layer, $\dfrac{(H-1)}{H\sqrt{c_f/2}}$
q	dynamic pressure, $\frac{1}{2}\rho U^2$
q_1	local free-stream dynamic pressure
q_0	free-stream dynamic pressure at $x=0$ position
$K(y)$	u-correlation coefficient between points spaced in y, $\overline{u_1 u_2}/u_1' u_2'$
L_y	mean correlation length in xy-plane, $\displaystyle\int_0^\infty K(y)\mathrm{d}y$

References p. 142

σ turbulent normal stress, $-\rho\overline{u^2}$

$-\rho\overline{uv}$ turbulent shear stress

Pr   local turbulence-production rate, $-\rho\overline{uv}\ \partial U/\partial y$.

C_τ turbulent-shear-stress coefficient, $-\rho\overline{uv}/q_1$

2. INTRODUCTION

The necessary condition for boundary-layer flow into regions of higher pressure is a transfer of momentum from the fluid farther from the bounding wall to the more retarded fluid nearer the wall. If the transfer is insufficient to maintain flow against the adverse pressure gradient, the commonly experienced condition of flow separation takes place. It is likewise known that the behavior of the layer and its development are greatly affected by the pressure gradient and the extent of the pressure change. In a turbulent boundary layer, which is the subject of this study, the transfer across the major part of the layer is predominantly due to turbulent motions, and here the mean-flow characteristics are determined also by these effects on the turbulence itself.

A case of considerable interest is that in which a streamwise pressure distribution is chosen to attain maximum pressure recovery in a minimum distance, and perhaps with minimum losses, without incurring boundary-layer separation. Several investigators have agreed on the general form of pressure-gradient profile to accomplish this objective. This gradient is initially steep and then progressively relaxes just sufficiently to continuously exploit the maximum ability of the turbulent boundary layer to overcome the local gradient without separation. The idealized limit of all the proposals is probably defined by Stratford's (1959) proposed gradient which produces a continuously zero skin friction and which has a pressure recovery starting infinitely steep and then progressively relaxing just enough to maintain the zero skin-friction condition.

In previous studies of this problem attention was focused on the effect of the adverse pressure gradient on the turbulent mean flow; or upon finding whether the properties of the mean flow within the boundary layer conformed with some theoretical prediction. In this study, rather than establishing a particular pressure distribution or a set of boundary layer profiles having some common property, the pressure gradient was adjusted by successive trials to attain the maximum pressure recovery without flow separation. This was accomplished by introducing, after an initial length of uniform pressure, the maximum gradient that could be produced in the duct and then reducing the gradient so that at all positions the flow was barely attached as shown by the intermittent appearance of small areas of transitory stall with visual indicators. Two slightly different flow conditions were used, one putting the boundary layer closer to separation than the other as judged by the behavior of tufts in regions of transitory stall. For both of these conditions, distributions of mean velocity and some of the properties of the turbulence were measured to determine the effect of going from one condition to the other and to find which of the two was the more favorable from the standpoint of energy losses. The experiments were conducted in air with the boundary layers developed on a smooth, flat wall.

3. TEST APPARATUS AND PROCEDURE

The special-purpose wind tunnel is shown in figure 1. Except for minor changes required for this investigation, it is the same as that used by Schubauer & Spangenberg (1960). It is supplied with air under positive pressure from a multi-bladed centrifugal blower with adjustable radial inlet vanes for volume-flow control. The test surface is a smooth*, flat, horizontal wall of birch-faced plywood 66 inches wide and 24 feet long. A trip is placed on the test surface near its leading edge to fix the position of transition to turbulent flow. Boundary-layer control in the duct corners was applied through a 3-inch wide gap between the outer edges of the test surface and the vertical test chamber side walls. A honeycomb, damping screens, and tunnel contraction ratio of 11 to 1 in area provided a uniform stream with a turbulence level of 0.4 percent.

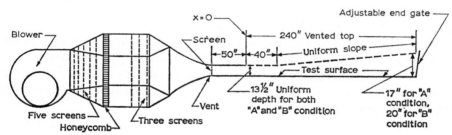

Figure 1. Wind-tunnel configuration.

A constant free-stream dynamic pressure, q_0, was maintained at the $x=0$ position for all of the tests. This corresponded to a velocity of 84 feet per second and an x-Reynolds number of about 2 million if the pressure and temperature of the air were assumed to be 760 mm of mercury and 15 °C, respectively. The velocity and Reynolds number were permitted to vary from day to day as the temperature and barometric pressure changed.

---

* No measurement of surface quality was made but an effectively smooth condition prevailed as judged by aerodynamic behavior.

References p. 142

The pressure-gradient adjustment was made by a combination of venting and sloping the test-chamber wall opposite the flat test surface, and regulating the pressure differential between the test chamber and the room by controlling the amount of air released at the adjustable end-gate in the downstream end of the test channel.

Static pressures were measured with an inclined manometer connected to 1/16-inch diameter static-pressure taps set flush with the test surface on 10-inch centers along the duct longitudinal centerline.

A check of the dynamic-pressure profiles and static pressures at points spaced laterally 15 inches on either side of the duct centerline showed essentially the same mean-flow conditions across the duct at each station in x. This indicated that the stream was well alined with the test channel with no gradient in the z-direction over this span.

The boundary layer was permitted to develop naturally, except for the laminar-to-turbulent trip, under uniform pressure conditions for a distance of 50 inches from the control screen near the leading edge of the test surface before the adverse pressure gradient was applied. The start of the pressure rise was taken as the origin of x. A computation of the distance that a turbulent boundary layer would normally travel from the leading edge of a flat plate in zero pressure gradient to develop a momentum thickness equal to the measured momentum thickness at the $x=0$ position showed a value of 47.5 inches. This close check of the actual length, together with the conformance of the profile data with the universal "law of the wall", indicates that the initial boundary layer was probably representative of boundary layers developing on a smooth wall with zero pressure gradient.

Two series of tests under slightly different flow conditions are included in the present report. In all of the tests of both series the test-chamber pressure was monitored and adjusted so that the identical pressure recovery was indicated at the $x=40$-inch position. The venting configuration remained physically the same for all of the tests of both series.

Under both flow conditions the test channel was about $13\frac{1}{2}$ inches deep from the $x=-50$-inch to the $x=+40$-inch position as shown in the figure. For the first flow condition, designated as "A", the vented top wall was sloped uniformly upward with increasing x downstream from $x=40$ so that at the $x=240$-inch position its depth was 17 inches. The wall venting was then adjusted starting at $x=0$ to achieve by successive trials the maximum total pressure recovery possible in the test channel. In the first two feet the maximum pressure gradient was limited by the capacity of the blower and the geometry of the test chamber, but in the remainder of the test chamber the pressure gradient could be adjusted upward to cause separated flow at any position. The condition of maximum pressure recovery was checked by changing the pressure distribution locally throughout the test-chamber length. It was established that any greater local gradient would cause stalled flow at all points downstream with a reduced overall pressure recovery, and any lesser gradient would not permit the pressure to reach the experimentally determined maximum.

The second flow condition, designated as "B", was obtained by increasing the slope of the test-duct top downstream from the 40-inch position so that the duct was increased in depth from its original 17 inches to 20 inches at the $x = 240$-inch position, as indicated in the figure. This was the maximum slope which would permit the flow to be continuously maintained along the wall. When the duct top was given additional slope so that the maximum channel depth was 21 inches rather than 20 inches, the flow was intermittently stalled at all points downstream from the $x = 80$-inch position.

Under this latter condition visual indicators showed sluggish intermittent movements in random directions in areas randomly distributed over the test surface. However, there was no massive circulation of the type generally associated with separation, and the overall pressure recovery remained about the same as it was for the two conditions investigated. This peculiar hovering behavior of the flow is apparently a characteristic of the effect of the gradually decreasing pressure gradient on the near-separated flow along a flat wall. When the adverse pressure gradient was made steeper, or a lesser gradient was maintained without progressive downstream relaxation, separation did take place suddenly and catastrophically, which involved both a loss of pressure recovery and drastic changes in the pressure distribution and flow field.

In both of the series of tests reported the near-separated condition of the flow was recognized by the detection of highly-disturbed flow with intermittently appearing areas of transitory stall along a large portion of the test-surface length. Transistory stall here manifests itself as a local condition in which the flow is not proceeding in a generally downstream direction. It includes both the condition of random cross-stream currents and reverse flow. The impression given with visual indicators, such as tufts fixed on the test surface, is that the flow is whipping violently from side to side with an occasional upstream burst. Visual indicators released in the flow follow random, zig-zag paths when travelling through the regions of intermittent stall. The nearness to separation was judged qualitatively by the prevalence of these phenomena as shown by the indicators. The wide variation in both speed and direction of the near-separated flow when the isolated areas of transitory stall were appearing intermittently in both time and space caused many instrumentation problems and probably adversely affected the accuracy of the results.

Distributions of u', v', $\overline{uv}$, $K(y)$, and $\overline{uv}/(u'v')$ were derived from hot-wire anemometer data. Both the single wire normal to the flow and the X-wire arrangements were used for the measurements as required. The constant-current system of anemometry was used. The uncompensated amplifier had a frequency response ranging from 1 cycle to 300 kilocycles. The response was down less than 30 percent at 1 cycle and 300 kilocycles, and less than 3 percent at 10 cycles and 75 kilocycles. The data were run with the high-frequency cut-off filter set to eliminate frequencies above 5 kilocycles, to reduce the unnecessary amplifier noise, without any detectable loss in additional signal from the wire when it was heated. The square-wave method was used to adjust the compensation for time lag.

All wires used for the measurements were 0.0001-inch diameter platinum. The single wires for use normal to the flow were about 0.040-inch long, and the X-wire configurations were made with wire-support spacings of about 0.040 inch with wire lengths of about 0.060 inch. When the boundary layer thickness exceeded about $1\frac{1}{4}$ inches or so, the X-wire instruments checked the single-wire data very closely, but in the regions of steep velocity gradients in thinner boundary layers the X-wire instruments were apparently too large relative to the boundary-layer thickness because the u' values derived from them were always less than those given by a single-wire arrangement in the same position.

Velocity profiles were measured with both a total-head tube of 0.040-inch outside diameter, 0.003-inch wall thickness, flattened to a 0.005-inch opening height, and also with the hot-wire anemometer. The velocity pressure was taken as the difference between the local total pressure and the static pressure measured at the wall orifice at the station of the particular traverse. The hot-wire anemometer was calibrated in the free stream at the $x=0$ position where the velocity determination was based on this same Pitot-static combination.

The hot-wire anemometer and the flattened total-pressure tube generally indicated essentially the same velocity at distances from the wall greater than about 10 percent of the local boundary-layer thickness. At positions closer to the wall the velocities indicated by the total-head tube were consistently higher than those indicated by the hot-wire anemometer and by increasing amounts as the wall was approached. The greatest spread between the indications of the two instruments was shown in the steep velocity gradients near the wall in the thin boundary layers rather than in the regions where the high local turbulence was indicated in the near-separated layers, but it does not appear that any reasonable displacement of the effective center of the total-head tube due to velocity gradient would be sufficient to account for the differences. In the near-separated layers the differences between the velocities indicated by the two instruments ranged up to about 13 percent of the local velocity at a distance from the wall equal to 5 percent of the boundary-layer thickness. This corresponded to differences in indicated mean velocity between the two instruments ranging from 0.3 up to 1.3 feet per second. At a distance from the wall equal to 2 percent of the boundary-layer thickness the differences in indicated velocities between the two instruments ranged up to 17 percent, which corresponded to differences in indicated mean velocities ranging from 0.3 to 1.1 feet per second. At lesser distances from the wall these differences ranged up to about 50 percent of the velocity derived from the total-pressure tube data.

Computations of the probable errors in mean-velocity measurements by the methods outlined by Hinze (1959) and Parthasarathy & Tritton (1963) showed that the effect of the indicated local turbulence on the total-pressure tube would cause the indicated velocity to be up to 15 percent too high and the velocity indicated by

TABLE 1

MEAN-VELOCITY DISTRIBUTION NORMAL TO SURFACE. TOTAL-PRESSURE TUBE TRAVERSES

Gradient A&B $x = 0$		Gradient A&B $x = 20$ in		Gradient A&B $x = 40$ in		Gradient A $x = 80$ in		Gradient B $x = 80$ in		Gradient B $x = 110$ in	
y, in	U/U_1	y, in	U/U_1	y, in	U/U_1	y, in	U/U_1	y, in	U/U_1	y, in	U/U_1
0.006	0.392	0.006	0.247	0.007	0.130	0.009	0.087	0.007	0.125	0.007	0.111
.025	.593	.025	.412	.009	.167	.030	.173	.015	.150	.015	.148
.047	.634	.047	.445	.032	.255	.054	.194	.026	.172	.026	.194
.066	.670	.066	.468	.075	.290	.075	.218	.052	.207	.052	.199
.112	.713	.112	.490	.100	.302	.100	.214	.104	.210	.104	.208
.180	.757	.180	.560	.300	.428	.127	.252	.178	.268	.178	.221
.297	.842	.297	.650	.500	.489	.159	.225	.294	.282	.294	.246
.300	.840	.350	.694	.700	.552	.200	.259	.600	.311	.600	.257
.350	.862	.450	.746	.900	.628	.284	.269	1.00	.372	1.00	.281
.400	.886	.550	.792	1.10	.696	.400	.295	1.40	.439	1.40	.325
.450	.906	.650	.834	1.30	.766	.800	.348	1.80	.505	1.80	.365
.500	.926	.750	.875	1.50	.831	1.20	.401	2.20	.558	2.20	.400
.550	.941	.850	.905	1.70	.891	1.60	.456	2.60	.638	2.60	.451
.600	.957	.950	.937	1.90	.949	2.00	.530	3.00	.695	3.00	.496
.650	.970	1.05	.958	2.10	.986	2.40	.596	3.40	.775	3.40	.531
.700	.978	1.15	.979	2.30	1.00	2.80	.675	3.80	.831	3.80	.583
.750	.986	1.25	.990			3.20	.746	4.20	.898	4.20	.619
.800	.990	1.35	.997			3.60	.806	4.60	.951	4.60	.671
.850	.996	1.45	1.00			4.00	.870	5.00	.983	5.00	.759
.900	1.00					4.40	.930	5.40	1.00	5.40	.800
						4.80	.975			5.80	.848
						5.20	.995			6.20	.881
						5.60	1.00			6.60	.912
										7.00	.938
										7.40	.959
										7.80	.972
										8.20	.985
										8.60	.991
										9.00	.996
										9.40	.999
										9.80	1.00

References p. 142

TABLE 1 (*continued*)

Gradient A x = 130 in		Gradient B x = 130 in		Gradient A x = 165 in		Gradient B x = 165 in		Gradient B x = 200 in		Gradient A x = 220 in	
y, in	U/U₁	y, in	U/U₁	y, in	U/U₁	y, in	U/U₁	y, in	U/U₁	y, in	U/U₁
0.009	0.156	0.007	0.048	0.009	0.132	0.006	0.125	0.007	0.140	0.009	0.172
.030	.220	.015	.069	.030	.181	.035	.165	.015	.112	.025	.170
.054	.251	.026	.119	.054	.213	.064	.180	.026	.127	.050	.198
.075	.263	.052	.129	.075	.237	.116	.200	.052	.144	.250	.251
.100	.278	.104	.110	.100	.257	.168	.215	.104	.152	.400	.169
.127	.272	.163	.145	.159	.279	.287	.235	.163	.158	.600	.169
.159	.273	.287	.164	.200	.297	.300	.237	.287	.176	.800	.288
.250	.305	.600	.180	.400	.332	.600	.259	.500	.204	1.50	.316
.284	.300	.800	.185	1.20	.364	1.20	.270	1.50	.257	2.50	.380
.300	.310	1.00	.192	2.00	.406	1.80	.290	2.50	.316	3.50	.406
.500	.339	1.50	.235	2.80	.457	2.40	.335	3.50	.354	4.00	.436
1.00	.367	2.00	.290	3.60	.503	3.00	.367	4.50	.418	5.50	.497
2.00	.449	3.00	.362	4.40	.565	3.60	.396	5.50	.454	6.50	.548
3.00	.528	4.00	.443	5.20	.612	4.20	.411	6.50	.500	7.40	.575
4.00	.620	5.00	.539	6.00	.655	4.80	.462	7.50	.548	8.80	.636
5.00	.714	6.00	.634	6.80	.711	5.40	.486	8.50	.581	9.90	.697
6.00	.796	7.00	.710	7.60	.763	6.00	.520	9.50	.603	10.5	.718
7.00	.892	8.00	.805	8.40	.805	6.60	.540	10.5	.652	11.5	.775
8.00	.950	9.00	.862	9.20	.858	7.20	.590	11.5	.689	12.0	.780
9.00	.980	10.0	.936	10.0	.896	7.80	.627	12.5	.716	12.5	.819
10.0	.994	11.0	.966	10.8	.932	8.40	.662	13.5	.758	13.6	.856
11.0	1.00	12.0	.984	11.6	.961	9.00	.687	14.5	.775	14.5	.910
		13.0	.995	12.4	.974	9.60	.742	16.5	.865	15.5	.950
		14.0	1.00	13.2	.988	10.2	.772	17.5	.902	*	*
				14.0	1.00	10.8	.808	*	*		
						11.4	.861				
						12.0	.893				
						12.6	.930				
						13.2	.948				
						13.8	.966				
						14.4	.983				
						15.0	.995				
						15.6	1.00				

* The boundary-layer thickness exceeded the depth of the test channel at all positions downstream from about x = 185 inches. The U₁ velocities at these positions were computed from the local static pressure recovery at the test wall. Extrapolations were used for obtaining δ* and θ in these cases.

the constant-current hot-wire anemometer to be about 2 percent too low because of the nonlinearity of the response of the instrument to changes in velocity. Calibrations of the flattened total-pressure tube with flow angle showed that it registered the axial component of velocity with a maximum error of 5 percent. This difference occurred when the tube was facing 30 degrees from the flow direction, and lesser errors were indicated for all angles up to 50 degrees, the limit of the calibration. If static tests are meaningful, this tube would eliminate most of the cross-stream components of the turbulence, and the error would be numerically essentially the same as that given by Hinze, if, unlike the case considered by Hinze, there is no turbulence effect on the measurement of static pressure. In our case, static pressures were taken at the wall orifices.

Static-pressure distributions were also measured across the boundary layer with a 0.040-inch diameter static-pressure tube of conventional type with spherical nose. These distributions indicated that when the static tube was within a few diameters of the wall there may be some interference effect; at greater distances the static-pressure tube showed pressures near the center of the boundary layer less than that at the wall orifice, the difference amounting to a maximum of about 4 percent of the free-stream dynamic pressure. In the free stream the difference was generally reversed, ranging up to a positive value of about 3 percent.

TABLE 2

MEAN-VELOCITY DISTRIBUTION NORMAL TO SURFACE
HOT-WIRE ANEMOMETER TRAVERSES

Gradient A&B $x = 0$		Gradient A&B $x = 20$ in		Gradient A $x = 80$ in		Gradient B $x = 80$ in		Gradient B $x = 110$ in	
y, in	U/U_1	y, in	U/U_1	y, in	U/U_1	y, in	U/U_1	y, in	U/U_1
0.010	0.403	0.005	0.200	0.010	0.127	0.025	0.141	0.020	0.112
.020	.501	.010	.278	.040	.178	.050	.184	.035	.140
.040	.583	.020	.354	.090	.209	.100	.202	.050	.169
.060	.637	.030	.386	.140	.222	.200	.236	.100	.190
.080	.665	.040	.414	.200	.242	.400	.259	.200	.214
.100	.688	.050	.433	.240	.247	.700	.320	.300	.224
.150	.729	.075	.464	.340	.260	1.00	.384	.400	.233
.200	.764	.100	.495	.440	.275	1.50	.447	.500	.246
.250	.808	.200	.577	.640	.314	2.00	.524	.750	.261
.300	.846	.300	.652	.940	.368	2.50	.620	1.00	.269
.350	.888	.400	.703	1.44	.453	3.00	.693	1.50	.309
.400	.904	.500	.753	1.94	.542	3.50	.773	2.00	.365
.450	.921	.600	.790	2.44	.624	4.00	.856	2.50	.445
.500	.936	.700	.831	3.00	.718	4.50	.929	3.00	.467
.550	.954	.800	.882	4.00	.870	5.00	.977	3.50	.551
.600	.963	.950	.921	5.00	.985	5.50	.996	4.00	.612
.650	.975	1.00	.950	5.50	1.00	6.00	1.00	4.50	.667
.700	.985	1.10	.971					5.00	.733
.750	.989	1.20	.990					6.00	.855
.800	.994	1.30	.993					7.00	.941
.850	.998	1.40	1.00					8.00	.984
.900	1.00							9.00	.994
								10.0	1.00

References p. 142

TABLE 2 (*continued*)

Gradient A x = 130 in		Gradient B x = 130 in		Gradient A x = 165 in		Gradient B x = 165 in		Gradient A x = 220 in	
y, in	U/U_1	y, in	U/U_1	y, in	U/U_1	y, in	U/U_1	y, in	U/U_1
0.030	0.154	0.015	0.044	0.038	0.127	0.028	0.142	0.021	0.128
.050	.194	.100	.103	.100	.237	.040	.150	.050	.159
.070	.217	.200	.135	.300	.282	.075	.165	.070	.182
.100	.231	.300	.138	.500	.314	.100	.170	.100	.201
.200	.265	.400	.144	1.00	.357	.500	.213	.150	.224
.300	.291	.500	.154	1.50	.387	1.00	.248	.200	.224
.400	.300	.600	.165	2.00	.414	1.50	.283	1.00	.282
.600	.330	1.00	.193	2.50	.431	2.00	.300	2.00	.351
.800	.354	1.50	.232	3.00	.479	2.50	.317	2.50	.362
1.00	.374	2.00	.287	3.50	.509	3.00	.341	3.50	.425
1.50	.415	2.50	.311	4.50	.569	3.50	.370	4.50	.469
2.00	.448	3.00	.355	5.50	.636	4.00	.395	5.50	.510
3.50	.554	3.50	.402	6.50	.706	4.50	.422	6.50	.526
4.50	.655	4.00	.446	7.50	.783	5.00	.446	8.00	.603
5.00	.720	4.50	.478	8.50	.838	5.50	.467	9.00	.633
5.50	.776	5.00	.530	9.50	.898	6.00	.497	10.0	.688
6.00	.803	5.50	.572	10.5	.938	6.50	.516	11.0	.743
6.50	.859	6.00	.630	11.5	.958	7.50	.587	12.0	.792
7.00	.901	7.00	.733	12.5	.990	8.00	.615	13.0	.833
8.00	.955	8.00	.818	13.5	.998	8.50	.631	15.0	.940
8.50	.964	9.00	.874	14.5	1.00	9.00	.699	*	*
9.00	.980	10.0	.946			9.50	.699		
9.50	.993	11.0	.983			10.0	.752		
10.0	.998	12.0	.991			10.5	.781		
10.5	1.00	13.0	1.00			11.0	.826		
						11.5	.855		
						12.0	.895		
						12.5	.915		
						13.0	.940		
						13.5	.957		
						14.0	.972		
						14.5	.982		
						15.0	.993		
						15.5	1.00		

* The boundary-layer thickness exceeded the depth of the test channel at all positions downstream from about $x = 185$ inches. The U_1 velocities at these positions were computed from the local static pressure recovery at the test wall. Extrapolations were used for obtaining δ^* and θ in these cases.

Since the corrective procedures for the effects here discussed seemed uncertain and the application of the accepted corrections did not cause the data from the hot-wire anemometer and the total-pressure tube to define a single curve, particularly in the regions very near the wall, no corrections were applied to the data from either source. Since most of the measurements were made with the hot-wire anemometer, for internal consistency the velocity profiles presented in the figures are those indicated with this instrument. The total-head tube data were used in combination with the hot-wire anemometer data in the estimation of the local skin-friction coefficients. The velocity-profile data are recorded in tables 1 and 2.

4. PRESSURE DISTRIBUTIONS

The pressure distributions and the computed pressure gradients are shown in figure 2, with the solid lines and the plotted circles indicating flow conditions "A" and "B", respectively. The differences between the two pressure distributions are of the same order as the reading errors, and no consistent change is indicated. The perceptible differences resulting from the change in test-section geometry appear in the redistribution of the Reynolds stresses and other boundary layer parameters.

With flow condition "A" highly perturbed flow was indicated with tufts at all positions downstream from the $x = 80$-inch position, with a maximum perturbation indicated at the $x = 130$-inch position. With flow condition "B" random areas of transitory stall appeared intermittently in the entire region between $x = 110$ and $x = 165$ inches. Under this condition it was estimated from chemical smoke observations that the flow at the 130-inch position showed areas of transitory stall up to about 50 percent of the time, and then recovered farther downstream so that at the 165-inch position the transitory spots appeared only about 15 percent of the time.

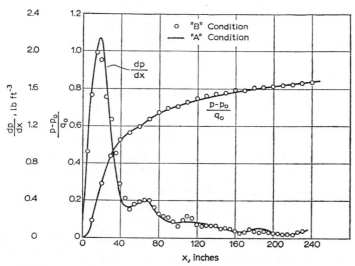

Figure 2. Static-pressure distributions and pressure-gradient profiles.

References p. 142

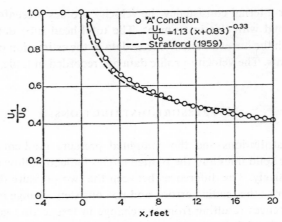

Figure 3. Free-stream velocity distributions. The *x*-dimension is given in units of feet to be consistent with the units of the given empirical equation.

Figure 3 shows the free-stream velocity distribution wherein the plotted points are those derived from the static-pressure readings of pressure distribution "A". The solid line is given by the equation

$$U_1/U_0 = 1.13(x + 0.83)^{-0.33}$$

fitted empirically to the observed data. This indicates that this velocity distribution established by successive trials closely approximates a power law within the range of self-preserving flow predicted by Townsend (1956). The broken line represents the free-stream velocity distribution proposed by Stratford (1959) to produce zero skin friction throughout the length of the pressure recovery path.

5. BOUNDARY-LAYER PROFILES

The boundary-layer velocity profiles are shown in figure 4. The skin friction could not have been zero for any of these profiles because they all show a steep step-up near the wall, and also in no case did the dynamic pressure near the wall vary linearly with distance from the wall as predicted by Stratford (1959) for a boundary layer with zero skin friction. Nevertheless incipient separation was near at hand as indicated by the local intermittent areas of transitory stall shown by visual indicators. The "B" condition, with its reduced skin friction and greater areas of transitory stall, caused the expected deformation of the profiles and the usual decrease in velocity gradient across the boundary layer associated with the decrease in skin friction.

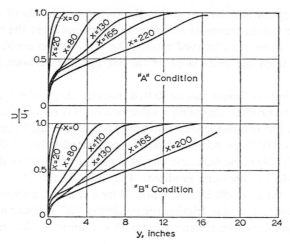

Figure 4. Boundary-layer velocity profiles.

To estimate the effects of transitory stall on the indicated velocities, comparative measurements were made with both forward- and reverse-facing total-pressure tubes. The reverse-facing tube in the near-separating layer here reported indicated sensibly zero velocity pressure, while the forward-facing tube definitely indicated forward flow. This simple experiment showed that there was in fact forward flow, even very close to the wall.

When these data were plotted logarithmically, the straight-line portion in the inner reaches of the layer indicated that they may all follow the universal law of the wall which has been so well established and checked experimentally for a wide range of conditions. The law of the wall is of the form:

$$U/u^* = (1/k)(\ln yu^*/v) + c.$$

If this equation is multiplied by u^*/U_1 and differentiated with respect to $\ln y$, the expression

$$\frac{y}{U_1}\frac{dU}{dy} = (1/k)(u^*/U_1) = (1/k)(\sqrt{c_f/2})$$

results. If a suitable value for k is chosen and U/U_1 is plotted against $\ln y$, a value of c_f may be estimated from the slope of the linear inner portion of the profile.

Velocity-profile data were obtained with both the hot-wire anemometer and the total-pressure tube. The latter data always indicated a consistently higher velocity than did the hot-wire data, particularly in the region very near the wall, but the two instruments generally agreed closely at greater distances from the wall. Both sets of data showed a straight-line portion on the logarithmic plots but of different slope. Since computations indicated that the turbulence would affect the velocity indicated by the two instruments in opposite directions from the true value, and this was borne out by the observed results, the skin-friction coefficients recorded were computed from the mean slope of the average line between the two sets of data.

The skin-friction coefficient was estimated from the slope of the semilogarithmic plots for all of the profiles, assuming a value of $k = 0.4$ (or its equivalent $1/k = 5.75$ if $\log_{10}$ is used). The results are shown in figure 5. The indicated skin friction at the $x = 0$ position is 0.0030 as compared with a computed value of 0.0029 with the Squire–Young (1938) formula. These curves show the usual sharp decrease in skin friction with adverse pressure gradient. The skin friction for condition "A" reaches a minimum at $x = 80$ inches, followed by a rise and a second decrease beyond $x = 165$ inches. The skin friction for condition "B" is lower and the trend is generally downward with increasing x but with variations as shown by the plotted points.

If the velocity-profile data are plotted with U/u^* as a function of $\log yu^*/v$, using the value of skin friction as determined from the mean plots, figure 6, the data

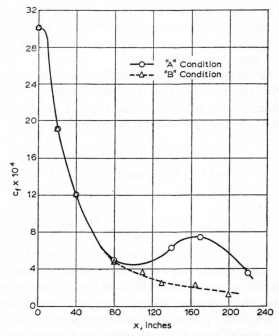

Figure 5. Skin-friction coefficients as derived from slopes of semilogarithmic plots of velocity-profile data.

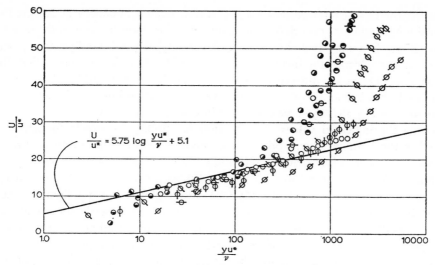

Figure 6. Universal semilogarithmic plot of velocity profiles.

Condition "A": O $x = 0$; ϕ 20; $\ominus$ 80; $\mathbb{Q}$ 130; $\varnothing$ 165 inches

Condition "B": O $x = 0$; ϕ 20; $\bullet$ 80; $\bullet$ 110; $\bullet$ 130; $\bullet$ 165 inches

scatter is not much greater than that normally expected in this type of plot, even under uniform pressure conditions. The greatest deviation is shown not at the different x-stations, but between the two sets of the data at the $x = 165$-inch position. The spread comes about principally because of differences in the intercept in the logarithmic plots among the several sets of data. The empirically determined constants to define the universal profiles are apparently not applicable to all the profiles measured under this extended range of flow conditions and it is further noted that the logarithmic profile extends to much lower values of yu^*/v than is normally shown in profiles measured in a uniform pressure.

When any boundary-layer-profile data is plotted in the manner described, it defines a curve consisting of a portion near the wall where $U/u^* = yu^*/v$, the straight-line portion described above, and an outer region where divergence from the straight line again occurs as the free-stream is approached. Transitional regions of gradually-changing slope connect the two ends of the straight-line portion to the inner and outer regions, respectively. Near the wall, the transitional region normally extends from a value of yu^*/v of somewhat less than 10 in the laminar sublayer up to perhaps 20 to 50; and under adverse-pressure gradient conditions the divergence from the straight line in the outer region may extend down to a value of yu^*/v of 100 or less. This leaves a greatly reduced length of the straight-line portion of the curve upon which to base an estimate of skin friction. The present

References p. 142

data follow this general pattern. In the near-separated boundary layers the two transitional regions approach one another so that a straight line drawn through the laboratory data may include some of the points in the bounding transitional regions. The effect of the inclusion of transitional data points in the straight-line portion would give the differences from the usual "law of the wall" in the direction indicated above; and also the estimated values of skin friction based upon these data may be too high by some corresponding amount.

Using the indicated values of skin friction, checks were made to determine whether the boundary-layer profiles comprised a set of equilibrium profiles as defined by Clauser (1954). Such a set would describe a single point on a plot of the nondimensional pressure force, $(\delta^*/\tau_w)(dp/dx)$, as a function of "G", which was defined by Clauser as $G=(H-1)/(H\sqrt{c_f/2})$. Such a plot is shown in figure 7. These data show that the boundary layers in these tests do not describe an equilibrium family. Neither G nor the force parameter are constant for all of the profiles. For comparison, Clauser's three points defining the equilibrium-profile sets which he studied and the point defining the set more recently studied by Bradshaw & Ferriss (1965) are shown on the plot. One remarkable thing is that all of the data

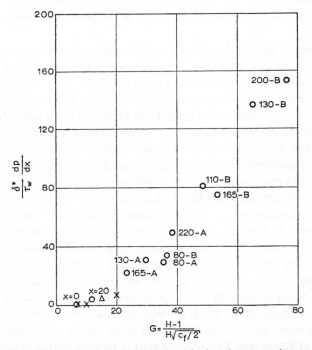

Figure 7. Test of velocity-profile data to determine whether they comprise a set of equilibrium profiles. $\times$ Clauser (1954); $\triangle$ Bradshaw & Ferriss (1965).

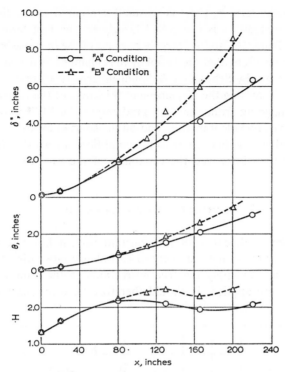

Figure 8. Displacement thickness, momentum thickness, and H-distributions.

shown appear to describe a function connecting the two parameters. It is not clear why velocity distributions such as those of the present investigation should produce such a well-behaved function.

The displacement and momentum thicknesses, derived from integrations of the boundary layer profiles, and their ratio, H, are shown in figure 8. In this figure the solid lines represent the data pertaining to flow condition "A" and the broken lines represent the data pertaining to flow condition "B". The greatest difference between the two sets of data is in the increased value of the displacement thickness for the "B" condition. Since the fractional change in θ was not as great as that in δ^*, the value of H likewise increased in going from condition "A" to condition "B".

The increase in θ, even though the skin friction decreased in going from "A" to "B", is readily explained in terms of the von Kármán momentum equation, written as follows for two-dimensional flow and with the Reynolds normal-stress terms omitted:

$$\frac{\mathrm{d}\theta}{\mathrm{d}x} = \frac{\theta}{q_1}\frac{\mathrm{d}p}{\mathrm{d}x}\left(\frac{\delta^*}{2\theta} + 1\right) + \frac{\tau_w}{2q_1}$$

References p. 142

In this equation the term $\tau_w/(2q_1)$ is so small compared to the first term on the right-hand side that $d\theta/dx$ is controlled largely by the first term. This term increased in going from "A" to "B" largely because of the increase in δ^* since, as we have seen from figure 2, neither dp/dx nor q_1 were changed by a measurable amount.

It was brought out by Schubauer & Spangenberg (1960) that turbulent mixing has the effect of decreasing the displacement thickness of the boundary layer. The increase in δ^* in going from the "A" gradient to the "B" gradient suggests a possible decrease of turbulent mixing, and on the basis of mean-flow parameters at least, it appears that in going nearer to the condition of zero skin friction we have worsened rather than improved the capability of the flow to proceed to higher pressures.

6. TURBULENCE INTENSITIES

The effects of the nonlinearity of the constant-current hot-wire anemometer is reflected noticeably in the measurement of turbulence intensities. Since all the information necessary to apply the true corrections to the data were not readily available, none were applied. It should therefore be recognized that these data

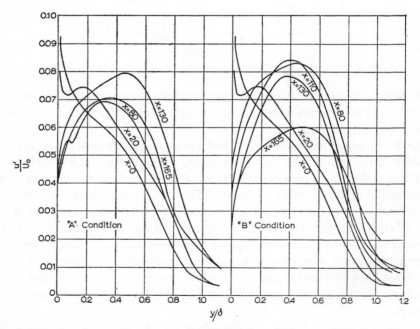

Figure 9. Intensity of *u*-component of turbulence relative to free-stream velocity at the $x = 0$ position.

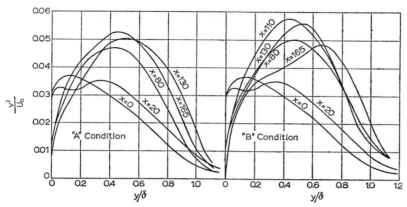

Figure 10. Intensity of v-component of turbulence relative to free-stream velocity at the $x = 0$ position.

probably indicate absolute turbulence intensities too low by amounts ranging from zero up to 20 percent of the indicated value, with the larger errors in the regions of high indicated turbulence intensities. However, even with these known errors, because of their similarity the data are probably closely indicative of the trends when they are intercompared among the various stations.

The longitudinal components of turbulence measured with a wire normal to the flow, and the normal components measured with an X-wire are shown in figures 9 and 10, respectively. In the redistribution of the turbulence across the boundary layer in the adverse pressure gradient the total turbulent energy probably increases as indicated by the greater areas under the curves, but the absolute value of the turbulence intensity adjacent to the wall actually decays in both the u and the v components. If the "A" curves are compared with the "B" curves in these figures, the principal change in intensity of the longitudinal components with the increased pressure gradient, i.e. in going from "A" to "B", is at the $x = 80$-inch position where the velocity profile has scarcely changed except very near the wall. At the $x = 130$-inch position, where the flow shows areas of transitory stall up to 50 percent of the time for the "B" condition, the absolute turbulence intensity has actually decayed and an additional decay is shown at the $x = 165$-inch position where the transitory stall has disappeared and the skin-friction coefficient has increased. This observation implies that conditions involving wall friction are essential to the maintenance of turbulence near the wall and some delay time occurs before the effect of changes in local conditions are felt.

If the data for u' are replotted relative to the local mean velocity, as in figure 11, the intensity in the "A" condition first increases as the free-stream velocity decreases and then remains about the same for all of the x-positions in the near-

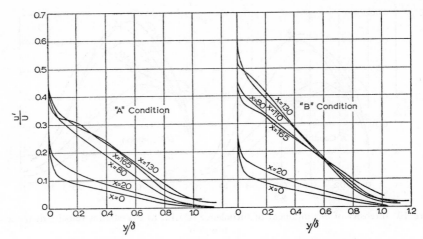

Figure 11. Intensity of *u*-component of turbulence relative to local velocity.

separated region. The increase is the greater for the "B" condition in the regions where the flow is more retarded, so that an increase in relative intensity is indicated as separation is approached. This is a combined effect of an absolute turbulence decrease and a mean-velocity decrease, the two not taking place at the same rate.

The intermittent appearance of areas of transitory stall shown by tufts or smoke can be correlated with the turbulent intensity relative to the local mean velocity. Areas of transitory stall are indicated only when the root-mean-square intensity in the inner 10 percent of the boundary layer exceeds about 33 percent of the local mean velocity, and the greater this percentage above 33, the greater the proportion of the time that the flow is intermittently stalled. This observation has been interpreted as a manifestation of one step in the separation process. In the adverse pressure gradient the mean velocity in the boundary layer near the wall decreases at a greater rate than the turbulent fluctuations decrease. When the mean forward velocity near the wall becomes less than the half-amplitude of the largest turbulence fluctuations, which occurs when the r.m.s. fluctuations are about 1/3 of the mean velocity, the instantaneous $(U+u)$ vector becomes zero or negative in an area corresponding to the size of the local turbulence eddy, and forward velocity is indicated only when this vector is positive. One now views the flow from his fixed position almost as if he were travelling at local mean velocity. With a suitable indicator such as smoke or tufts, all components of the turbulence in the region of reduced velocity near the wall are detectable. The indicator moves in random directions relative to the wall much more vigorously than it did in a region of greater forward velocity, and the result is that the turbulent fluctuations appear to become predominant. As separation is approached, more and more negative turbulent excursions exceed the local mean forward velocity in absolute value so that in the limit one would observe turbulence with no forward flow. After this occurs, the weakened driving force of the stresses within the fluid becomes less than the retarding effects of the adverse pressure gradient so that full separation ensues.

7. CORRELATION LENGTHS

If u_1 and u_2 represent the instantaneous longitudinal velocity fluctuations at points 1 and 2 which are spaced a distance y apart, and u'_1 and u'_2 represent the local root-mean-square velocity fluctuations at these same points, a correlation coefficient may be defined as

$$K(y) = \overline{u_1 u_2}/u'_1 u'_2 .$$

Turbulence is comprised of a mixture of many eddy sizes the mean correlation length of which may be determined through the measurements of correlation coefficients. The mean correlation length, L_y, is given by

$$L_y = \int_0^\infty K(y)\mathrm{d}y .$$

$K(y)$ generally becomes negligible within a finite distance so that outside this distance it contributes a negligible amount to the mean length.

Correlation coefficients were measured with two hot-wire anemometers, movable in the y-direction both relative to the wall and to one another, the wires being oriented normal to the flow and parallel to the wall. With the system of anemometry used, the outputs of the two wires were mixed before amplification. This required that the two wires in different mean-speed regions be run at different temperatures to make their time lapse equal. Sensitivity to mean speed did not enter into the determination of the correlation coefficient. The proper relative temperatures of the two wires were determined by a graphical solution of the characteristic equation defining the time lag in terms of wire temperature and electrical current, and then adjusting the electrical current.

The results were plotted in the form of contours of equal correlation coefficients. An example is shown in figure 12.

Because of the inhomogeneity, the correlation coefficient $K(y)$ and the correlation length L_y are functions of the position of measurement, which is taken to be

$$\tfrac{1}{2}(y_1 + y_2) ,$$

with their respective velocities u_1 and u_2.

References p. 142

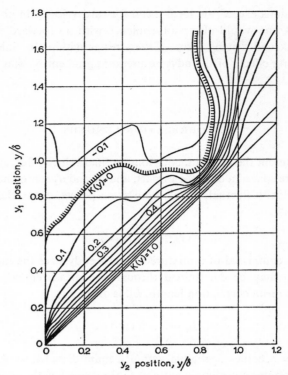

Figure 12. Contour plot of correlation coefficients along a line perpendicular to the test surface; $x = 80$ inches, condition "A".

If the field were homogeneous we would have a family of straight lines. The fact that they are not straight lines shows that the flow is inhomogeneous. Thus the correlation coefficient depends on the position $\frac{1}{2}(y_1 + y_2)$, and on the spacing $y_1 - y_2$, which is represented by an axis inclined at $-45°$ from the y_1-axis.

The contour plots for all of the stations were similar in most respects, and they showed a greatest distance over which there is a positive correlation ranging from about 0.9δ at $x = 0$ to about 0.5δ at the $x = 130$-inch position. These greatest distances of positive correlation reached a maximum near the center of the boundary layer, and a minimum in the region between 0.7 and 0.9δ. The negative correlations indicated as centered about y/δ of 0.8 are probably caused by the oscillatory fluctuations associated with intermittency.

The distribution of L_y across the boundary layer for each of the several x-positions is shown plotted in figure 13. In these results only the positive correlations were included in the integration because the contributions of the negative correlations to L_y were unknown.

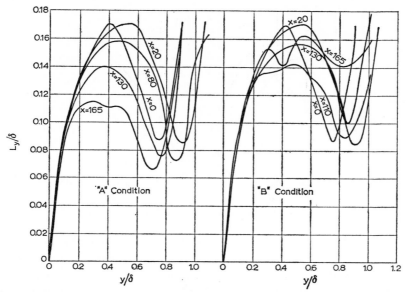

Figure 13. Distributions of mean correlation lengths of turbulence, along lines normal to the test surface.

This figure shows that the L_y distributions are similar for the several x-positions only in the region very near the wall. The adverse pressure gradient apparently has two effects on L_y in the remainder of the boundary layer. The region of both the maximum L_y near the center of the boundary layer and also the local minimum in the outer $\frac{1}{3}$ of the boundary layer first move outward from the wall for condition "A", and then as separation is approached, they move closer to the wall. Apparently the gradient has affected not only the correlation length of the turbulence but also the position of the intermittency region relative to the wall. The curves further show that the maximum mean correlation length of the turbulence decreases relative to the boundary layer thickness as the flow proceeds.

A comparison of these data with the condition "B" data shows larger values of L_y for "B" in the intermittent region; this suggests a decrease in the oscillatory motions associated with intermittency. A greater L_y is also indicated over a large portion of the boundary layer at the $x=165$-inch position after the flow has recovered from the nearly stalled condition farther upstream.

8. SHEAR-STRESS DISTRIBUTIONS

The distributions of the $\overline{uv}$-correlation coefficient, $-\overline{uv}/u'v'$, at the various positions

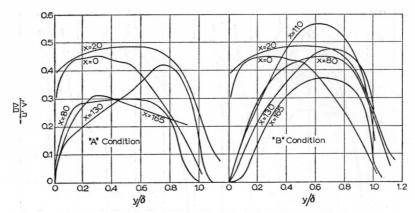

Figure 14. Distributions of $\overline{uv}$-correlation coefficients.

in x are shown in figure 14. At the $x=0$ position a maximum of 0.45 is shown at about a y/δ of 0.3, and as the pressure increases, the maximum value moves outward from the wall, as at $x=20$ inches. For condition "A" the remaining measurements show reduced correlation coefficients, particularly in the region near the wall. There is a more consistent pattern of behavior in the data taken in the reduced skin-friction case of condition "B". In all of these latter profiles a maximum $\overline{uv}$-correlation coefficient is shown in the outer half of the boundary layer, and this maximum value apparently bears some relationship to the flow history. At the $x=110$-inch position, where areas of transitory stall were first detected, the correlation coefficient reaches a maximum of 0.56, but this high degree of correlation decreases for succeeding stations downstream to a maximum of only 0.37 at the 165-inch position where the flow has nearly recovered from intermittently stalled areas. In addition to this behavior, the conditions causing the reduced skin friction apparently also cause an expanding region of nearly zero $\overline{uv}$-correlation coefficient near the wall.

The turbulent shear stress, $-\rho\overline{uv}$, was derived in two ways, first by direct measurement with the hot-wire anemometer, and second by measuring the correlation coefficient, $\overline{uv}/u'v'$, and the turbulence intensities, u' and v', independently and forming the product,

$$-(\overline{uv}/u'v')(\rho u'v')$$

Both methods gave essentially the same values except in the regions of high velocity gradients near the wall at the $x=0$ and the $x=20$-inch positions. When the above product was evaluated at these positions the result approximated the shear stress at the wall indicated by the logarithmic-profile plots much more closely than did the directly-measured values of $-\rho\overline{uv}$. The difference was apparently in the low values of the u-fluctuations indicated by the X-wire in these high-gradient regions. Since the values from the product were apparently more reliable, they were accepted in the other regions also.

The distributions of total shear stress,

$$\tau = -\rho\overline{uv} + \mu(\partial u/\partial y),$$

are shown in figure 15, as a fraction of free-stream dynamic pressure. In these data the viscous term is negligible relative to the turbulence term at all positions except those of high velocity gradient near the wall where the turbulent shear stress term is essentially zero. The reduction in turbulent shear stress in the region near the wall is caused by the disappearance of correlation between the u- and the v-components of the turbulence. In this area the flow is highly turbulent but even in the steep velocity gradient near the wall the two components remain uncorrelated. This leads to the conclusion that these turbulence components which are present must have originated from sources other than the local velocity gradient.

In two-dimensional flow near a wall, the mean-flow equation reduces to

$$\frac{\partial \tau}{\partial y} = \frac{\partial p}{\partial x}$$

when it is assumed that the remaining terms of that equation are negligible in the

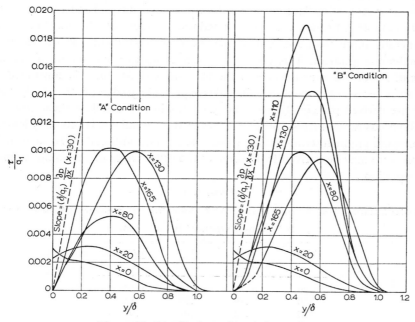

Figure 15. Distributions of total shear stress.

vicinity of the wall. This property has been utilized under more favorable conditions in estimating skin friction from the distribution of the shear stress across the boundary layer.

The shear-stress measurements in this investigation show that in no case in the near-separating layer did the $\partial\tau/\partial y$ term equal the $\partial p/\partial x$ term in the region near the wall. As separation is approached the region of increasing turbulent shear stress shifts outward from the wall, maintaining a slope somewhat less than the pressure gradient but leaving a region of near-zero shear stress near the wall. In this region the forces required to overcome the gradient must be derived from some source other than the shear stress in the xz-plane. Apparently none of the terms of the mean-flow equations can be ignored without further examination in the extremely disturbed flow in the near-separated boundary layer, particularly in the presence of areas of transitory stall.

A consideration of the terms in the mean-flow equation which are usually assumed to be negligible revealed that the most likely source of the force near the wall to overcome the gradient in pressure is in the Reynolds-normal-stress term, $\partial\sigma/\partial x$. It will be recalled that the turbulence decays near the wall in the near-separating layer. As the flow proceeds in x the pressure force opposing the pressure gradient is probably derived from this reduction in the longitudinal turbulence components. The pressures derived from this source were computed from the data in the near-separating layer. The results for a constant y-distance of $\frac{1}{2}$ inch are shown in table 3. From these tabulated values, it is seen that the pressure gradient is generally more than the sum of the shear-stress gradient and the Reynolds-normal-stress gradient. This discrepancy ranges up to a maximum of about 25 percent. From this near-balance of the mean-flow equation, it is concluded that the forces necessary to overcome the adverse pressure gradient in the nearly stalled layer are derived principally from the gradients in the turbulent shear stress and the Reynolds normal stress. Since the sum of these gradients is generally less than the pressure-gradient term, excluding possible errors, additional forces to overcome the pressure may be derived from some of the other terms of the complete mean-flow equation.

TABLE 3

COMPARISON OF SOME FORCE-GRADIENT TERMS IN THE MEAN-FLOW EQUATION

(lb ft^{-3}, pressure gradient "B", $y = \frac{1}{2}$ inch)

x, in	$\dfrac{\partial p}{\partial x}$	$\dfrac{\partial \tau}{\partial y}$	$\dfrac{\partial \sigma}{\partial x}$
80	0.25	0.16	0.12
110	.19	.04	.12
130	.12	.02	.07
165	.06	.00	.05

9. ENERGY CONVERSION

Neglecting the effect of the normal stresses, the local rate of energy conversion from the mean flow to turbulence is given by the product of the turbulent shear stress and the local velocity gradient

$$\text{Pr} = -\rho \overline{uv} \, \partial U / \partial y \, .$$

The measured turbulence-production rates per unit volume per unit of dynamic pressure are shown plotted in figure 16. When the adverse pressure gradient is encountered, the greater contribution to turbulence production shifts from the velocity-gradient factor to the Reynolds-stress factor. In the near-separating layer the maximum turbulence-production rate coincides with the region of maximum Reynolds stress rather than with the region of high local velocity gradient near the wall. The steeper velocity gradients near the wall with their relatively high viscous shear stresses are associated with the regions of low turbulent shear stress and no turbulence can be produced without the latter.

The "B"-gradient data indicate that in the reduced $\partial U / \partial y$ gradient associated with the thicker boundary layer the turbulence-production rate is greater because the local turbulent shear stress increases faster than the velocity gradient decreases. As the flow proceeds farther, Pr/q_1 always diminishes.

The rate of energy loss (per unit volume now being understood from here on)

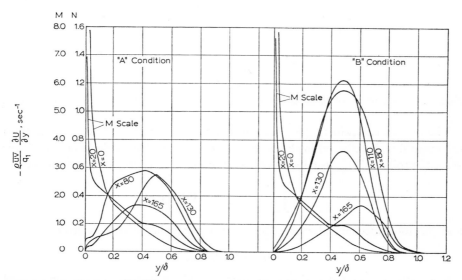

Figure 16. Turbulent-energy production rates. The "M" scale applies to the $x = 0$ and $x = 20$-inch data only; the "N" scale applies to the remainder of the data.

through direct dissipation is given by

$$\int_0^\infty \mu(\partial U/\partial y)^2 \, dy$$

This quantity in ratio to the total rate of energy dissipation from the mean flow is shown in figure 17. At the start of the pressure rise, 37 percent of the energy lost from the free stream is through direct viscous action while 63 percent is consumed in the production of turbulence. As the flow proceeds the turbulence-production rate increases relative to the direct-dissipation rate so that finally nearly all of the energy lost by the mean flow is through the production of turbulence.

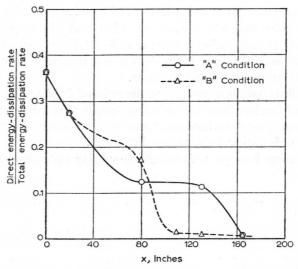

Figure 17. Ratio of rate of direct viscous dissipation of energy to the total energy-dissipation rate.

The mechanical (kinetic plus pressure) energy lost in the boundary layer from the mean flow is reflected in the defect in energy indicated by the boundary layer velocity profile. This is usually expressed in terms of an energy thickness defined as

$$\delta^{**} = \int_0^\infty (U/U_1)(1-(U/U_1)^2) \, dy$$

and the total mechanical-energy defect at a particular station is given by

$$(\rho/2)(U_1^3 \delta^{**}).$$

This latter expression is shown in figure 18. The principal observation derived from a comparison of these curves is that, contrary to predictions, there is a greater

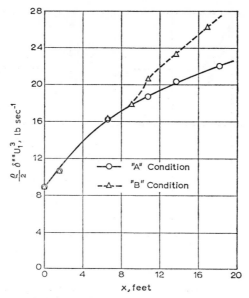

Figure 18. Defect of energy in boundary layer. The x-dimension is given in feet so that the local slopes are consistent with the ordinate of figure 19.

energy loss in the flow distribution "B" with its reduced skin friction. The conclusion to be drawn is that the condition which reduced the skin friction imposed a condition of greater energy defect in this case. This additional energy is absorbed in the production of turbulence in the region well away from the wall. There is no apparent trend toward minimum energy losses as the skin friction approaches zero.

As a final check on the data the measured values were compared through the relationship

$$\int_0^\infty \left(\mu \frac{\partial U}{\partial y} - \rho\overline{uv} \right) \frac{\partial U}{\partial y} \, dy = \frac{d}{dx} \left(\frac{\rho}{2} U_1^3 \delta^{**} \right) \tag{1}$$

where the terms on the left-hand side are the rates of energy loss by direct dissipation and turbulence production and the term on the right-hand side is the rate of growth of energy defect. This relationship is usually considered valid in boundary layer theory but the present data indicate that this equality is not sufficient under the present flow conditions. Any failure of this relationship is an indication of either an omission of contributing terms or errors in measurements.

The experimentally-determined right- and left-hand sides of the equation are plotted separately as functions of x in figure 19. These data show a large systematic discrepancy over the entire range of measurements. This discrepancy is greatest where the near-separated flow condition exists and the rate of energy loss is least.

References p. 142

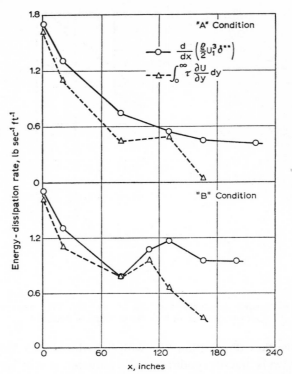

Figure 19. Comparison of the energy-dissipation rates as derived from mean-speed and shear-stress measurements.

The error in the mean-velocity data is probably negligible and all of the losses are included in the energy defect derived from these data. We should perhaps suspect the measured dissipation rates rather than the energy defect for causing the differences between the two sets of measurements. The instrument corrections suggested by Parthasarathy and Tritton (1963), based upon estimates of factors for which no data were available, indicate that local values of measured shear stress may be in error by amounts ranging up to 50 percent, particularly in regions where the higher turbulence intensity and shear stress exist, because of the nonlinearity of the response of the constant-current hot-wire anemometer; but this large discrepancy should not extend to the total energy-dissipation rate at any given x-position. The indicated differences far exceed any inaccuracy attributable to the instrument. On the other hand the total contributions of all the terms not included in the measured dissipation rates are unknown, but pressure recovery derived from the gradient in Reynolds normal stress, particularly in the region near the wall, may account for some of this discrepancy.

In comparing the near-separating flow regions of "A" and "B", both the energy-defect data and also the dissipation-rate data show consistently larger values of energy loss for "B" than for "A". Preference should be given to the indicated growth rates of energy defect rather than to the direct measurement of energy dissipation because of possible errors and omissions in the latter. These data show a monotonically decreasing growth rate of the energy defect with "A", whereas that for "B" does not decrease downstream nearly to the extent as does that for "A". Again we conclude that in going from "A" to "B" conditions were worsened, and we might go farther and surmise that if the boundary-layer conditions were such that the skin friction were greater than for "A", the rate of energy loss might be further decreased for the same pressure recovery.

10. CONCLUDING REMARKS

These data are basically similar to corresponding data observed in other investigations where the adverse pressure gradient had a pronounced effect on the results, such as that reported by Schubauer & Klebanoff (1950). To find all the features which may emerge as being unique to the boundary layer maintained in a near-separating condition would require a detailed comparison of the present results with results obtained under different conditions. This has not been done.

The extended range of near-separated flow obtaining in these tests suggests the following observations:

Classical boundary layer theory as based upon equation (1) suggests that in reducing the shear stress, which is proportional to the left-hand side of that equation, one would reduce the gradient in energy defect which is represented by the right-hand side of that equation. The experimental data, as shown by figure 19, shows that no such equality is suggested. Apart from the difference due to experimental inaccuracy, this indicates that minimum losses may not be associated with minimum skin friction and that some other feature, for example the normal stress, σ, or other factors usually assumed to be negligible, may play an important role in the energy balance.

In the near-separating boundary layer the turbulent shear stress nearly vanishes in a considerable region near the wall while the Reynolds normal stresses are present. Apparently the force necessary to cause the flow to advance against the adverse pressure in this region is principally derived from the Reynolds normal stress rather than from the shear stress as has been previously indicated by measurements made under other flow conditions.

References p. 142

ACKNOWLEDGEMENT

The authors acknowledge the active interest and support of Dr. G. B. Schubauer during this investigation.

REFERENCES

Bradshaw, P. & Ferriss, D. H. (1965) *The Response of a Retarded Equilibrium Turbulent Boundary Layer to a Sudden Removal of Pressure Gradient*. NPL Aero Report 1145, British Aero. Res. Counc. 26758.

Clauser, Francis H. (1954) *Turbulent Boundary Layers in Adverse Pressure Gradients*. J. Aero. Sci. **21**, 91–108.

Hinze, J. O. (1959) *Turbulence*. McGraw-Hill Book Co., New York.

Parthasarathy, S. P. & Tritton, D. J. (1963) *Impossibility of Linearizing a Hot-Wire Anemometer for Measurements in Turbulent Flows*. AIAA J. **1**, 1210–1.

Schubauer, G. B. & Klebanoff, P. S. (1950) *Investigation of Separation of the Turbulent Boundary Layer*. NACA T.N. 2133.

Schubauer, G. B. & Spangenberg, W. G. (1960) *Forced Mixing in Boundary Layers*. J. Fluid Mech. **8**, 10–32. Following publication, the authors felt that it was important to add certain information and accordingly supplied two footnotes to be attached to the paper. These were distributed by an amendment sheet included between the covers of the November 1963 number of JFM. They are quoted here, see below*.

Squire, H. B. & Young, A. D. (1938) *The Calculation of the Profile Drag of Aerofoils*. R. and M. No. 1838, British Aero. Res. Counc.

Stratford, B. S. (1959) *Prediction of Separation of the Turbulent Boundary Layer*. J. Fluid Mech. **5**, 1–16.

Townsend, A. A. (1956) *The Structure of Turbulent Shear Flow*. Cambridge Univ. Press, London.

---

* Vol. 8, part 1, J. Fluid Mech.

Page 15: "The 'scale effects' mentioned in the text apply only to the performance of the experimental setup. For all the results presented herein the velocity was 82 ft per sec. No attention was given to possible Reynolds-number effects on the performance of any of the mixing devices, nor to the general question of such effects in connexion with forced mixing."

Page 20: "Devices (A), (B), and (C) were given a 10° angle of attack to provide a tripping action which caused the boundary layer of the top surface to become turbulent near the sharp leading edge and prevent laminar flow separation. This was effective under existing conditions. Scale effects, which might impair [or otherwise change] the performance of a device, were not investigated for any of the devices." (*Note*: "[or otherwise change]" not in original; inserted now to bring out better the original intent of these footnotes.)

Addendum

In addition to the tests and experiments here reported, duplicate tests, to be incorporated and reported elsewhere, were made in the same test equipment with the same mechanical configuration after the free-stream turbulence had been increased by a factor of five. This was accomplished by installing a $1\frac{1}{2}$-inch square mesh by 0.168-inch diameter wire grid at the $x = -48$-inch position normal to the flow, 2 inches downstream from the control screen shown in figure 1. The grid was oriented with the wires at 45° to the wall and with the apex of each square in contact with the surface. This increased the free-stream turbulence intensity from 0.4 percent to 2.0 percent at the $x=0$ position.

The results of these tests were generally similar to those here reported, but with the following deviations:

1. The boundary layer profile shape was distorted at the $x=0$ position in a direction to indicate a higher skin friction. This was possibly due to the way in which the grid affected the initial conditions of the flow as well as to the turbulence produced by it. These effects require further study.

2. The free-stream turbulence level of 2.0 percent at the $x=0$ position altered the correlation coefficients, $K(y)$. Negative correlations, attributed to oscillations attending intermittency, were absent, suggesting that the higher free-stream turbulence had effectively wiped out the oscillatory motions. This resulted in a monotonically increasing integral scale of the turbulence from the wall outward toward the free stream.

3. The grid-induced turbulence decayed as the flow proceeded downstream, and as it did so the negative correlations associated with intermittency again appeared, and the boundary layer recovered characteristic features similar to those reported in the body of this paper for the stream of lesser turbulence.

4. For the same duct configuration that originally produced the "B" gradient, the boundary layer now showed a greater tendency toward separation. Specifically, the near-separating turbulent boundary layer developing in the presence of the more-turbulent free stream showed: (a) lesser skin friction coefficient, (b) greater areas of transitory stall, (c) the region of near-zero $\overline{uv}$-correlation extending farther from the wall, and (d) a lesser total pressure recovery than was indicated with pressure gradient "B" here reported.

These observations indicate that, in addition to the factors usually considered, the free-stream turbulence and its history may also have an important bearing upon the behavior of the boundary layer in the near-separating condition.

Discussion

S. J. KLINE (*Stanford University, Stanford, California*)

I would like to ask a semantics question. At Stanford we used the term transitory stall some time ago to describe diffuser flows in which large regions of backflow occurred. Then we used some other words, unfortunately two different sets, to describe small bits of backflow like those which I talked about in the last zone of the first figure of my paper. I am not clear which kind you are talking about when you refer to transitory stall.

W. G. SPANGENBERG

I am talking about the small scale backflows which you described. I would consider the intermittent transitory stall to be of very small scale, within the possible scale of the turbulence present within the boundary layer.

S. J. KLINE

We have some confusion of nomenclature I'm afraid. They were momentary backflows with considerable transverse scale? They didn't go clear across the flow?

W. G. SPANGENBERG

They were little tiny bits—just intermittent spots of transitory stall. I think you used this term in the first place to describe such things. I feel I'm seeing exactly the same thing that you reported in some of your earlier papers. The intermittent stall, on the other hand, I would consider a massive type of thing in which the entire boundary-layer-separation line surges, both upstream and downstream, with very violent fluctuations in pressure. There were no such violent fluctuations of pressure in the type of transitory stall that I described.

B. S. STRATFORD (*Rolls Royce Ltd., Derby, England*)

Mr. Spangenberg and the team of the NBS are to be congratulated for this magnificent mass of experimental information that we have all been clamoring for. One particular point that I would like to emphasize is their very large pressure rise and the long distance over which they have been operating. The main sort of problem in this type of experiment is the threat of secondary flows, and I understand that Mr. Spangenberg's team spent two or three months solidly testing in order to prevent such flows happening. The difficulties probably increase exponentially with the length of the surface you are trying to operate with. For Mr. Spangenberg's surface, the length of the pressure-rise region is about 5 times the length of the test surface before the start of the pressure rise, and his pressure recoveries are in the order of 85 % of the inlet dynamic head. To maintain two-dimensional conditions over this sort of distance with that kind of pressure rise is a very big achievement.

I would like to comment on two other points. Using the pressure distributions of figure 2 of Mr. Spangenberg's paper (figure 20), it can be seen that the main difference between pressure distributions A and B is that curve B rises locally above curve A at some intermediate point along the length of diffusion, while curve A has the larger value at the end of the distributions. Now if we use figure 4 and look at the velocity profiles in the region of overlap (figure 21) we see that the profiles for

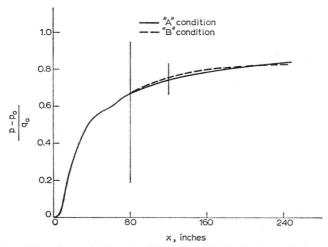

Figure 20. Comparison of static-pressure distributions. The "B" condition has been slightly exaggerated to emphasize the difference between the curves.

pressure distribution A come towards a value of 0.2 near the wall, while for distribution B they come towards 0.1. One of my hobbies is plotting velocity profiles in terms of U^2, instead of U as is done here. If we replot them as velocity squared, the 0.2 becomes 0.04 and the 0.1 becomes 0.01, and they look approximately as follows (figure 22). You'll have to take my word for this, but I did have the advantage of being able to speak to Mr. Spangenberg about a week ago. The A profile is not a very straight line, while the B profile is reasonably straight near the wall. Also, in Mr. Spangenberg's actual measurements he showed that skin friction was virtually zero at the wall, and it is generally accepted that the level of skin friction is very closely related to the level of velocity or dynamic head close to the wall. We can say, from all points of view, that it is pretty certain that the skin friction in both of these flows is very close to zero, even though not quite zero. In

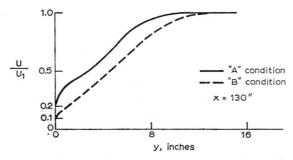

Figure 21. Comparison of velocity profiles in overlap region of figure 20.

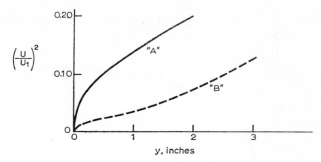

Figure 22. Comparison of dynamic-head profiles in overlap region of figure 20.

figure 5, in fact, Mr. Spangenberg showed that the skin friction fell to roughly 1/10 or less of the initial value.

Now if we consider the difference between these two results, in going from flow A to flow B we have dropped the skin friction just a little bit closer to zero (figure 5) and dropped the value of the actual dynamic head at the wall by 2 or 3 percentage points. This was started from a position of about $x = 80$ inches (figure 20) and resulted in an increase in pressure rise at the peak point on curve B of something like 1 % of the initial dynamic head over that at the corresponding point on A. So by dropping to a skin friction which is virtually zero and a dynamic head which varies essentially linearly from zero at the wall we have obtained this marginal increase in pressure rise at the particular station.

So far, so good; this lines up with what we tended to expect. Now the interesting thing which Mr. Spangenberg shows is that having obtained this higher pressure curve with virtually zero skin friction, we then find that we lose again because, in order to avoid separation, we have had to allow the pressure rise to flatten off downstream. His later analysis showed that the dissipation in flow B is very considerably higher than that in flow A. So we therefore seem to have two conclusions: if you consider just *local* conditions, then the steepest pressure rise corresponds to zero skin friction, or very close to zero skin friction. But if you are concerned about *overall* conditions over a long distance (and remember that this is a large distance in terms of the initial distance, and a very large pressure rise), it is better to have a skin friction marginally greater than zero because it appears to reduce the local dissipation. This is something that we hadn't expected. The increase in dissipation makes the boundary layer somewhat thicker downstream and it can only accept a shallower pressure gradient. So, in the long run you lose by extracting the last bit of skin friction.

The second point I wanted to make is more in the way of a question and it concerns the measured distribution of total shear stress. I know that Mr. Spangenberg has spent many hours considering this very difficult problem and he finds that the distribution behaves according to his figure 15. Just looking at the boundary layer equations one expects a linear variation near the wall (figure 23) since $\partial \tau / \partial y \approx \partial p / \partial x$ in this region. However, the measurements show a different sort of line. Now, the horizontal displacement of the two curves is in the order of 0.1 of the boundary layer thickness. It is not enormous, but on the other hand it's on the order of an inch so that it certainly isn't an experimental error. An inch is something which is on the order of probably a hundred times the size of the instrumentation involved so there is no question about the realness of this displacement. If you look at the curves along a vertical line, the actual shear stress at a point near the wall is only a tiny fraction of the shear stress that you would expect. So there does seem to be a very real puzzle here.

Mr. Spangenberg has suggested that this is perhaps due to the Reynolds-normal-stress term, $\partial \sigma / \partial x$, and this certainly seems like one suggestion that is worth following up. He has mentioned to me privately that $\partial(\rho U^2)/\partial x$ is negligible compared with this term, i.e., the ordinary inertia terms seem to be almost irrelevant. I wonder if I could suggest one other possibility. I happen to know that it has been

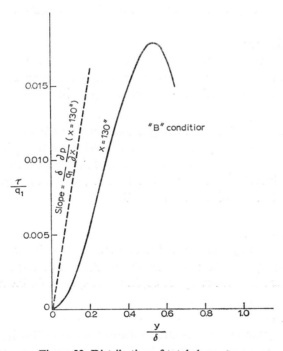

Figure 23. Distribution of total shear stress.

looked at but I would still like to suggest it. In this sort of flow the u-component of the turbulence velocity near the wall (i.e., the root-mean-square value, u') is of the order of 1/3 of the local mean value (figure 11). If you multiply this by the $\sqrt{2}$ on the assumption of a sine profile for the time variation of the turbulence component, it brings you up to about 0.5 for the corresponding maximum value. Now the distribution of turbulence velocity is nothing like a sine profile so you can easily imagine a maximum that is appreciably larger than 0.5, and the actual very-local velocity peaks which tend to contribute a lot to the shear stress could perhaps exceed unity. This would be in line with Mr. Spangenberg's observations that there are momentary conditions of reversed flow. If you have a v term of comparable magnitude, then you have a situation in which the flow is reversed and there is also a strong component of velocity at 90° to the direction of mean flow; these conditions are so far removed from the usual conditions under which this type of instrument is used that one wonders if there is not some sort of calibration effect present; I leave this for further comment.

H. W. LIEPMANN (*California Institute of Technology, Pasadena, California*)

I think that this is a good point; at these high turbulence levels one really ought to discuss what accuracy constant-current hot wire anemometers can achieve.

W. G. SPANGENBERG

I know that this application is outside the range of the usual use of a hot-wire anemometer, but the data were so consistent. It may be off by a few percent but I don't think it's off by hundreds or thousands of percent.

G. B. SCHUBAUER (*National Bureau of Standards, Washington, D.C.*)

Mr. Spangenberg told me, perhaps he is a little reluctant to say it here, that what Dr. Stratford has said was borne out when he tried it. The gradient in the Reynolds normal stress did just about make up the difference between the expected and measured total shear-stress gradient near the wall.

W. G. SPANGENBERG

The gradient in the Reynolds normal stress (i.e., $\partial\sigma/\partial x \equiv \partial(-\overline{\rho u^2})/\partial x$) accounted for approximately 2/3 of the difference (Table 3). If this term is added to the $\partial\tau/\partial y$ term, the sum just about equals $\partial p/\partial x$ (i.e., $\partial\tau/\partial y + \partial\sigma/\partial x \cong \partial p/\partial x$).

G. B. SCHUBAUER

I believe that may tend to answer Dr. Stratford's question. The hot-wire measurements may be in error to some extent, but here we apparently have evidence of a gradient of turbulent normal stress opposing a pressure gradient and acting to keep fluid moving downstream.

I want to make one more point. Holding this layer in a near-separating condition for 13 feet was no small task. Mr. Spangenberg and his co-workers spent a lot of time adjusting the layer; if they went too far they encountered massive separation (a condition of extensive, continuous stall), so you see it's a bit tricky. You are pushing as near to separation as you can without having it actually occur, and if even something small happens to the boundary layer (we don't know all the things that can happen to make it separate accidentally) you are in trouble. Separation occurring suddenly and without warning comes to mind, but one must not overlook other effects, some of which are probably likewise of a catastrophic nature. I would not now venture to predict all that could occur in situations of this kind, and one must always be aware of the inherent dangers whatever they may be.

H. W. LIEPMANN

What is the situation with $\partial p/\partial y$?

W. G. SPANGENBERG

In addition to a total-head rake and a hot-wire anemometer, I also traversed the boundary layers with a pitot-static tube. The gradients in pressure normal to the wall were really very minor when compared with $\partial p/\partial x$. They were very small across the boundary layer, and had their greatest value well upstream of the station where the critical nearly-separating condition became established.

G. K. SEROVY (*Iowa State University, Ames, Iowa*)

Did you have a number of rows of static-pressure taps across the tunnel?

W. G. SPANGENBERG

Yes, I had rows of static pressure taps across the tunnel and that is one way that I determined whether the flow was actually aligned with the box. I had 3 rows, one down the center and one on either side, fifteen inches from the center. I had to tailor the gradient by venting and a lot of other things to give not only a uniform pressure-recovery across the test chamber but also to give similar boundary layer profiles in each of the three positions. These measurements showed that the flow was fairly well aligned with the box and that there was no great cross-stream gradient.

G. K. SEROVY

Your total-head velocity surveys and hot-wire surveys were both at the center of the tunnel, approximately?

W. G. SPANGENBERG

Yes. I should add that I was worrying about this difference in total shear-stress distribution near the wall and I thought that there might be some 3-dimensional effects present, some w and v velocities perhaps, and consequently some striated flow. I could not detect any striated flow; it didn't make any difference where I measured across the box, I got the same answer.

B. G. NEWMAN (*McGill University, Montreal, Quebec, Canada*)

You presumably also got information on v from the crossed wires. Did $p + \overline{\varrho v^2}$ remain essentially constant near the wall?

W. G. SPANGENBERG

I never checked that. I do have v' data but we had so much information I didn't present it. We were rushing to get this paper together in time for the symposium and we didn't have very much time to do a great deal of analysis. (Note that v' values are given in figure 10 of the paper.)

S. J. KLINE

On the question about the meaning of the hot-wire measurements, if there are bits of flow going upstream the wire reads this as a "u" because it presumably only indicates the magnitude of a normal component of velocity and can't determine its direction. Actually, it is a negative u. Was this accounted for in any way in the measurements?

W. G. SPANGENBERG

No. The pitot-static velocity readings checked my hot-wire measurements very closely. If there were any rectification effects, as you suggest, I would think that the velocity indicated by the hot-wire anemometer would be greater than that shown by the pitot-static tube in this highly turbulent region. This was not the case. I thought for some time that perhaps there was a rectification in regions of transitory stall but there is no indication whatsoever in the data that the hot-wire mean-speed readings were, in fact, too high.

S. J. KLINE

Wouldn't this make the $\overline{uv}$ reading too low rather than too high?

W. G. SPANGENBERG

It could affect the u and v individually but it shouldn't affect the correlation. This comes about by the nature of the $\overline{uv}$ correlation, I believe.

S. J. KLINE

But if you are talking about the Reynolds stress (i.e., the fact that fluid is transported from a region of one value of U to another) the wire reads what is actually $-u$ as $+u$. This will give too low a reading for the correlation because the $-u$ will tend to give a much stronger Reynolds stress than a $+u$ because it has more difference of velocity.

W. G. Spangenberg

I just don't know. There are some defects in the data taking. However, I did determine the $\overline{\varrho uv}$ shearing stress in two ways. First, by direct measurement with the usual hot-wire anemometry. Second, I took the product of the $\overline{uv}$ correlation coefficient (figure 14) and $u'v'$. The answers were not identical, but in the region adjacent or very close to the wall, the product of the correlation coefficient and $u'v'$ came much closer to the actual indicated skin friction at $x = 0$ than did the directly measured $\overline{\varrho uv}$. Therefore, I adopted this method of evaluation for $\overline{\varrho uv}$.*

E. S. Taylor (*Massachusetts Institute of Technology, Cambridge, Massachusetts*)

Isn't there some question about what you say the static pressure taps read? The static pressure taps also read $\overline{\varrho v^2}$.

W. G. Spangenberg

The static pressure taps were flush with the floor.

E. S. Taylor

Of course, but they also read $\overline{\varrho v^2}$. They don't just read $\overline{\varrho u^2}$.

W. G. Spangenberg

The v-components, of course, have decayed close to the floor much faster than the u-components of turbulence. They could affect the pressure reading but I don't think they are going to account for as large a discrepancy as the one we are considering.

G. B. Schubauer

May I make just one more little comment. The explanation we have been talking about came after Dr. Stratford visited us. We discussed it with him first. We had been very mystified, and we would like to thank him very much for making us think a little more about it. We don't want to take credit for having done this all by ourselves. We did have his help in thinking about it.

---

* A reconsideration of this problem indicates to me also that intermittent flow reversal can cause a reduction in the absolute value of the correlation coefficient as measured by the hot wire as suggested by Dr. Kline. Since, however, the regions of transitory stall extended in the y-direction across only a small fraction of the region wherein the correlation coefficient had vanished, the reduction in turbulent shear stress in this entire region cannot be explained by this effect.

The Applicability of Turbulence Research to the Solution of Internal Flow Problems

J. L. LUMLEY

The Pennsylvania State University, University Park, Pennsylvania

SUMMARY

The needs of the engineer for knowledge about turbulence are examined. The state of present knowledge and directions of current research in several parts of this field are briefly outlined. The extent to, and ways by, which the engineer's needs may be met from this current knowledge and research are discussed.

INTRODUCTION

Much of the information on turbulence available to the engineer in expository form (e.g. Schlichting 1951) represents ideas having their origin in the period immediately preceding World War Two (although some more recent material is referred to). In the decade and-a-half just passed, two monographs on the subject have been published (Batchelor 1953; Townsend 1956) together with innumerable papers. Much of this material is available in expository form (Hinze 1959) though not directed specifically to engineers. It is evident to even the casual reader that this more recent material differs in character from the earlier in being more mathematical, more statistical, and placing smaller reliance on *ad-hoc* assumptions. It is legitimate to enquire as to the applicability of this material to the problems of the engineer, particularly with regard to internal flows.

In examining the applicability of current turbulence research, I would like to limit the discussion by excluding as much as possible two aspects of this subject. The first is the wealth of experimental data available in the literature. This is clearly applicable to problems involving similar flows. The second is similarity. One of the most powerful techniques in fluid mechanics is the reduction of the number of variables describing a flow by the recognition of invariance groups. In its simplest use this permits data measured in one circumstance to be taken as representative of a group of circumstances. Flows possessing invariances are often more tractable than more general ones. Occasionally an invariance is discovered which is a basic feature of a flow; without quibbling about the definition of "basic", I would like to leave out of discussion all but the last aspect.

I would prefer to direct the discussion to some of the ideas which motivate, and which have arisen from recent and current turbulence research. We can never make measurements in all possible configurations. Our goal must be to predict quantitatively the flow in an unfamiliar configuration from existing data in other situations which are not similar; and eventually from "first principles". In order to do this, we must understand the principles which govern a turbulent flow. Hence, my emphasis is on ideas.

It is as well to face from the outset the fact that, in the restricted sense of applicability defined above, current turbulence research is in a position to offer very little quantitative help to the engineer concerned with internal flow. In much of what follows I will be reduced to explaining why this is so. The turbulence problem has proven so difficult that an engineer presently having a particular flow problem in hand cannot expect more than qualitative indications and order-of-magnitude estimates. Although these can, of course, be extremely helpful, quantitative answers will at this stage almost always require the engineer's getting up a small experimental research program of his own.

THE NEEDS OF THE ENGINEER

The engineer working in internal flow problems needs to predict boundary layer growth in non-circular passages of changing cross section; the location of separation and reattachment; the occurrence of large-scale unsteady phenomena, such as oscillating stall in a diffuser; the sizes, frequencies and intensities of unsteady forces on flow boundaries; heat transfer rates on all these boundaries; mass transfer rates from boundaries and from droplets suspended in the flow; heat and mass transfer rates and reaction rates within the flow, as for example in a combustion chamber; and noise, both due to structural vibration induced by unsteady forces at the boundaries, and caused directly from open jets and shear layers. He needs to do this not only in a steady flow but also in pulsating unsteady flows. Occasionally he needs to predict the location of transition.

Although much of the work of the internal flow engineer is likely to be concerned with gases, a large class of problems arise in liquids. If the liquid is a Newtonian liquid, such as water or lubricating oil, we may expect the turbulence to be dynamically similar in every way to that in a gas of such a density as to be describable by continuum ideas (see Lumley 1963)*.

---

* Where possible reference is given to general works and literature surveys.

References p. 164

The only exception to this is cavitation which is, of course, a phenomenon peculiar to liquids. We can therefore describe the differences and similarities between turbulence in the two phases by the different values of the various non-dimensional parameters which occur, and in what follows we will make no distinction between liquids and gases.*

These problems can conveniently be placed in five categories which are more or less distinct:

1. The prediction of transition;
2. The prediction of radiated noise from a turbulent shear flow;
3. The prediction of the motion of suspended particles in a turbulent flow;
4. The prediction of separation; and
5. The prediction of the structure of turbulent shear flows, particularly as this influences the transport of momentum, heat, contamination and so forth by fluctuating velocities.

In a survey as brief as this it is evident that I cannot discuss all five areas. The first four are reasonably well defined areas of specialization in each of which there is an extensive literature; I would prefer to give my attention to the fifth which is at once the broadest, in scope and significance, and the least well understood.

THE PRESENT STATE OF KNOWLEDGE ABOUT TURBULENCE

The so-called "statistical theory" of turbulence has been concerned largely with *description* of the turbulent velocity field. As the name implies, this involves averages of various kinds: time averages for stationary quantities (those whose statistics do not change in time), space averages for homogeneous quantities (those whose statistics are constant in a spacial direction), ensemble averages (averages over a collection of superficially identical experiments) and so forth. At first the quantities of interest were the so-called mean quantities (although all averaged quantities are mean quantities); for example the mean velocity $\overline{U}$. Since the time of Reynolds, fluctuations have been defined by forming $u = U - \overline{U}$, and the moments are of interest, for example $\overline{u^2}$. The turbulence level is defined as $\sqrt{\overline{u^2}}/\overline{U}$. Because of its appearance in the equation of mean motion, correlations such as $\overline{uv}$ are of interest.

---

* One interesting possibility which may have relevance for the internal flow engineer exists in liquids and does not exist in gases (see Lumley 1964). This is the demonstrated possibility of controlling the presence and structure of the turbulence by using liquids whose constitutive relations are not Newtonian. For each such liquid the engineer needs to be able to predict all of the phenomena described above and of course each new constitutive relation is to a large extent a new problem. This area is the subject of active current research, and understanding of observed phenomena is presently almost completely lacking.

The beginning of the modern period may perhaps be taken from the beginning of interest in correlations between two quantities not at the same point. These were used in 1921 by Taylor in discussing turbulent transport: if $Y(t)$ and $v(t)$ are the position and velocity of a point of the fluid, then one can write ($Y(0) = 0$)

$$Y(t) = \int_0^t v(t')\mathrm{d}t' \tag{1}$$

$$\overline{Y^2(t)} = \int_0^t \int \overline{v(t')v(t'')}\mathrm{d}t'\,\mathrm{d}t'' \tag{2}$$

and $\overline{v(t')v(t'')}$ is an auto-correlation. It was not until 1935, however, that interest in such quantities became intense. At that time it was recognized (Taylor 1935) that, if $v(t)$ is stationary, so that $\overline{v(t)v(t')} = R(t'-t)$, then $v(t)$ may be decomposed into harmonic components (with some restrictions which need not concern us here)*

$$v(t) = \sum_\omega a(\omega)\cos \omega t + b(\omega)\sin \omega t = \sum_\omega \alpha(\omega)\mathrm{e}^{i\omega t} \tag{3}$$

and the "energy spectrum", $\overline{a^2(\omega)} + \overline{b^2(\omega)} = F(\omega) = |\alpha|^2$, is related to the correlation by

$$R(t) = \sum_\omega \cos \omega t\, F(\omega) \tag{4}$$

The time correlation, of course, could be measured (with difficulty), and the spectrum was even easier to measure with a narrow band filter.

The spectrum of fluctuations measured at a fixed place in a flow, or on a boundary, became an object of interest in itself (see figure 1) and attempts were made to predict its form in various ranges and under various circumstances.

Greatest success, of course, can be expected in circumstances in which the number of relevant variables can be reduced by a group invariance; the similarity theory of Kolmogorov recognizes a naturally occurring invariance which is in a sense basic (see figure 2). This predicted that if the eddies influenced by viscosity were sufficiently smaller than those containing most of the energy (a circumstance which becomes increasingly true with increasing Reynolds numbers) then the smaller eddies would have a universal structure dependent only on the viscosity v and the rate at which they were being supplied with energy, ε (called an equilibrium range of eddies). The largest of these smaller eddies might even be uninfluenced by v, so that their structure would be determined solely by ε (called an inertial sub-range).

---

* More properly, of course, these should be Stieltjes integrals, but operationally the distinction is irrelevant.

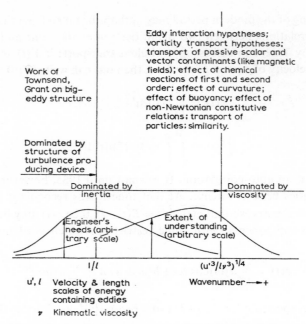

Figure 1. A guide to current research activity in turbulence.

It was soon realized that one- and two-dimensional turbulence could not exist. This is because, to complete the energy balance, viscosity must convert the mechanical energy to heat. Viscous effects are negligible at the largest scales of the motion, however. The energy must be gradually transferred to smaller scales (at which viscosity is effective) by stretching of vorticity: an eddy of a given size stretches in its strain field the smaller eddies imbedded in it, reducing their scale and doing work on them (see figure 3). Only in a three-dimensional flow can the velocity field stretch the vorticity. By the same token, a real turbulence must be rotational, and it must be non-linear (since vortex stretching is a non-linear phenomenon). As a result of these realizations, the statistical description was extended to vectors in three dimensions giving rise to quantities like

$$\overline{u_i(x, t)u_j(x', t')} = R_{ij}(x,x', t,t') \tag{5}$$

and attempts were made to find simplifications (not completely at variance with the physics) to replace the classical ones of irrotationality, two-dimensionality and linearization, none of which was permissible. The search is still going on.

The statistical theory has provided considerable insight into the basic mechanism of the smaller eddies in turbulent flow. It has made it possible to answer such questions as "what is the probability of two droplets colliding", which is relevant to the formation of raindrops, and the dynamics of aerosol clouds and fuel sprays. This insight has been extended to include the effect of gravitation, rotation, magnetic fields, chemical reactions of various orders and a change of constitutive relation on the structure of these high-wave-number eddies. This work is essential for an eventual understanding of the entire turbulence phenomenon.

It has also provided descriptive tools. For example, an engineer concerned with panel flutter knows that he must be concerned with quantities such as

$$\overline{p(x, t)\, p(x', t')} = P(x' - x, t' - t) \tag{6}$$

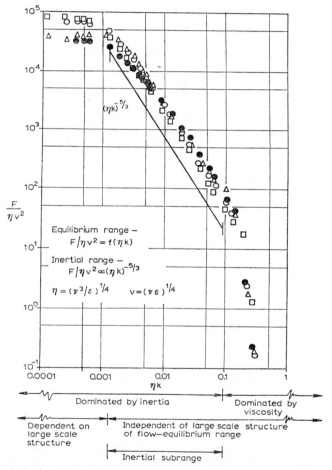

Figure 2. The similarity theory of Kolmogorov applied to some spectra measured in a curved mixing layer (Margolis, Ph. D. Thesis, Penn. State 1963).

References p. 164

where x is a position on the panel, and p is a pressure fluctuation. It has provided concepts. For example, the same engineer may be interested in pressure patterns of a given spacial extent $2\pi/\kappa$,

$$p(x, t) = \Sigma\, e^{i\kappa \cdot x}\, \Pi(\kappa, t) \tag{7}$$

and he may inquire about the convection velocity (Wills 1964) of a given size pattern by decomposing further,

$$p(x, t) = \Sigma\, e^{i(\kappa \cdot x - \kappa ct)}\, \Omega(\kappa, c) \tag{8}$$

(using $-\kappa c$ instead of frequency). The spectrum $|\Omega|^2$ is given by the transform of the autocorrelation

$$\overline{p(x, t)\, p(x + \xi, t + \tau)} = \Sigma\, e^{i(\kappa \cdot \xi - \kappa c \tau)}\, \overline{|\Omega|^2} \tag{9}$$

and from the peaks of $\overline{|\Omega|^2}$ he can tell at what speed most of the energy of scale κ

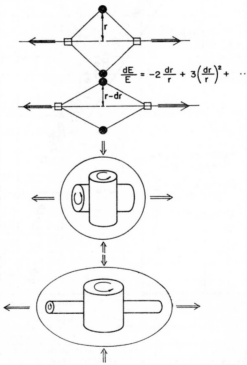

$$\frac{dE}{E} = -2\,\frac{dr}{r} + 3\left(\frac{dr}{r}\right)^2 + \cdots$$

Figure 3. Inertial transfer by the interaction of a strain-rate field and vorticity; applicable either to turbulent production or inertial spectral transfer. The lengthened vortex gains more energy than the shortened one looses, so that net energy is removed from the strain-rate field, and this appears at smaller scale.

is convected. He is then in a position to construct a surface having no modes of scale κ with propagation velocities matching those of the most energetic eddies of scale κ.

This concept is relatively sophisticated. A simple one is the integral scale

$$\int_0^\infty \frac{\overline{v(t)v(t+\tau)}}{\overline{v^2}} \, d\tau = T \tag{10}$$

which can be shown to give essentially the "color" of a random quantity, in the sense that its inverse is near the frequency containing the most energy.

The statistical theory has as yet, however, contributed far less to the understanding of the large scale motions in turbulent shear flows, the part of the spectrum which is intensely dependent on the overall geometry and history of the flow, and the end of the spectrum of greatest interest to the engineer. This is primarily because turbulent flows can be ranked in order of complexity and difficulty in the following way*:

1. Homogeneous and isotropic:
   no variation of turbulent quantities with position or direction; mean strain-rate tensor vanishes; no production of turbulent energy.
2. Homogeneous anisotropic:
   no variation of turbulent quantities with position; mean strain-rate tensor not a function of position; production of turbulent energy.
3. Inhomogeneous anisotropic two-dimensional:
   turbulent quantities and mean-velocity field are functions of one variable only; production of turbulent energy.
4. Inhomogeneous anisotropic three-dimensional (boundary layer type):
   turbulent quantities and mean-velocity field are functions of two variables only; production of turbulent energy; secondary motion present.
5. Inhomogeneous anisotropic fully three-dimensional:
   turbulent quantities and mean-velocity field are functions of three variables; production of turbulent energy; secondary motions present.

The list could be extended to include dynamically interacting fields (such as temperature), etc. Only the first category has received extensive and detailed theoretical and experimental investigation sufficient to display the mechanisms involved. The first detailed experimental investigation of the second has just been completed (Rose 1965). The third category has been investigated extensively (including as it does pipes, channels, plane boundary layers, plane and axi-symmetric wakes and jets, etc.) but only recently has an investigation reached the intensiveness characterizing 1) (Bradshaw & Ferriss 1965). No detailed investigation exists of 4) and an

---

* It should be noted that this ranking is by the number of invariance groups displayed.

References p. 164

investigation of 5) is only beginning at NPL (the shear layer between two ortho-gonal streams).

The only attempt at a theory of flows which are self-maintaining (in the sense of supplying the energy which is dissipated) is Townsend (1956); this is highly speculative, somewhat phenomenological, rests heavily on similarity arguments and meager experimental evidence, and is probably something like the truth. It is strictly applicable only to 3).

The central difficulty in the construction of a theory for any of the flows more complicated than 1) is still the relation of the Reynolds stress to the mean flow (similar remarks may be made regarding the temperature–velocity and concen-tration–velocity correlations). Several decades of work have not produced a relationship substantially more satisfactory than the eddy viscosity, although it is now known with some precision why and in what ways this is not satisfactory. Briefly, in molecular transport in a gas at large Knudsen numbers the transporting motions have length and time scales that are small relative to length and time scales in the mean motion, so that the stress depends only on local properties, i.e. the present value of the first derivative of the mean-velocity field. In addition, the structure of the transporting motion is isotropic; that is, in the process of trans-mission of mean-flow energy to the scales of the molecular motion, information on the organized character of the mean motion is lost—the stress thus depends iso-tropically on the first derivative. Finally, the shortness of the time-scale ratio also implies that the dependence is linear; that is, a consistent higher approximation involves both time derivatives and second order terms (Coleman & Noll 1961). Now, in a general turbulent flow the length and time scales of the transporting motion are of the same order as those of the mean motion (empirical observation) and the transporting motions retain much of the organization of the mean motion; we may therefore expect that the stress will depend in some integral manner on the entire deformation field over the whole past, and that the dependence will be neither isotropic nor linear.

This is a pretty discouraging picture, but fortunately there are some bright spots. It is observed (Townsend 1956) that turbulent shear flows can be (very approxi-mately) split into two types of motions; big eddies, of length scales similar to the mean motion, highly anisotropic, long lived and weak (perhaps 20% of the tur-bulent energy); and small eddies, of scales 1/3 to 1/5 that of the mean motion, more nearly isotropic, shorter lived and strong (perhaps 80% of the turbulent energy). The intensity of the smaller eddies is nearly uniform in the turbulent fluid, since a blob of fluid will have wandered over most of the flow during its lifetime. For these smaller eddies the idea of an eddy viscosity is not such a serious violation of the physics.

The time and length scales of the small eddies are a good deal smaller than the time and length scales of the mean motion or the large eddies, so that a linear dependence on the local, present value of the strain rate may be a satisfactory first approximation (although the order of approximation is not likely to be high); an isotropic dependence is probably as satisfactory, although this implies that the principal axes of the stress and strain rate are the same, which is known to not be quite true. It must also be remembered that this approximation is likely to be poor in regions where the strain rate vanishes; the stress is known not always to vanish there, so presumably a proper approximation would include dependence on higher derivatives. This, however, would be a higher order correction. The coefficients, of course, should depend on the length and time scales of the smaller eddies, thus:

$$- \overline{u_i u_j} + \overline{u'^2} \delta_{ij} = \alpha \overline{u'^2} t^* S_{ij} = 2\nu_T S_{ij} \overline{u'^2} \tag{11}$$

$$\overline{u'^2} = \frac{\overline{u_1^2} + \overline{u_2^2} + \overline{u_3^2}}{3}; \quad S_{ij} = \tfrac{1}{2}(\overline{U}_{i,j} + \overline{U}_{j,i}); \quad \overline{U}_{i,j} = \partial \overline{U}_i / \partial x_j$$

(t^* is the time scale of these eddies and α is a supposedly-universal constant).

In a flow which is nearly in equilibrium, in the sense that any changes in structure take place very slowly compared to the time scale of the small eddies, we may write

$$\langle -\overline{u_i u_j} S_{ij} \rangle_{\mathrm{av}} = \overline{u'^2} / t^* \tag{12}$$

where the brackets indicate an average over the flow cross section. This gives a value of

$$t^* = [\alpha \langle S_{pq} S_{pq} \rangle_{\mathrm{av}}]^{-\frac{1}{2}} \tag{13}$$

or

$$- \frac{\overline{u_i u_j}}{\overline{u'^2}} + \delta_{ij} = \sqrt{\alpha} \frac{S_{ij}}{\sqrt{\langle S_{pq} S_{pq} \rangle_{\mathrm{av}}}} \tag{14}$$

A value of $\sqrt{\alpha} = 0.45\sqrt{2}$ fits the (sparse) available data quite well. Equation (14) states that under the action of a steady uniform strain rate of given geometry, the *structure* of the turbulence acquires an equilibrium value regardless of the intensity of the strain rate. A way to interpret (11) is to say that under the action of a strain-rate field, the turbulence adopts the same structure as an isotropic turbulence would to first order in its own characteristic time. Under the application of a rapid deformation by a large eddy (still slow relative to the small eddies) the structure of the small eddies is changed according to (14), but the length and time scales of the small eddies do not have time to change. For flows whose development cannot be regarded as slow, we must revert to (11), where the eddy viscosity may be taken as constant over a flow cross section and slowly varying in the flow direction. The slightly more explicit form in (14) is of no great advantage, since we do not know $\overline{u'^2}$.

References p. 164

What is the advantage of having an expression for the Reynolds stress produced by these small eddies if they represent only part of the energy present (although a major part)? And how should we determine the eddy viscosity? Townsend has suggested the following: Let us presume for a minute that we know the structure of the big eddies. We need not assume that we know their intensity; only their size and orientation in the flow. If we assume that we know the mean velocity profile* then we can estimate the rate at which the large eddies extract energy from the mean flow. At the same time we may estimate the rate at which these eddies lose energy to the small eddies, expressing it in terms of the eddy viscosity whose magnitude is not known (using expression (11) with S_{ij} being the sum of the strain rates of the mean field and the big eddy). The requirement that these large eddies should be in equilibrium (that is, losing energy through the small scale motion at the same rate at which they gain energy from the mean motion) gives another relationship. This relationship is in the form of a Reynolds number made up of the local velocity and length scales and the eddy viscosity. This Reynolds number is a numerical constant whose value lies roughly between 15 and 30 in all flows which have been studied. This value compares very favorably with experiment.

The number which is obtained for the turbulent Reynolds number is not particularly sensitive to the choice of large eddy structure, which is fortunate because there is currently considerable controversy about the proper structure (Grant 1958).

We have not said what these large eddies are, nor where they come from and in fact this is not entirely clear. The most consistent picture seems to be the following: that in a homogeneous direction sines and cosines are the appropriate functions into which to decompose the velocity field; across the flow, however, (in inhomogeneous directions) this is not the case and the flow is most suitably decomposed into discrete structures, eigenmodes if you like, which occur with random amplitudes (Payne & Lumley 1965), the amplitudes of the various eigenmodes being uncorrelated with each other. Higher modes, having length scales small compared with the width of the flow, will look very much like sines and cosines; the first few modes however, whose length scales are of the order of the width of the flow, are quite distinctive in structure. An equation can be obtained for the structure of these eigenmodes and of course the equation resembles the Navier–Stokes equation. There is, however, an interaction term representing the interchange of energy among the various eigenmodes. An approximate way of solving this equation is to represent all modes above the first by an eddy viscosity, as we have done. If an expansion is formed in the amplitude of the first eigenmode (since we know it to be weak), the equation becomes a stability equation, similar to the Orr–Sommerfeld

---

* which is given, for reasons no one quite understands, to an adequate approximation by an eddy viscosity assumption for the whole Reynolds stress.

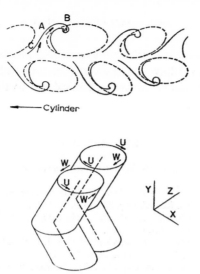

Figure 4. Large eddy structure of the turbulent wake suggested in Grant (1958). The total structure is a combination of the two shown.

equation, for the stability of the mean flow against a disturbance represented by the first eigenmode. The eddy viscosity is now determined by the requirement that the flow should just be neutrally stable to this lowest mode which is the same as the requirement of equilibrium discussed above.

In order to obtain reasonable amplitudes it is probably necessary to carry the solution to second order terms. It is interesting to note that this results in the big eddy having the same structure as the three-dimensional disturbance in a similar laminar flow just before transition.

CONCLUSIONS

The engineer dealing with internal flows needs to understand general turbulent shear flows. While most of the statistical theory of turbulence provides little help on this problem (since it deals largely with the high wave-numbers) Townsend's somewhat speculative theory does provide a model: small eddies whose momentum transport can be represented by an eddy viscosity; large eddies whose structure can be obtained from a stability-like equation; and an energy equilibrium between the two to determine the value of the eddy viscosity. Much calculation is required before comparison with experiment is possible, to show whether quantitative help can be expected from this source; simple preliminary results for the eddy viscosity do compare favorably with experiment.

References p. 164

ACKNOWLEDGEMENTS

The material presented here on turbulent shear flows places me overwhelmingly in debt to Townsend (1956); I have made several deletions, additions and changes for which I take full responsibility, however. I wish also to thank my colleagues for many helpful discussions.

REFERENCES

Batchelor, G. K. (1953; 2nd ed. 1956) *Homogeneous Turbulence*. Cambridge University Press, London.
Bradshaw, P. & Ferriss, D. H. (1965) *The Spectral Energy Balance in a Turbulent Mixing Layer*. NPL Aero Report 1144, Aero. Res. Counc. 26 743 F.M. 3574.
Coleman, B. D. & Noll, W. (1961) *Recent Results in the Continuum Theory of Viscoelastic Fluids*. Ann. New York Acad. Sciences **89**, 672–714.
Grant, H. L. (1958) *The Large Eddies of Turbulent Motion*. J. Fluid Mech. **4**, 149–90.
Hinze, J. O. (1959) *Turbulence*. McGraw-Hill, New York.
Lumley, J. L. (1963) "Turbulence in Liquids", in *The Encyclopaedic Dictionary of Physics*, Pergamon Press, Oxford.
Lumley, J. L. (1964) *The Reduction of Skin Friction Drag*. Proceedings of 5th International Symposium on Naval Hydrodynamics, Bergen. Office of Naval Research.
Payne, F. R. & Lumley, J. L. (1965) *Big-Eddy Structure of Turbulent Shear Flows*. SP6 American Physical Society, Honolulu.
Rose, W. G. (1965) *Results of an Attempt to Generate a Homogeneous Turbulent Shear Flow*. Dept. of Mechanics, the Johns Hopkins University, August 16.
Schlichting, H. (1951; 4th ed. 1960) *Boundary Layer Theory*. McGraw-Hill, New York.
Taylor, G. I. (1921) *Diffusion by Continuous Movements*. Proc. Lond. Math. Soc. **20**, 196–211.
Taylor, G. I. (1935) *Statistical Theory of Turbulence*. Proc. Roy. Soc. A, **151**, 421–90.
Townsend A. A. (1956) *The Structure of Turbulent Shear Flow*. Cambridge University Press, London.
Wills, J. A. B. (1964) *On Convection Velocity in Turbulent Shear Flows*. J. Fluid Mech. **20**, 417–32.

Discussion

S. ESKINAZI (*Syracuse University, Syracuse, New York*)

If there are such ways of separating the turbulence into two parts with small eddies in one and big eddies in another, have you given any thought to how you ultimately anticipate putting this together to determine the mean flow while somehow including turbulence terms? It's already hard enough to have one eddy viscosity for the entire flow; when you break the flow into two parts, how do you bring all this information together? Is it through the energy spectrum?

J. L. LUMLEY

No, you would have a new expression for the Reynolds stress which would be composed of two terms. One would be the conventional eddy viscosity and the other would account for the Reynolds stress produced by the big eddies. Let's say that from somewhere you assume a mean-velocity profile; then you can get something like $\overline{a_1^2}\phi_i\phi_j + \nu_T S_{ij}$ (where S_{ij} is the mean strain rate). You see that you have an additional term arising from the Reynolds stress produced by the big eddies. You can now put this back into the mean equation and get a better mean-velocity profile; if you still had strength you could use this new mean-velocity profile to get a slightly better form for the big eddy and continue until the process converged.

H. W. LIEPMANN (*California Institute of Technology, Pasadena, California*)

There is an excellent reference to this in the thesis of S. I. Pai from Cal Tech between 1938 and 1939. He investigated flow between rotating cylinders. In the turbulent case, Taylor eddies appeared in addition to the turbulence stress. Von Kármán decomposed the momentum transport into that arising from these Taylor eddies plus an eddy viscosity by turbulence; this is very much in line with what you have been saying. This was reported as a T.N. of the old NACA reports.*

M. V. MORKOVIN (*The Martin Company, Baltimore, Maryland*)

I think that the decay of von Kármán vortex streets at a relatively low Reynolds number has some of the very same features that you are talking about, and I think that a fair amount of the literature of Roshko** actually could be used to follow this thing in detail. However, I would like to suggest that what you are introducing is the requirement that the eddy viscosity of the smaller eddies always be in step with the larger eddies if there is going to be a local picture. I think that one can probably be a little bit more general, in the sense that you don't have to impose that requirement if you know something about the uniformity of the developments of the particular flow—if there is some sort of quasi-similarity you know about so that, even though it is not really true locally, it is as if it were true because of the past experience. To put across the idea by an analogy, we know that if we look locally across a supersonic conical flow it seems to be an elliptic differential equation that we can solve as if it were locally interacting, even though we know that the disturbances are non-local and always propagated hyperbolically downstream. The conical flow acts as if there were something upstream that was contributing to this local picture. I suggest, then, that for many of the flow fields that we can call quasi-similar (quasi-similar in the gross profile, for instance), it's safe to use an eddy viscosity or eddy conductivity because a milder condition is satisfied.

---

* NACA T.N. 892 (1943).
** NACA Tech. Rep. No. 1191 (also T.N. No. 2913).

J. L. LUMLEY

I am not sure that I completely understand what you have said. Do you mean that it is not necessary to break the flow into a large- and small-scale structure in such a flow?

M. V. MORKOVIN

Yes.

J. L. LUMLEY

I think that some of the data, let's say that in Townsend's book, would disagree with that. I think that it depends on what you are trying to predict. What you say is quite true for some things because, as you point out, you know they aren't really determined by local values but they act as if they were. If you are trying to predict the mean-velocity profile, for example, I think this is quite satisfactory. But if you are trying to predict the transport of contaminants at the outer edges of shear flows or something like that, then I think the eddy viscosity is inadequate simply because it does not bring in transport. It doesn't act like gradient transport; it doesn't go the right way.

M. V. MORKOVIN

Chances are you know more references on that than I. The one that Townsend was quoting was with respect to transporting the kinetic energy of the turbulence itself and that's the one that most people are aware of. But I am not so sure that you can apply the transport process through the local kinetic energy in this complete framework. I would say that's somewhat of an exception.

J. L. LUMLEY

What about temperature?

M. V. MORKOVIN

Well I can't really argue* that Townsend overstated that claim; but if he is correct you must have absolutely a large-scale transport in order to explain a number of these quasi-similar fields.

J. LAUFER (*University of Southern California, Los Angeles, California*)

I would like to remark that, quite independently, we are thinking very much along the same lines as Professor Lumley. However, our approach is an experimen-

---

* M. W. Morkovin (1965) *On Eddy Diffusivity, Quasi-Similarity and Diffusion Experiments in Turbulent Boundary Layers*, Int. J. Heat and Mass Transfer **8**, especially pp. 133 and 142.

tal one. We are asking ourselves the following question: if we really accept this picture of the double structure of turbulence, is it at all possible to somehow experimentally extract information about the large-scale motion? Is it then possible to study the large-scale motion and see whether its behavior resembles the Orr–Sommerfeld type of stability motion? We propose to do this by studying the motion of the interface in a turbulent boundary layer. I feel that the motion of this interface (i.e., the line of demarcation between the fully turbulent flow and the irrotational field outside of the boundary layer) must be closely associated with the large-scale motion of the fully turbulent shear flow.

H. W. LIEPMANN
Is this called the superlayer?

J. LAUFER
Yes.

J. L. LUMLEY
Could I make one comment in connection with that? It's only mildly related, but Capt. Payne, who has been working with me, has taken the data of Grant for the cylinder wake and obtained the eigenfunctions of the auto-correlation tensors. The most energetic ones look remarkably like the structures that Grant has proposed. But in that connection, I want to say that I have always thought of Grant's data as being the final word on the wake; that after Grant measured the wake, no one need ever do it again. That's not true. In particular, you must have correlations between dissimilar velocities. These he did not measure and they are vital to the whole thing. You get eddies whose velocities in orthogonal directions are unrelated unless you have the correlations relating velocities in the orthogonal directions. So you need the 1,2 and the 2,3 correlations. You also need separations which aren't all along the axes, which is all that anyone has ever measured. You need to cover the entire plane.

M. H. BLOOM (*Polytechnic Institute of Brooklyn, Farmingdale, New York*)
Are you describing here a sequence of frequency-dependent transports that would be applicable to an array of frequency bands? It is reasonable to expect that for a flow in which low-frequency motion coexists over a period of time with high-frequency motion, the two associated transports must be different. Are you proposing here a systematic method for determining the cascading process and the transports within that cascade system?

J. L. LUMLEY
Yes, and I will only add that apparently all shear flows have such a structure.

H. W. LIEPMANN

I should like to add that there *are* flows in which the large eddies and small eddies are really distinct; it *does* happen that there really is a big break, so to speak, in the spectrum. In such cases, this idea is even more applicable.

G. L. MELLOR (*Princeton University, Princeton, New Jersey*)

How far along are we towards a closed problem?

J. L. LUMLEY

I think we are quite close to a closed problem. We have an equation which we must now solve and Prof. Reynolds of Stanford has actually already made the first steps on its solution. Clearly there are some things about it which we don't understand but which we will discover after we begin trying to solve the equation. I think we have at least a suggestion of what a big eddy might be. We have an equation which describes it. The equation is, at least for parallel shear flows, solvable and we can go ahead from there.

I. S. GARTSHORE (*McGill University, Montreal, Quebec, Canada*)

I would like to make a remark about Prof. Laufer's comment on the relation between the superlayer and the large-eddy characteristics. Some recent experiments that I have done at McGill indicate that if you make the assumption that the standard deviation of the superlayer from its mean position is directly proportional to the scale of the largest eddies in a shear flow, and if you use this in conjunction with the hypothesis of large-eddy equilibrium as Townsend has proposed, then you can check the large-eddy-equilibrium hypothesis in a quantitative fashion. You can show that most similar shear flows (i.e., self-preversing shear flows) do obey this hypothesis, thus relating the shear stress at the center of the flow to the scale of the largest eddy as represented by the standard deviation of the superlayer from its mean position. This is going part way toward relating the characteristics of the large eddies directly to the superlayer as you mentioned.

R. E. KRONAUER (*Harvard University, Cambridge, Massachusetts*)

I would just like to inject one word of caution here. There is a tendency, I think, to feel that the non-linear interactions between waves of different wave lengths is always going to feed turbulent energy toward the smaller eddies. Depending on the situation, it can go in either direction. There is one rather startling piece of evidence that I encountered which illustrates this. If you place a small circular cylinder across a fully turbulent flow in a pipe you would think that energy would be added at the Strouhal frequency. We did the experiment, and if we measured a couple of diameters downstream of the cylinder we found that this was the case. However, if we went eight diameters downstream of the cylinder we found that the energy had interchanged and two-thirds of it had gone as the dominant wave length of the pipe. I think this direction of transport should be considered in many of these problems.

J. L. LUMLEY

The suggestion that it may be all right to use an eddy viscosity for the second and higher eigenfunctions, which essentially assumes that the energy transport is always going toward the smaller scales, is only on the grounds that it is certainly better than applying it to the first and higher. It may not be good enough, but we won't really know until we try it. Certainly all the appearances are that it should be better than the present situation.

Turbulent Jets and Wakes in a Pressure Gradient

B. G. NEWMAN

Canadair Professor of Aerodynamics, McGill University, Montreal, Canada

SUMMARY

Symmetrical jets and wakes in streaming flow with a pressure gradient are examined. The fluid density is assumed to be constant and the rotational flow is turbulent. Particular pressure fields are identified which give time-mean profiles that are similar for all downstream stations. The experimental results for the particular cases of a jet with still surroundings and a small-perturbation jet or wake are examined in some detail. These form the basis for approximate integral methods for predicting more general cases. The methods are reviewed and it is shown that those methods based on Townsend's hypotheses of large-eddy equilibrium and universal eddy structure are generally consistent with the few available experimental results.

NOTATION

A_0, A_1, A_2 coefficients in the polynomial equation for rate of growth (section 4.1)

A $= \partial U/\partial y$ ($= \partial U_1/\partial x_2$ in section 4.2): area of a round orifice (in Appendix)

B $= \partial U/\partial x$ ($= \partial U_1/\partial x_1$ in section 4.2).

b slot width or hole diameter; body width or diameter

C_1, C_2 constants in equation (16) and the equation preceding (18)

C_D drag coefficient of wake-producing body (using b and U_1)

f function of η for the mean-velocity profile

F "function of"

g functions of η for components of the turbulence stress tensor (eqn. (4))

H $= (\delta^*/\theta)^{r+1}$

k $= \log_e 2 = 0.693$, or subscript in tensor notation

L_0 scaling length for mean-velocity profile (figure 1)

L_B scaling length for large eddies

L_{B_0}	scaling length for large eddies when $B=0$
m	exponent for the free-stream velocity variation with x (section 2)
r	$=0$ for two-dimensional flow, $=1$ for axisymmetric flow
R_T	$=(|U_0|L_0/\nu_T)_{y=L_0}$
R_{T_0}	value of R_T when $B=0$
T_B	average lifetime of a large eddy
u	local turbulent fluctuation in the x direction
u_i	local turbulent fluctuation in the ith direction
U	local mean velocity in the x direction
U_i	local mean velocity in the ith direction
U_1	streaming-flow velocity in the x direction (except in section 4.2)
U_0	scaling velocity for mean-velocity profile (figure 1): negative for a wake
U_J	central jet velocity at the slot
U_{10}	streaming-flow velocity at a reference station
v	local turbulent fluctuation in the y direction
V	local mean velocity in the y direction
x_i	Cartesian coordinates in tensor notation: $x_1 = x$, $x_2 = y$
x	downstream distance
x_0	position of fictitious origin of the flow upstream of either the orifice or the trailing edge of the body (figure 4)
y	cross-stream distance measured from the axis of symmetry
$\delta*$	$=$ displacement thickness: eqn. (8)
η	$=y/L_0$
θ	$=$ momentum increment thickness: eqn. (8)
λ_1, λ_2	constants in equation (24)
ν	fluid kinematic viscosity
ν_T	turbulent eddy viscosity $= \dfrac{-\overline{uv}}{\partial U/\partial y}$ (see also eqn. (28))
ρ	fluid density
τ	turbulent, apparent, shearing stress, $-\rho\overline{uv}$
ω_B	vorticity scale for large eddies.
ω_{B_0}	vorticity scale for large eddies when $B=0$
ω_i	turbulent vorticity in the ith direction
Ω_i	mean vorticity in the ith direction
$-$	time averages at a point are denoted by bars

1. INTRODUCTION

The purpose of the present paper is to review and to extend the available theoretical methods for predicting the mean velocity in symmetrical turbulent jets and wakes in streaming flow with a pressure gradient. The study is limited to incompressible and isothermal conditions.

This class of flows is of considerable practical interest in that it represents an idealization of the flow in both variable area ducts with upstream bodies, and in models of combustion chambers. It is also similar to the outer part of the flow in a jet-augmented boundary layer, such as occurs in the application of blowing to prevent separation over flapped wings and other shapes.

Since the mean-velocity profiles when normalized are closely similar for all cases that have been measured (see, for example, Forstall & Shapiro (1950)) the aim becomes simply to predict the normalizing length scale L_0 and the perturbation velocity scale U_0 for the motion. The integral momentum equation taken across the complete flow provides one equation. The difficulty is to find a second equation which is sufficiently realistic.

Various methods have been proposed for zero pressure gradient. Relativistic arguments have been used (Küchemann & Weber 1953; Eskinazi & Kruka 1964) to generalize the still-fluid jet to a jet in a moving stream. Perhaps the least empirical of these methods is that developed by Abramovich (1963), and this method may be readily extended to cases with variable pressure.

Weinstein et al. (1956) have applied Reichardt's inductive theory of turbulence (Schlichting 1960) to a two-dimensional jet at constant pressure. This permits an analysis of the two-dimensional jet by superposition of the flow from a series of very small round jets, the difference between the square of the local velocity and the square of the streaming-flow velocity being the superimposed quantity. It is easily shown that this approach gives the same linear rate of growth for both a round jet and a two-dimensional jet in still fluid, a conclusion which is about 20 % in error (see Appendix and Knystautas (1964)).

Squire & Trouncer (1944) developed the second equation from the momentum equation integrated halfway across the jet. The required shearing stress at the outer limit of the integral was obtained from Prandtl's mixing-length theory and the assumption that the mixing length is a constant proportion of the width of the flow. Forstall & Shapiro's (1950) measurements on a round jet at constant pressure were in fair agreement.

The integral moment-of-momentum or integral energy equations have also been used, in conjunction with an eddy viscosity v_T which is assumed to be constant across the flow. The eddy-viscosity Reynolds number $|U_0|L_0/v_T$ has also been taken as constant in the downstream direction x (Hill et al. 1963; Bradbury 1963) or varying in the direction x according to the rate of strain of the mean flow at a typical point in the jet or wake (Gartshore 1964; Bradbury 1963). Hill (1965) has avoided the necessity for such an assumption by invoking Spalding's (1958) argument that, at constant pressure, the only significant length dimensions for the developing flow are the momentum thickness θ and the downstream distance x so that L_0/θ is a universal function of x/θ and is obtained from still-fluid data.

In the present paper those methods which may be readily applied to variable-pressure jets and wakes are examined. These include Abramovich's method and extensions of it (e.g. Ribner 1946) and the half momentum-integral method of Gartshore using both constant and variable $U_0 L_0/\nu_T$. These methods are more likely to be correct for self-preserving flows and thus the paper begins with a discussion of the requirements for self preservation and a careful reexamination of the experimental data on the extreme self-preserving cases, i.e. a jet with still surroundings and a small-perturbation jet or wake. This information is then used in applying Abramovich's and Gartshore's methods to predict the streamwise development of the few two-dimensional jets and wakes in a pressure gradient which have been measured.

2. SELF-PRESERVING WAKES AND JETS IN STREAMING FLOW WITH CHANGING PRESSURE

Following Townsend (1956), the author has identified those conditions for which a two-dimensional turbulent wake or jet in streaming flow may be self-preserving (Patel & Newman 1961).

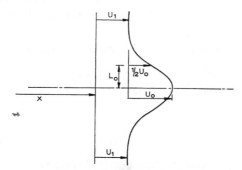

Figure 1. Symmetrical jet in streaming flow.

Considering either a symmetrical, two-dimensional, or an axisymmetrical three-dimensional, jet or wake (figure 1), the time-averaged boundary-layer equation in the downstream direction x (for constant density, ρ, and making use of the approximate equation in the y direction) is:

$$U\frac{\partial U}{\partial x} + V\frac{\partial U}{\partial x} + \frac{\partial}{\partial x}(\overline{u^2} - \overline{v^2}) + \frac{1}{y^r}\frac{\partial}{\partial y}(\overline{uv}\,y^r) = U_1\frac{dU_1}{dx} + \frac{v}{y^r}\frac{\partial}{\partial y}\left(y^r\frac{\partial U}{\partial y}\right) \quad (1)$$

where U and V are the mean velocities in directions x and y $(U \gg V)$,

u and v are the associated turbulent fluctuations about the mean, and

U_1 is the velocity of the external irrotational flow and varies with x in general.

The time-averaged continuity equation is

$$\frac{\partial U}{\partial x} + \frac{1}{y^r}\frac{\partial}{\partial y}(Vy^r) = 0 \tag{2}$$

$r = 0$ for two-dimensional flow

$= 1$ for axisymmetric three-dimensional flow., $V_\varphi = 0$ in cylindrical coordinate

The flows are self-preserving or self-similar for all x if (following Townsend's (1956) formulation):

$$U = U_1 + U_0 f(y/L_0) \tag{3}$$

and if the components of the kinematic turbulence stress tensor are given by

$$\overline{u^2} = U_0^2 g_{11}(y/L_0)$$

$$\overline{v^2} = U_0^2 g_{22}(y/L_0)$$

$$\overline{uv} = U_0^2 g_{12}(y/L_0) \tag{4}$$

where the bars again denote a time average.

The functions f and g are independent of both x and y for a given self-preserving flow. For clarity the scaling length L_0, and the scaling velocity U_0 are specifically identified in figure 1.

Substituting (3) and (4) in (2) gives, for the cross-stream velocity V,

$$-V = \frac{L_0 \eta}{r+1}\frac{dU_1}{dx} + \frac{1}{(\eta L_0)^r}\frac{d}{dx}(U_0 L_0^{r+1})\int_0^\eta f\eta^r\,d\eta - U_0\frac{dL_0}{dx}\eta f$$

where

$$\eta = \frac{y}{L_0} \tag{5}$$

Using equations (3), (4) and (5), equation (1) becomes the master equation

$$\left\{\frac{L_0}{U_0}\frac{dU_0}{dx}\right\}[f^2 + 2(g_{11} - g_{22})] + \left\{\frac{L_0}{U_0^2}\frac{d}{dx}(U_1 U_0)\right\}[f] -$$

$$-\left\{\frac{1}{r+1}\frac{1}{U_0 L_0^r}\frac{d}{dx}(U_1 L_0^{r+1})\right\}[\eta f'] - \left\{\frac{1}{U_0 L_0^r}\frac{d}{dx}(U_0 L_0^{r+1})\right\}\left[\frac{f'}{\eta^r}\int_0^\eta f\eta^r\,d\eta\right] -$$

$$-\left\{\frac{dL_0}{dx}\right\}[\eta(g'_{11} - g'_{22})] + \left[\frac{1}{\eta^r}\frac{d}{d\eta}(\eta^r g_{12})\right] = \left\{\frac{\nu}{U_0 L_0}\right\}\left[\frac{1}{\eta^r}\frac{\partial}{\partial\eta}(\eta^r f')\right] \tag{6}$$

where dashes denote differentiation with respect to η.

This equation is identical to that given by Townsend for the particular case, $r=0$ and $U_1=$constant. The terms in the square brackets are functions of η only, and the terms in the curly brackets are functions of x only. Since there is no curly bracket in the final term on the left-hand side, self preservation is possible only if the six curly-bracket terms are constant. At sufficiently large $U_0 L_0/\nu$, the term on the right-hand side may be neglected, and it is then readily seen that the remaining terms are constant if

$$\frac{\mathrm{d}L_0}{\mathrm{d}x}, \ \frac{U_0}{U_1} \ \text{and} \ \frac{L_0}{U_0}\frac{\mathrm{d}U_0}{\mathrm{d}x} \ \text{are constant.}$$

Thus L_0 varies linearly with x, $L_0 \propto (x+x_0)$, and both U_0 and U_1 are proportional to $(x+x_0)^m$ where x_0 is a constant which, when the origin of coordinates for x has been chosen, identifies the position of the hypothetical origin for the flow*. The exponent m is not arbitrary but depends on U_0/U_1.

Integrating equation (1) from $y=0$ to y very large and neglecting the normal stresses, gives the integral momentum equation:

$$\frac{\mathrm{d}}{\mathrm{d}x}(\theta^{r+1}U_1^2) + (\delta^*)^{r+1}U_1\frac{\mathrm{d}U_1}{\mathrm{d}x} = 0 \tag{7}$$

i.e.

$$\theta^{r+1}U_1^{H+2} = \text{constant, if } H \text{ is constant}$$

where

$$\theta^{r+1}U_1^2 = \frac{2}{r+1}\int_0^\infty U(U-U_1)y^r\mathrm{d}y \tag{8}$$

$$(\delta^*)^{r+1}U_1 = \frac{2}{r+1}\int_0^\infty (U-U_1)y^r\mathrm{d}y$$

and

$$H = \left(\frac{\delta^*}{\theta}\right)^{r+1}$$

Thus for self-similar profiles

$$L_0^{r+1}U_0^{(H+2)} = \text{constant} \tag{9}$$

where

$$\frac{1}{H} = \frac{\displaystyle\int_0^\infty \left(1 + \frac{U_0}{U_1}f\right)f\eta^r\mathrm{d}\eta}{\displaystyle\int_0^\infty f\eta^r\mathrm{d}\eta} \tag{10}$$

---

* As in the Falkner–Skan analysis of laminar flow, an additional possible solution is that U_0 and U_1 are proportional to $\exp[(\text{constant})(x + x_0)]$ for the particular case $L_0 = \text{constant}$.

References p. 200–201

and

$$m = -\frac{1+r}{H+2} \tag{11}$$

One extreme case of self-preserving flow is the jet in virtually still surroundings:

$$\frac{U_0}{U_1} \to \infty, \ H = 0$$

$$m = -\frac{1+r}{2}$$

Thus $U_0 \propto x^{-\frac{1}{2}}$ for two-dimensional flow
$\propto x^{-1}$ for axisymmetric three-dimensional flow.

A special intermediate case is the *exact* self-preserving small-increment jet or small-deficit wake

$$\frac{U_0}{U_1} \to 0, \ H \to 1$$

and

$$m = -\frac{1+r}{3}$$

Thus, $m = -\frac{1}{3}$ for two-dimensional flow
$= -\frac{2}{3}$ for axisymmetric three-dimensional flow.

If a Gaussian form is assumed for the mean-velocity distribution, which is justified by comparison with experiment (figure 2)

$$f = e^{-k\eta^2}$$

where $k = \log_e 2 = 0.693$.

Equation (10) gives:

$$\frac{1}{H} = 1 + \left(\frac{U_0}{U_1}\right) \frac{1}{2^{(r+1)/2}} \ \text{for} \ r = 0 \ \text{or} \ 1 \tag{12}$$

This shows what is evident physically, that the required exponent m to achieve a self-preserving flow depends on the chosen value of U_0/U_1.

Values of m for the other extreme case of a wake with zero central velocity can now be stated. In this case $U_0/U_1 = -1$ and
$m = -0.1843$ for two-dimensional flow
$= -\frac{1}{2}$ for axisymmetric, three-dimensional flow.

The jet or wake in zero pressure gradient ($U_1 = $ constant) is not strictly self-preserving, and is therefore a more complicated case to study. However if U_0/U_1 is $\ll 1$, the flow is approximately self-preserving because the master equation (6) approximates to

$$\left\{\frac{L_0}{U_0^2}\frac{\mathrm{d}}{\mathrm{d}x}(U_1 U_0)\right\}[f] - \left\{\frac{1}{r+1}\frac{1}{U_0 L_0^r}\frac{\mathrm{d}}{\mathrm{d}x}(U_1 L_0^{r+1})\right\}[\eta f']$$

$$+ \left[\frac{1}{\eta^r}\frac{\mathrm{d}}{\mathrm{d}\eta}(\eta^r g_{12})\right] = 0 \qquad (13)$$

if both the normal-turbulent-stress term and the viscous term are neglected. Thus the requirement becomes that both

$$\frac{U_1 L_0}{U_0^2}\frac{\mathrm{d}U_0}{\mathrm{d}x} \quad \text{and} \quad \frac{U_1}{U_0}\frac{\mathrm{d}L_0}{\mathrm{d}x} \quad \text{are constant,}$$

while equation (7) gives $\theta^{r+1} = \text{constant}$.

Therefore

$$U_0 L_0^{r+1} = \text{constant}.$$

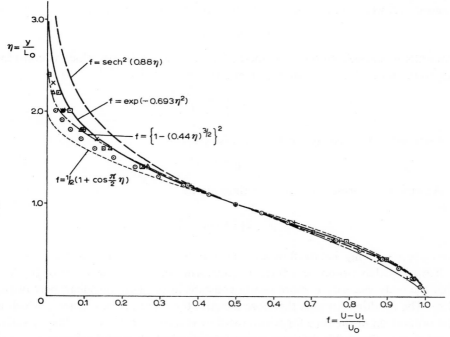

Figure 2. Mean velocity in two-dimensional, turbulent, shear flows.
  ⊙ Bradbury (1963): jets in zero pressure gradient.
  + Gartshore (1965): wakes in self-preserving pressure gradient.
  × Patel & Newman (1961): self-preserving wall jets.
  ⊡ Halleen (1964): jets in still surroundings.
  △ Halleen (1964): wakes in zero pressure gradient.

References p. 200–201

Thus

$$L_0 \propto (x+x_0)^{1/(r+2)}$$

$$U_0 \propto (x+x_0)^{-\{(r+1)/(r+2)\}}$$

	$r=0$		$r=1$
$L_0 \propto (x+x_0)^{1/(r+2)}$	$\frac{1}{2}$	and	$\frac{1}{3}$
$U_0 \propto (x+x_0)^{-\{(r+1)/(r+2)\}}$	$-\frac{1}{2}$	and	$-\frac{2}{3}$

for the approximate self-preserving small-perturbation cases in *zero* pressure gradient (Schlichting 1960).

3. COMPARISON WITH EXPERIMENT

3.1. *Mean-Velocity Profile*

The mean-velocity profile $f(\eta)$ may be predicted if a form for the turbulent shearing stress is assumed. For a jet in still air the assumption of a constant eddy viscosity (Görtler in Schlichting (1960)) across the flow gives:

$$f = \mathrm{sech}^2 (0.88\eta)$$

Prandtl's mixing-length theory combined with a mixing length which is constant across the flow, gives for a small-perturbation wake or jet:

$$f = \left[1 - \left(\frac{\eta}{2.27} \right)^{\frac{3}{2}} \right]^2$$

Constant eddy viscosity for the same case gives:

$$f = e^{-0.693\eta^2}$$

An empirical formula is also sometimes used:

$$f = \frac{1}{2} \left(1 + \cos \frac{\pi\eta}{2} \right)$$

for $2 > \eta > -2$ only, i.e. the flow is assumed to have a finite width of $4L_0$

Townsend has proposed a further refinement which takes account of the fact that the eddy viscosity is more nearly constant in the *fully* turbulent part of the flow. The resulting formula therefore includes the intermittency factor γ which is the proportion of the time for which the flow is turbulent. However since γ varies from flow to flow* this does not represent a particularly useful refinement at the present time.

It seems that most flows can be represented with fair accuracy by a Gaussian

---

* For example the intermittent region is only about $\frac{2}{3}$ as wide for a still-air jet as it is for a small-perturbation jet or wake with the same L_0.

profile, a fact which Reichardt used in developing his inductive theory of turbulence. It will therefore be assumed that

$$f = e^{-k\eta^2}$$

where $\eta = y/L_0$ and $k = 0.693$ by definition of L_0.

A comparison with several sets of average experimental results is given in figure 2.

3.2. *The Jet With Still Surroundings* ($U_1/U_0 = 0$)

It is well established experimentally that, as predicted, the flow grows linearly, with nearly constant mean-flow momentum (Miller & Comings 1958). A table of experimental data is given in Table 1.

The notation is explained in figure 3. U_J is the central jet velocity at the slot, that is the velocity between the internal boundary layers at the slot lip; b is the slot width or hole diameter.

It is seen from Table 1 that there is no clear variation of jet growth with Reynolds number, and therefore that the assumption of viscous independence is not refuted. Furthermore any dependence on slot conditions, changes of which are apparent in the small variations of x_0/b and $(U_0/U_J)[(x+x_0)/b]^{\frac{1}{2}}$, are apparently quite unimportant a few tens-of-slot-widths downstream. These variations are affected by the internal slot boundary layers and, in the latter case, also by the geometry of the structure which supports the slot. A slight negative pressure is built up on this structure due to jet entrainment of the surrounding fluid, a negative pressure which reduces the momentum of the jet downstream. The variations in rate of growth $L_0/(x+x_0)$ are apparently largely due to end effects. The earlier measurements were made with low-aspect-ratio slots, and insufficient care was taken to provide fairings on the end plates or to make them adequately large. These results give rates of growth which, with the exception of Reichardt's measurements, are too low. Presumably vortices forming at the edge of the end plates induce spanwise flows

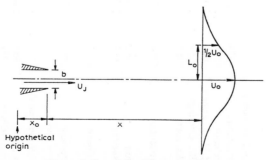

Figure 3. Jet with still surroundings.

References p. 200–201

TABLE 1
JETS WITH STILL SURROUNDINGS

Experimenter(s)	Year	$\dfrac{U_J b}{\nu} \times 10^{-4}$	Slot Aspect Ratio $\dfrac{\text{Slot Length}}{b}$	Max. $\dfrac{x}{b}$	$\dfrac{L_0}{(x+x_0)}$	$\dfrac{x_0}{b}$	$\dfrac{U_0}{U_J}\left(\dfrac{x+x_0}{b}\right)^{\frac{1}{2}}$	Remarks
Two-Dimensional								
Förthmann	1934	7.1	20	25	0.0985	+ 2.0	2.40	
Reichardt	1951	2.4	21	100	0.115	0		
v. d. Hegge Zijnen	1949	1.3	25	40	0.099	− 0.6	2.22	
Miller–Comings	1958	1.8	40	40	0.096	− 1.6	2.47	
Nakaguchi	1961	0.9–1.6	133	100	0.106	+ 0.3	2.30	Width of end plates ≈ slot length
Knystautas	1964	0.7–1.3	98–195	350	0.106 0.1035	+ 1.5	2.41	Tapered end plates
Olson	1962	0.9	12	16	0.106	− 1.5		Slot Mach No. = 0.66
Heskestad	1963	2.4(?)	120	216	0.106	− 1.5	2.40(?)	Width of end plates ≈ slot length
Bradbury	1963		48	66	0.080		2.38	In small streaming flow $U_1/U_J = 0.07$
Gartshore	1965	1.7	167	200	0.102	+ 2.0	2.47	Fairings fitted to end plates
Axi-Symmetric								
Reichardt	1951	5.0		47	0.0848	0		
Corrsin–Uberoi	1951*	2.0–7.0						
Hinze– v. d. Hegge Zijnen	1949*			40	0.0842	0		
Johannesen	1962	45		95	0.0856	− 6.0		Slot flow supersonic: $M_J = 1.4$

* Townsend's collection.

Note: Some values have been determined by replotting the original data and may differ slightly from those stated in previous work.

which usually thin the shear flow. This trouble is not present for round jets and it is comforting to note that the variations in their rate of growth are much less (Table 1). The low-aspect-ratio measurements of Olson are satisfactory probably because the entrained flow was ducted into the centre of a surrounding chamber.

If the earlier more doubtful measurements are neglected, an average value of $L_0/(x+x_0)$ is 0.104 with a $\pm 2\%$ variation, a variation which is certainly within typical experimental accuracy. As a matter of interest the corresponding value of $(U_0/U_J)[(x+x_0)/b]^{\frac{1}{2}}$ if the downstream jet momentum were fully $\rho U_J^2 b$, would be 2.53 for a Gaussian mean-velocity profile.

The eddy viscosity Reynolds number at $y=L_0$, will be required later and is defined as

$$R_{\mathrm{T}} = \left(\frac{U_0 L_0 \,\partial U/\partial y}{-\overline{uv}}\right)_{y=L_0} = \left(\frac{U_0 L_0}{\nu_{\mathrm{T}}}\right)_{y=L_0} \tag{14}$$

It may be readily computed from the rate of growth by integrating equation (6) (again neglecting the viscous terms and the normal-turbulent-stress terms). The value is 32.9.

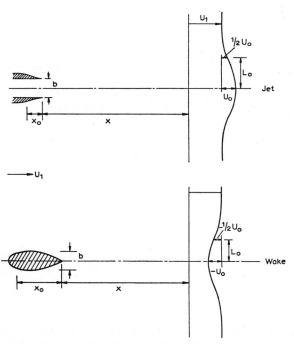

Figure 4. Small-perturbation jet and wake in flow at constant pressure.

Average values for the round jet are:

$$\frac{L_0}{x+x_0} = 0.085$$

and

$$R_T = 45.3.$$

It is interesting to note that Bradbury's measurements on a two-dimensional jet indicate that the rate of spread is severely reduced by even a small amount of streaming flow,

$$\frac{L_0}{x+x_0} \approx 0.08 \text{ with } \frac{U_1}{U_J} = 0.07.$$

3.3. The Small-Perturbation Jet or Wake in Flow at Constant Pressure (figure 4)

The predicted variations of U_0 and L_0 with x are again well supported by experiment.

Far downstream the pressure is almost constant and the momentum increment or deficit is conserved. Thus θ (eqn. (8)) may be a more relevant reference-length dimension than the slot or body width b.

For a Gaussian profile,

$$f = e^{-k\eta^2} \text{ and } U_0 \ll U_1$$

$$|\theta| = (2.13)L_0 \left|\frac{U_0}{U_1}\right| \text{ for a two-dimensional jet or wake}$$

$$|\theta| = (1.20)L_0 \left|\frac{U_0}{U_1}\right|^{\frac{1}{2}} \text{ for a round jet or wake} \tag{15}$$

The eddy viscosity Reynolds number at $y=L_0$, $R_T = (U_0 L_0/\nu_T)_{y=L_0}$ is related directly to the growth parameter by the equation

$$\frac{L_0}{(x+x_0)^{1/(r+2)}|\theta|^{(r+1)/(r+2)}} = \left(\frac{N}{R_T}\right)^{1/(2+r)}$$

where $N = 1.30$ for $r = 0$

$N = 2.88$ for $r = 1$.

It is noted that if the drag coefficient of the wake-producing body is C_D (based on body dimension b) then

$$\frac{C_D}{2} = \left(-\frac{\theta}{b}\right)^{r+1}$$

Experimental data for two-dimensional small-perturbation jets and wakes is collected in Table 2.

TABLE 2

TWO-DIMENSIONAL, SMALL-PERTURBATION, WAKES AND JETS AT CONSTANT PRESSURE

Experimenter(s)	Year	$\dfrac{x}{b}$	$\dfrac{U_1|\theta|}{\nu}\cdot 10^{-4}$	Aspect Ratio $\dfrac{Length}{|\theta|}$	$\dfrac{x}{|\theta|}$	Range of $\dfrac{|U_0|}{|U_1|}$	$\dfrac{L_0}{(x+x_0)^{\frac{1}{2}}|\theta|^{\frac{1}{2}}}$	$\dfrac{x_0}{|\theta|}$	R_T	Remarks
Reichardt	1951				300–600	0.080–0.057	0.354	~0	10.4	Circular Cylinder
Schlichting	1960				600–3400	0.061–0.025	0.316	~0	13.0	Circular Cylinder
Townsend	1956	500–950	0.4	~200	1120–2280	0.045–0.031	0.313	−2	13.3	Circular Cylinder
Gartshore	1965*	80–220	0.45	146	100–270	0.111–0.071	0.398	+25	8.6	Square Cylinder
Silverstein et al.	1939	17	1.5	1850**	920		0.394	+40	8.4	Aerofoil NACA 0018
Bradbury	1963	25–70		39	20–56	0.41–0.21	0.250	+13.9	20.8	
Weinstein et al.	1956	20–100	1.2	32	27–133	0.402–0.196	0.23–0.21		23.8–24.9	

Wakes: Reichardt, Schlichting, Townsend, Gartshore, Silverstein et al.

Jets: Bradbury, Weinstein et al.

* Unpublished.
** No end plates.

References p. 200–201

It is clear that the jets cannot be regarded as small-perturbation flows even though L_0 varies linearly with $(x+x_0)^{\frac{1}{2}}$ for a significant number of measurements in both cases.

A satisfactory asymptotic value for wakes is:

$$\frac{L_0}{(x+x_0)^{\frac{1}{2}}|\theta|^{\frac{1}{2}}} = 0.316$$

Larger values are obtained closer to the wake-producing body and it seems, from the measurements of Silverstein, that the upstream history of the flow is a determining factor, for

$$\frac{L_0}{(x+x_0)^{\frac{1}{2}}|\theta|^{\frac{1}{2}}} \approx 0.4 \text{ even though } \frac{x}{\theta} = 920.$$

Townsend's (1956) measurements and his elucidation of them, also indicate that self-preservation is only obtained approximately 500 body widths downstream, and is only obtained accurately at about 1000 body widths downstream. Thus body width is an important parameter and the upstream history affects the development of the flow for $O(10^3)$ body widths downstream. Spalding's earlier concept of "jet-forgetfulness" is therefore limited in its application (Spalding 1958; Hill 1965). It might be noted in passing that the associated proof by dimensional analysis used the implicit, but strictly-incorrect, assumption that the fictitious origin of the flow is independent of the upstream conditions.

4. APPROXIMATE ANALYSES OF TWO-DIMENSIONAL JETS AND WAKES IN STREAMING FLOW IN ANY PRESSURE GRADIENT

A few integral methods have been developed for analysing two-dimensional flows and these are, of course, readily extendable to axi-symmetric three-dimensional flows. The fact that this has not yet been done in most cases is witness to the tentative confidence with which these theories are held at the present time. With the possible exception of Gartshore and Bradbury's recent theories, which are based on Townsend's hypotheses, they all have important shortcomings, and even these theories require a good deal more detailed comparison with experiment before they can be cheerfully accepted.

All the integral methods assume a form for the shape of the mean-velocity profile. There are then two unknowns U_0 and L_0 and thus two equations are required. The integral momentum equation across the complete flow provides one of them (eqn. (7)). The various methods differ in their choice of the second equation.

4.1. *Abramovich's Method*

The second equation due to Abramovich is derived from consideration of a mixing layer in constant pressure. This flow is of more than passing interest since two such layers form near the slot for a jet in streaming flow.

Assume constant density and pressure, and the notation explained in figure 5.

U_1 and U_2 are constant and the flow conforms to the requirements of self preservation in that the coefficients of eqn. (6) are constant.

U_0 may be defined as $U_2 - U_1$, $U_0/U_1 = $ constant, $(L_0/U_0)(dU_0/dx) = 0$ and $dL_0/dx = $ constant so that L_0 grows linearly with x.

It is reasonable to assume that the spatial rate of growth of the mixing layer will depend on the level of turbulence in the layer, which in turn depends on U_0.

Thus

$$\frac{dL_0}{dx} = F\left(\frac{U_0}{U_1}\right)$$

Since the rate of growth is unaffected if U_1 and U_2 are interchanged

$$\frac{dL_0}{dx} = F\left(\frac{-U_0}{U_1 + U_0}\right)$$

Thus

$$\frac{dL_0}{dx} = F\left[\frac{|U_0|}{U_1 + \dfrac{U_0}{2}}\right]$$

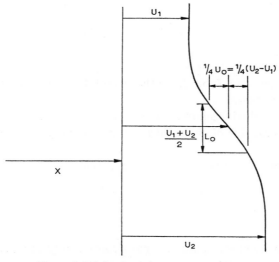

Figure 5. Mixing layer in constant pressure.

References p. 200–201

Expanding as a polynomial, this may be written:

$$= A_0 + A_1 \frac{|U_0|}{U_1 + \dfrac{U_0}{2}} + A_2 \frac{U_0^2}{\left(U_1 + \dfrac{U_0}{2}\right)^2} + \dots$$

If $U_0 = 0$, no mixing occurs, $dL_0/dx = 0$ and thus $A_0 = 0$.

Abramovich, following Prandtl, chooses only the first term A_1 in the above expansion on the grounds that the rate of spread is proportional to the cross-stream turbulence $(\overline{v^2})^{\frac{1}{2}}$, which in turn depends on U_0.

The extension of this analysis to a jet in uniform streaming flow involves a further, and less plausible, assumption that U_2 may be replaced by the central jet velocity $U_1 + U_0$ (figure 1).

$$\frac{dL_0}{dx} = C_1 \frac{|U_0|}{U_1 + \dfrac{U_0}{2}} \tag{16}$$

For still surroundings $dL_0/dx = 0.104$ and hence $C_1 = 0.052$. (Abramovich uses a slightly different value.)

This formulation enables the rate of growth for any streaming flow to be predicted. In particular, for a small-perturbation jet

$$\frac{dL_0}{dx} \frac{U_1}{|U_0|} = 0.052$$

Using eqn. (15), therefore

$$\frac{L_0}{(x + x_0)^{\frac{1}{3}} |\theta|^{\frac{1}{3}}} = 0.156$$

Despite the scatter in the experimental results, this is not even close to the measured values given in Table 2. To this extent, therefore, Abramovich's theory is limited in its application.

Despite this formal criticism of the theory however, it will be demonstrated later that the theory is capable of giving fairly good predictions for moderate to strong jets.

In a pressure gradient we continue to assume that

$$\frac{dL_0}{dx} = 0.052 \frac{|U_0|}{U_1 + \dfrac{U_0}{2}} \tag{16}$$

The integral momentum equation is most conveniently expressed in differential form. For a Gaussian profile

$$\frac{1}{L_0}\frac{dL_0}{dx} + \frac{d}{dx}\left(\frac{U_0}{U_1}\right)\left[\frac{U_1}{U_0} + \frac{1}{1 + \dfrac{U_0}{\sqrt{2}U_1}}\right] + \left[\frac{1}{1 + \dfrac{U_0}{\sqrt{2}U_1}} + 2\right]\frac{1}{U_1}\frac{dU_1}{dx} = 0 \quad (17)$$

These two equations may be solved numerically for comparison with experiment using, for example, the Runge–Kutta method.

Ribner (1946) suggests a modification to equation (16) in the form

$$\frac{dL_0}{dx} \propto \frac{|U_0|}{C_2 U_1 + \dfrac{U_0}{2}}$$

where $C_2 = 1.65$ is chosen to give improved agreement with the method of Squire & Trouncer for a round jet in zero pressure gradient. The new form is, of course, not consistent with the required functional form for a *mixing layer*. This criticism however does not apply to the application of the formula, in an empirical manner, to a jet in streaming flow, which was Ribner's aim.

It is interesting to note that if the second coefficient in the expansion for F is retained, a formula which is consistent with both the rate of growth for a still-fluid jet ($dL_0/dx = 0.104$) and the likely-value for a small-perturbation wake ($L_0/[(x+x_0)^{\frac{1}{2}}|\theta|^{\frac{1}{2}}] = 0.316$) is:

$$\frac{dL_0}{dx} = 0.212\,\frac{|U_0|}{U_1 + \dfrac{U_0}{2}} - 0.080\,\frac{U_0^2}{\left(U_1 + \dfrac{U_0}{2}\right)^2} \quad (18)$$

The extreme value of $|U_0|/(U_1 + U_0/2)$, if backflow is excluded, is 2.0. For this value the second term is almost as large as the first, indicating that it would be desirable to include further terms in the polynomial for $F[|U_0|/(U_1 + U_0/2)]$.

4.2. Gartshore's Method (Gartshore 1964, 1965a,b,c)

This appears to be the most sophisticated method currently available. It permits the eddy-viscosity Reynolds number, R_T, at $y=L_0$ to vary in the downstream direction in a particular flow, and also from one flow to another. The variation is related to $(\partial U/\partial x)/(\partial U/\partial y)$ at $y=L_0$. It therefore overcomes the objections to other theories which have assumed that R_T is constant (Hill et al. 1963) or that the mixing length is proportional to the width of the flow (Squire & Trouncer 1944). A similar approach to Gartshore's has been suggested independently by Bradbury (1963). Both are based on Townsend's hypotheses.

Derivation of the Equation for R_T

The equation for the instantaneous turbulent vorticity ω_i is obtained by subtracting from the Navier–Stokes equation for the instantaneous total vorticity,

$\Omega_i + \omega_i$, the same equation averaged over a sufficient period of time (for example subtract 2.6.2 from 2.6.1 in Townsend (1956)).

Introducing the substantial derivative

$$\frac{D}{Dt} = \frac{\partial}{\partial t} + (U_k + u_k)\frac{\partial}{\partial x_k}$$

the equation for the ith component of turbulent vorticity ω_i is then

$$\frac{D\omega_i}{Dt} + u_k\frac{\partial \Omega_i}{\partial x_k} - \overline{u_k\frac{\partial \omega_i}{\partial x_k}} = \Omega_k\frac{\partial u_i}{\partial x_k} + \omega_k\frac{\partial U_i}{\partial x_k} - \frac{\partial}{\partial x_k}\overline{(u_i\omega_k)} + v\frac{\partial^2 \omega_i}{\partial x_k^2} \quad (19)$$

where:

the instantaneous component of velocity in the ith direction is $U_i + u_i$, bars denote time averages e.g. $\overline{u_i} = \overline{\omega_i} = 0$, and the instantaneous component of vorticity in the ith direction is

$$\Omega_i + \omega_i = \varepsilon_{ijk}\frac{\partial}{\partial x_j}(U_k + u_k)$$

We consider a simple shear flow which, in the mean, is two-dimensional in planes perpendicular to the 3 axis and has a constant longitudinal rate of strain in the 1 direction.

Thus

$$U_3 = 0$$

$$\frac{\partial U_1}{\partial x_2} = A, \qquad \frac{\partial U_2}{\partial x_1} = 0$$

$$\frac{\partial U_1}{\partial x_1} = B = -\frac{\partial U_2}{\partial x_2}$$

Then $\Omega_1 = \Omega_2 = 0$, $\Omega_3 = -A$ and is constant.

The vorticity equation becomes

$$\frac{D\omega_i}{Dt} - \underset{(*)}{\underbrace{u_k\frac{\partial \omega_i}{\partial x_k}}} = -A\frac{\partial u_i}{\partial x_3} + \omega_1\frac{\partial U_i}{\partial x_1} + \omega_2\frac{\partial U_i}{\partial x_2} - \underset{(*)}{\underbrace{\frac{\partial}{\partial x_k}\overline{(u_i\omega_k)}}} + v\frac{\partial^2 \omega_i}{\partial x_k^2} \quad (20)$$

The two starred terms represent, respectively, the convection of vorticity by the turbulent motion and the apparent production of vorticity by rate of strain in the turbulent part of the motion.

If we consider only the average vorticity of the large-scale eddies, it may be postulated that the smaller, energy-containing eddies have a mainly diffusive effect on this average vorticity and thus the starred terms may be neglected. The viscous diffusion term may also be neglected.

Thus for the average vorticity of the large eddies

$$\frac{D\omega_i}{Dt} = -A\frac{\partial u_i}{\partial x_3} + \omega_1\frac{\partial U_i}{\partial x_1} + \omega_2\frac{\partial U_i}{\partial x_2} \tag{21}$$

where

$$
\begin{array}{ccc}
 & i=1 & i=2 \\
\hline
\frac{\partial U_i}{\partial x_1} = & B & 0 \\
\\
\frac{\partial U_i}{\partial x_2} = & A & -B
\end{array}
\tag{22}
$$

This equation is now applied to two similar fields of turbulence which are characterized by a length scale L_B, and a vorticity scale ω_B, both of which are positive quantities.

For the first field, A and B exist. The second field has the same A but has $B=0$; $L_B=L_{B_0}$; $\omega_B=\omega_{B_0}$.

Suppose two identical large eddies are suddenly born in both fields and that they have a circulation Γ. Each eddy will be strained longitudinally by the mean motion, and at a maximum rate when its axis is aligned at approximately 45° to the 1 axis. However, since the fields are similar*, $\Gamma \propto L_B^2\omega_B$ with the same constant of proportionality.

Thus

$$L_{B_0}^2\omega_{B_0} = L_B^2\omega_B \tag{23}$$

If T_B is the lifetime of the large eddy in the first field, equation (21) can be written approximately as

$$\frac{\omega_B}{T_B} = |\lambda_1 A + \lambda_2 B|\omega_B \tag{24}$$

where λ_1 and λ_2 are constants (note that $\partial u_i/\partial x_3 \propto \omega_B$ and $D\omega_i/Dt$ has been approximated by an average value ω_B/T_B).

The lifetime T_B of the eddy is also characteristic of the field, and is thus proportional to $1/\omega_B$.

Hence

$$\omega_B \propto |\lambda_1 A + \lambda_2 B|(**) \tag{25}$$

---

* This presupposes that changes of B do not significantly affect the form of the eddies at birth.
** This equation may also be derived by more general considerations. In the model flow the turbulence of the large-scale eddies with vorticity scale ω_B and length scale L_B is contained in a mean flow with constant $A = \partial U/\partial y$ and $B = \partial U/\partial x$. Since the vorticity of the large eddies is maintained by stretching due to the rate of strain in the mean flow, ω_B is determined by A and

For the second field

$$\omega_{B_0} \propto |\lambda_1 A| \tag{26}$$

Townsend (1956) assumes that the typical lifetime of a large eddy is proportional to $1/|A|$, and this is consistent with the above assumption if $|B| \ll |A|$.

Combining with equation (23)

$$\frac{L_B^2}{L_{B_0}^2} = 1 + (\text{constant}) \left|\frac{B}{A}\right| \tag{27}$$

This equation is the same as Gartshore's but has been derived in a more general way. A similar equation is also proposed by Bradbury as an approximation to Townsend's expression at the bottom of p. 189 (Townsend 1956).

An inherent inconsistency in the analysis has been noted. We have postulated the initial existence of identical *large* eddies in fields which are themselves not identical but merely similar. This is perhaps excusable since the large eddies contain very little of the turbulence energy. However it is clear that the theory is again restricted to small B/A, a restriction which is fortunately true in most cases and, moreover, is required by the boundary-layer approximation.

Townsend's large-eddy-equilibrium hypothesis may also be applied to the large eddies. These eddies are continuously gaining energy from the mean motion while at the same time losing it to the eddies of next smaller scale (Townsend (1956) p. 115). Townsend argues that these rates of gain and loss are in balance. The energy equation for the large eddies may then be written (*loc. cit.*, eqn. 2.4.10)

$$\overline{u_i u_k} \frac{\partial U_i}{\partial x_k} = \overline{v_T u_i \frac{\partial^2 u_i}{\partial x_k^2}} \tag{28}$$

where the kinematic viscosity v has been replaced by an equivalent eddy viscosity v_T to provide terms which represent the transfer of energy to the eddies of next smaller scale. Note that it is intrinsically assumed here that this "v_T" is identical with, or at least proportional to, the eddy viscosity v_T which relates the turbulent shearing stress to the mean rate of shear strain. This is plausible if the energy-containing eddies have a universal structure.

B and is independent of the fluid density, the fluid viscosity and the magnitude of the mean fluid velocity.

Thus, since ω_B is positive

$$\frac{\omega_B}{|A|} = F\left(\left|\frac{B}{A}\right|\right)$$

$$\propto \left(1 + \text{constant} \left|\frac{B}{A}\right|\right) \quad \text{if} \quad \frac{B}{A} \text{ is small.}$$

Thus for the large eddies, which are superimposed on a mean flow with scales U_0 and L_0,

$$L_B^2 \omega_B^2 \frac{U_0}{L_0} \propto \nu_T \omega_B^2$$

i.e.

$$\frac{1}{R_T} = \left| \frac{\nu_T}{U_0 L_0} \right| \propto \frac{L_B^2}{L_0^2} \qquad (29)$$

Gartshore (1965b,c) has successfully compared this equation directly with experiment by measuring the extent of the intermittent region at the edge of various shear flows.

Combining with equation (27) this gives

$$\frac{1}{R_T} = \frac{1}{R_{T_0}} \left\{ 1 + \lambda \left| \frac{B}{A} \right| \right\}$$

The two constants R_{T_0}, the value of R_T when $B=0$, and λ may be obtained from the measured results for

(a) the jet with still surroundings; $R_T = 32.9$

$$\left(\frac{B}{A} \right)_{y=L_0} = 0.0665$$

(b) the small perturbation wake; $R_T = 13.0$

$$\left(\frac{B}{A} \right)_{y=L_0} \to 0 .$$

Thus

$$\frac{1}{R_T} = 0.077 \left\{ 1 - 9.1 \left| \frac{B}{A} \right| \right\} \qquad (30)$$

It is worth noting that, since $\nu_T = \dfrac{\tau}{\rho \partial U/\partial y}$, equation (29) may also be written $\tau/\rho \propto L_B^2(\partial U/\partial y)^2$, which would be applicable even if the mean-velocity profile were not universal. This equation is the same as that obtained from Prandtl's mixing-length theory with the difference that L_B is now the scale of the *large* eddies and is not universally proportional to the width of the flow. These lengths are, of course, proportional to one another for a given self-preserving flow, but the constant of proportionality varies from one self-preserving flow to another (Townsend 1956).

The assumption that the rate of change of turbulent vorticity following the mean motion is proportional on the average to ω_B/T_B (eqn. (24)) implies that the field of turbulence is not varying greatly from place to place. This apart, nothing else in the derivation implies that R_T is constant across the flow at a given x (the constants

λ_1 and λ_2, for example, can vary from one part of the field to another). Gartshore therefore applies the theory specifically to obtain the shearing stress at $y=L_0$ and then states the "half" momentum-integral equation with limits $y=0$ and $y=L_0$ (Squire & Trouncer 1944).

$$\int_0^{L_0} \frac{\partial}{\partial x}[U(U-U_1)]y^r\,dy + \frac{dU_1}{dx}\int_0^{L_0}(U-U_1)y^r\,dy - (U-U_1)_{y=L_0}\int_0^{L_0}\frac{\partial U}{\partial x}\,y^r\,dy$$

$$= L_0^r\left(v_T\frac{\partial U}{\partial y}\right)_{y=L_0} \qquad (31)$$

where $r=0$ for two-dimensional flow and

$$\frac{1}{R_T} = \left|\frac{v_T}{U_0 L_0}\right| = (0.077)\left[1 - 9.1\left|\frac{\partial U/\partial x}{\partial U/\partial y}\right|_{y=L_0}\right]$$

using the previous notation (e.g. U_1 is again the streaming-flow velocity).

Bradbury (1963) applies equation (30) using the integral energy equation assuming constant R_T across the flow, and obtains a closed-form solution for a jet in zero pressure gradient. It should be acknowledged that one probably gets very similar results using either the integral energy or the integral moment-of-momentum equation together with constant R_T across the flow. Indeed Hill *et al.* (1963) prove this analytically. The essential improvement of Gartshore's and Bradbury's work is that some allowance has been made for variations of R_T *downstream*, even if this allowance is based on somewhat shaky assumptions.

Gartshore's method (equations (17), (31) and (30)) has been programmed using the Runge–Kutta technique. Details may be found in Gartshore (1965a,b).

5. COMPARISON WITH EXPERIMENT

The theories which have been reviewed are now compared with available experimental data. In all cases measured data at a suitable downstream station has been used as a starting value for the theoretical calculations.

5.1. *Gartshore* (1965a,b): *Near-Self-Preserving Wakes*

This is the only free-jet or wake data which approximates self-preserving conditions in a pressure gradient. Two wakes were investigated. Wake A had a somewhat stronger adverse pressure gradient (the exponent $-m$ was larger) and due to this and a very slight misalignment of the "two-dimensional" body, the "invariant" $|\theta|U_1^{H+2}$ (eqn. (7)) decreased by 14% over the range of measurements. The results for wake B are much better however, and the change of $|\theta|U_1^{H+2}$ was

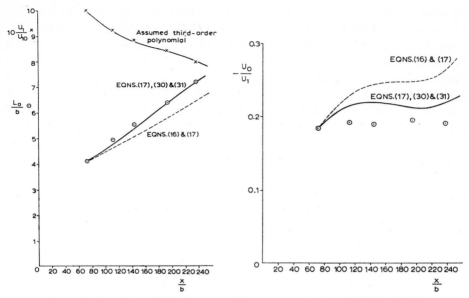

Figure 6. Gartshore (1965a,b): near-self-preserving wake A. $(U_1b/v)_0 = 6,300$.

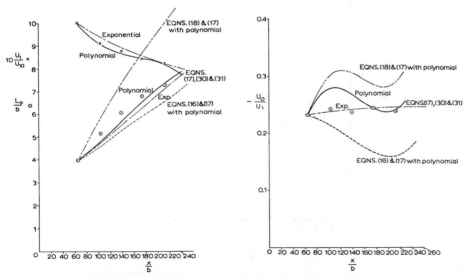

Figure 7. Gartshore (1965a,b): near-self-preserving wake B. $(U_1b/v)_0 = 7,300$.

variable and was less than $\pm$ 2%. A best-fit third-order polynomial was fitted to the experimental external velocity distribution U_1/U_{10} and is shown in figure 6 for wake A. Gartshore's variable R_T theory (solid line in figure 6) gives almost perfect agreement with the measured width of the flow L_0 and much better agreement than Abramovich's theory (dotted line) for the velocity perturbation U_0. The results for wake B in figure 7 exhibit similar features. On figure 7 two other curves have been plotted. One refers to Gartshore's theory, but in conjunction with an exponential external velocity distribution; this is a valid modification because the longitudinal pressure distribution was measured by pressure plotting one of the end plates of the flow and may not be entirely accurate. The effect of choosing an exponential velocity distribution, $U_1 \propto x^m$, is shown by the chain dotted lines in figure 7. There is not quite such a good prediction of L_0 but a much better prediction of U_0. The double chain dotted line is included for interest: it shows the effect of using the modified Abramovich equation (18) and is apparently unsuccessful.

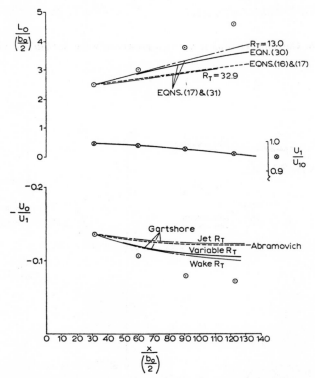

Figure 8. Hill, Schaub & Senoo (1963): wake in weak adverse pressure gradient. $b_0/2 = 0.182$ in., $b \approx 1$ in.

5.2. *Schaub: Wake in Weak Adverse Pressure Gradient (figure 8)*

Hill, Schaub & Senoo (1963) present data on three wakes. Unfortunately the two with the strongest adverse pressure gradients are apparently in rather poor agreement with the integral momentum equation (momentum loss thickness nearly twice what it should be) for it has been impossible to obtain theoretical solutions which incorporate this equation correctly. Hill *et al.* apparently got over the difficulty by assuming a constant value of $H(=1)$. The data for the third wake in a weak adverse pressure gradient is however quite satisfactory and makes an interesting comparison with the theories. In this case Gartshore's theory has been applied using both variable R_T, and R_T fixed at the extreme values for a small-perturbation wake and for a jet with still surroundings. In this case the wake-R_T and variable-R_T theories give the best agreement but this is still poor. Apparently developing wakes at nearly constant pressure have effective values of R_T which are lower than the ultimate small-perturbation values, as is clearly evident in the results given in Table 2. It is also interesting to notice that the jet-R_T results and Abramovich's theory are in close agreement with one another, as might be expected.

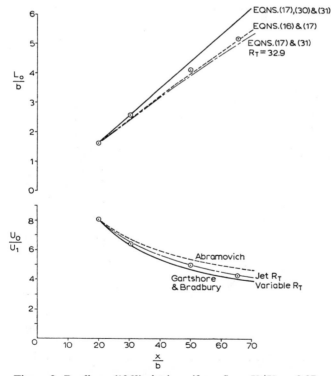

Figure 9. Bradbury (1963): jet in uniform flow. $U_1/U_J = 0.07$.

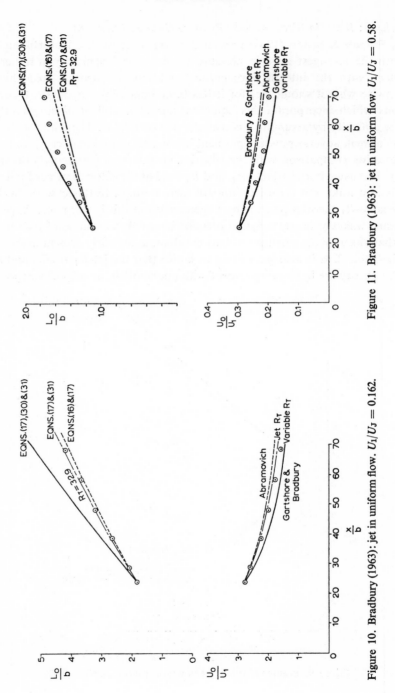

Figure 11. Bradbury (1963): jet in uniform flow. $U_1/U_J = 0.58$.

Figure 10. Bradbury (1963): jet in uniform flow. $U_1/U_J = 0.162$.

5.3. *Bradbury* (1963): *Jets at Constant Pressure*

This data is of fairly good quality, the streamwise variation of θ being only 4%. Three values of U_1/U_J were chosen and the results are shown in figures 9, 10 and 11. Abramovich's theory shows up well for the strong jets (U_1/U_J small) although it is perhaps not quite as good as Gartshore's theory if a constant R_T equal to the jet value is chosen. The variable-R_T theory is best for the weakest jet.

6. DISCUSSION AND CONCLUSIONS

It is concluded that the Gartshore–Bradbury formulation of Townsend's hypotheses leads to a fairly satisfactory prediction of U_0 and L_0 for a self-preserving wake or jet. Apparently the structure of the turbulent eddies in the vicinity of $y=L_0$ is sufficiently well represented by the idealized model of the flow. Experimental confirmation has of course only been obtained for a wake but there is good reason to suppose that the theory will also be valid for a jet. Values of $-\overline{uv}/\overline{u^2}$ at $y=L_0$ for a variety of jets and wakes are shown in Table 3 and none of the values differ greatly from 0.40, the value found by Townsend for large distortion of homogeneous

TABLE 3

COLLECTED VALUES OF TURBULENCE-STRESS RATIOS AT $y = L_0$

Type of flow	Experimenter(s)	$-\dfrac{\overline{uv}}{\overline{u^2}}$	$\dfrac{\overline{v^2}}{\overline{u^2}}$	Remarks
Two-Dimensional				
Jet in Almost Still Surroundings and in Streaming Flow	Bradbury (1963)	0.42	0.66	$\dfrac{U_1}{U_J} = 0.07, 0.162, 0.58$
Wall Jet in Still Surroundings	Eskinazi & Kruka (1962)	0.38	0.73	
Wall Jet in Equilibrium Pressure Gradient	Patel (unpublished)	0.38	1.10?	$\dfrac{U_0}{U_1} = 1.65$
Self-Preserving Wake B	Gartshore (1965a, b)	0.41		
Small-Deficit Wake	Townsend (1956)	0.36	0.73	
Axisymmetric Jet in Still Surroundings	Corrsin (1943)	0.43	0.59	

References p. 200–201

turbulence (Townsend (1956) p. 152). It must be noted, however, that the values of $\overline{v^2}/\overline{u^2}$ do exhibit a greater variation.

For the non-self-preserving flows the appropriate value of R_T seems to be an upstream value rather than the local value; this is, of course, reminiscent of the behaviour of the outer region of non-equilibrium turbulent boundary layers. It may be understood by considering the distance travelled by a large eddy during its lifetime. Townsend (1956) suggests that an eddy lives for about $2.4/|\partial U/\partial y|$, and this value will be assumed. During this time a particle with the local velocity $U_1 + U_0/2$ would travel a distance of some $3.5L_0(U_1/U_0 \pm \frac{1}{2})$, with $+$ for jets and $-$ for wakes. In the case of Gartshore's wake B at $x/b=200$, this distance is $90b$ and, since the flow was developing up to $x/b=70$ under nearly-self-preserving conditions before the theory was applied, it is expected that the theory will be fairly satisfactory. For Bradbury's second jet with $U_1/U_J=0.162$ and $x/b=60$, the eddy distance is $85b$ and hence it is not surprising that the value of R_T for a still-fluid jet is most appropriate for these measurements. For Schaub's weak wake at $x/(b_0/2)=160$, the eddy migration distance is $190(b_0/2)$ and again an estimated wake value near the body ($R_T \approx 8$ perhaps) would give best agreement. Thus the agreement and the discrepancies may be justified in terms of the distance required to stretch the large eddy during its lifetime. It is understandable that a very great distance is required to establish a true small-perturbation self-preserving flow since, almost by definition, $U_1/U_0 > 10$ and the eddy migration distance becomes almost $35L_0$ as self preservation is approached. In contrast the corresponding distance for a still-fluid jet is only $1.7L_0$.

The Gartshore–Bradbury equation is incapable of giving values of R_T which are less than 13.0 and yet such values are certainly found near the body (Table 2). Presumably the relatively high turbulence generated by the body leads to high values of v_T and these are not eradicated until the turbulence has been distorted sufficiently and for a long enough time.

From a purely pragmatic point of view, jets in uniform streaming flow with U_1/U_J less than about 0.3 can be satisfactorily predicted for most purposes using Abramovich's theory or by using a second integral equation with $R_T=32.9$. Weaker jets in uniform streaming flow may be predicted using Gartshore's method with variable R_T if one accepts an appropriate, modified value of the factor multiplying B/A in eqn. (30) (Gartshore 1965b). For wakes in uniform flow a value of $R_T < 13$ must be chosen and Table 2 provides some guidance as to the choice. Abramovich's theory is certainly not satisfactory for this case. Near-self-preserving flows in which the eddy migration distance is not much larger than the development length and in which B/A is small (certainly less than 0.11), are predicted with fair accuracy by Gartshore's method using variable R_T (eqn. (30)). The matching of the solution to the starting conditions at the body or the jet slot is most easily done

by equating both the momentum perturbation and the excess mass flux to that of
the theoretical flow. For a still-fluid jet with negligible slot boundary layers this
gives the reasonable value of $x_0 = 2.8b$ (Newman 1961). Gartshore (1965b) has
adopted this procedure with the refinement that, in the case of a jet, if the apparent
value of $U_1 + U_0$ exceeds U_J at the slot then the mass flux equation is replaced by
$U_1 + U_0 = U_J$.

Clearly there is a definite need for more good-quality experiments on jets and
wakes. The self-preserving jet should be studied over long downstream distances
both in axisymmetric three-dimensional, and in truly representative two-dimensional, conditions. As a start the measurements could be simply the mean velocity,
the intermittency and the turbulent stress tensor. The wake could also be usefully
studied in greater detail and it would be interesting to study the development of a
constant pressure wake as the condition of the turbulence at the body is artificially
modified.

ACKNOWLEDGEMENT

I am indebted to Dr. I. S. Gartshore for providing the computer programme for
his method, supplying his original experimental data and for discussing the con-
tents of this paper both constructively and critically.

The McGill experimental work on wakes and jets which is quoted in this paper
(Gartshore, Patel and Knystautas) was undertaken with the financial support of the
Defence Research Board of Canada (Grant Number 9551–12).

APPENDIX

RELATIONSHIP BETWEEN THE GROWTH OF TWO-DIMENSIONAL AND ROUND JETS IN STILL SURROUNDINGS

Knystautas (1964) has demonstrated experimentally that the jet emanating from a
series of round coplanar orifices eventually becomes two-dimensional. Reichardt's
inductive theory of turbulence (Alexander, Baron & Cumings 1953) may be applied
to this problem permitting the squares of the mean velocity for each flow to be
superimposed.

Thus, considering the two-dimensional jet from a thin slot of width b to be
equivalent to the jet from a series of many closely-spaced holes with spacing Δs and
area A, $A = b\Delta s$.

For the nth hole which is offset $n\Delta s$ from the plane of observation, the contribution to the central velocity squared is (eqns. (3), (7) with $U_1 = 0$ and $f = \exp[-k\eta^2]$)

$$\Delta U_0^2 = \frac{2k\,U_J^2\,A}{\pi L_0^2}\exp\left[-2k\left(\frac{n\Delta s}{L_0}\right)^2\right]$$

Summing for all the holes and proceeding to the limit, the central velocity U_0 is given by

$$\left(\frac{U_0}{U_J}\right)^2 = \frac{2kb}{\pi L_0^2}\int_{-\infty}^{+\infty}\exp\left[-2k\left(\frac{z}{L_0}\right)^2\right]dz$$

$$= \left(\frac{2k}{\pi}\right)^{\frac{1}{2}}\frac{b}{L_0}$$

An identical result is obtained for a truly two-dimensional jet, proving that L_0 is the same for each and that dL_0/dx should be the same for both a round jet and a two-dimensional jet. The measured values are respectively 0.085 and 0.104.

REFERENCES

Abramovich, G. N. (1963) *The Theory of Turbulent Jets*. M.I.T. Press, Cambridge, Mass.

Alexander, L. G., Baron, T. & Cumings, E. W. (1953) *Transport of Momentum, Mass and Heat in Turbulent Jets*. Engineering Experiment Station Bulletin no. 413, University of Illinois.

Bradbury, L. J. S. (1963) *An Investigation Into the Structure of a Turbulent Plane Jet*. Ph. D. Thesis, University of London.

Corrsin, S. (1943) *Investigation of Flow in an Axially-Symmetric Heated Jet of Air*. NACA Wartime Report W-94.

Eskinazi, S. & Kruka, V. (1962) *Turbulence Measurements in a Two-Dimensional Rectangular Wall Jet With a Longitudinal Stream*. Syracuse University, Rep. no. ME 937–6205P.

Eskinazi, S. & Kruka, V. (1964) *The Wall Jet in a Moving Stream*. J. Fluid Mech. **20**, 555–79.

Forstall, W. & Shapiro, A. H. (1950) *Momentum and Mass Transfer in Coaxial Gas Jets*. J. Applied Mech. **72**, 399–408.

Förthmann, E. (1934) *Turbulent Jet Expansion*. NACA Tech. Memo no. 789: Ing. Arch. **5**, 42–54.

Gartshore, I. S. (1964) *Jets and Wall Jets in Uniform Streaming Flow*. McGill University, Mech. Eng. Rep. no. 64–4.

Gartshore, I. S. (1965a) *The Streamwise Development of Certain Two-Dimensional Shear Flows*. McGill University Mech. Eng. Rep. no. 65–3.

Gartshore, I. S. (1965b) *The Streamwise Development of Two-Dimensional Wall Jets and Other Two-Dimensional Turbulent Shear Flows*. Mech. Eng. Ph. D. Thesis, McGill University.

Gartshore, I. S. (1965c) *An Experimental Examination of the Large-Eddy Equilibrium Hypothesis*. To be published in J. Fluid Mech.

Halleen, R. M. (1964) *Literature Review on Subsonic Free Turbulent Shear Flow*. Stanford University, Mech. Eng. Rep. no. MD-11.

Heskestad, G. (1963) *Two Turbulent Shear Flows*. Johns Hopkins University, Mech. Eng. Contract AF(638)–248.

Hill, P. G. (1965) *Turbulent Jets in Ducted Streams*. J. Fluid Mech. **22**, 161–86.

Hill, P. G., Schaub, U. W. & Senoo, Y. (1963) *Turbulent Wakes in Pressure Gradients*. ASME Paper no. 63-WA-5.

Hinze, J. O. & v. d. Hegge Zijnen, B. G. (1949) *Transfer of Heat and Matter in the Turbulent Mixing Zone of an Axially Symmetric Jet*. Appl. Sci. Res., The Hague, A, **1**, 435–61.

Johannesen, N. H. (1962) *Further Results on the Mixing of Free Axially-Symmetrical Jets of Mach Number 1.40*. Aero. Res. Counc. Tech. Rep. R. and M. no. 3292.

Knystautas, R. (1964) *The Turbulent Jet From a Series of Holes in Line*. Aero. Quart. **15**, 1–28.

Küchemann, D. & Weber, J. (1953) *Aerodynamics of Propulsion*. McGraw Hill, New York.

Liepmann, H. W. & Laufer, J. (1947) *Investigation of Free Turbulent Mixing*. NACA Tech. Note no. 1257.

Maczynski, J. F. J. (1962) *A Round Jet in an Ambient Co-Axial Stream*. J. Fluid Mech. **13**, 597–608.

Miller, D. R. & Comings, E. W. (1958) *Static Pressure Distribution in a Free Turbulent Jet*. J. Fluid Mech. **3**, 1–16.

Nakaguchi, H. (1961) *Jet Along a Curved Wall*. University of Tokyo Research Memo 4.

Newman, B. G. (1961) *Deflection of Plane Jets by Adjacent Boundaries—Coanda Effect*. Boundary Layer and Flow Control **1**, Pergamon Press, Oxford.

Olson, R. E. (1962) *An Analytical and Experimental Study of Two-Dimensional Submerged Jets*. Diamond Ordnance Labs, Proc. Fluid Amplification Symposium, 267–86.

Patel, R. & Newman, B. G. (1961) *Self-Preserving, Two-Dimensional Turbulent Jets and Wall Jets in a Moving Stream*. McGill University, Mech. Eng. Rep. no. Ae. 5.

Reichardt, H. (1951) *Gesetzmassigkeiten der Freien Turbulenz*. VDI-Forschungsheft **414**.

Ribner, H. S. (1946) *Field of Flow About a Jet and Effect of Jets on Stability of Jet-Propelled Airplanes*. NACA W.R. L-213.

Ricou, F. P. & Spalding, D. B. (1961) *Measurements of Entrainment by Axisymmetrical Turbulent Jets*. J. Fluid Mech. **11**, 21–32.

Sabin, C. M. (1963) *An Analytical and Experimental Study of the Plane Incompressible Turbulent Free Shear Layer With Arbitrary Velocity Ratio and Pressure Gradient*. Stanford University, Mech. Eng. Rep. no. MD-9.

Schlichting, H. (1960) *Boundary-Layer Theory*. 4th edition. McGraw-Hill, New York.

Silverstein, A., Katzoff, S. & Bullivant, W. K. (1939) *Downwash and Wake Behind Plain and Flapped Airfoils*. NACA Rep. no. 651.

Spalding, D. B. (1958) *Spread of Confined Turbulent Pre-Mixed Flames*. Seventh Symposium (International) on Combustion. Butterworth, London.

Squire, H. B. & Trouncer, J. (1944) *Round Jets in a General Stream*. Aero. Res. Counc. Tech. Rep. R. and M. no. 1974.

Townsend, A. A. (1948) *Momentum and Energy Diffusion in the Turbulent Wake of a Cylinder*. Proc. Roy. Soc. A, **197**, 124–40.

Townsend, A. A. (1956) *The Structure of Turbulent Shear Flow*. Cambridge University Press, London.

Weinstein, A. S., Osterle, J. F. & Forstall, W. (1956) *Momentum Diffusion From a Slot Jet Into a Moving Secondary*. J. Applied Mech. **78**, 437–43.

Discussion

H. W. EMMONS (*Harvard University, Cambridge, Massachusetts*)

We have just had a review of the attempts to explain the mean-velocity profile in turbulent wakes and jets by various theoretical methods. As you recall, yesterday we had the distinction made between the recognition of the detailed mechanisms and the attempt to find a procedure of some sort, based upon more-or-less plausible initial assumptions but largely *ad hoc* in nature, for explaining the gross features of the phenomenon. The review this morning on wakes and jets has been concentrated primarily in this second area.

S. Eskinazi (*Syracuse University, Syracuse, New York*)

I would like to compliment Prof. Newman for the nice survey he has made of an approach for dealing with turbulent mixing problems, whether they are wakes or adjacent jets of different kinds. This unique approach at least puts down the similarity between wake and jet flows.

I would like to make one comment and I think it was touched upon in nearly every other paper. Sometimes I think we create confusion about what is considered to be truly basic and what is understood as "laws". We should make it clear that some methods of approach are based on common sense and semi-empirical thinking which appear from the way we evaluate our experiments. I think that the self-similar or self-preserving law based on Townsend's similarity considerations for the turbulence production, that Prof. Newman has pointed out, should be stated with some care. Prof. Newman spoke of the necessity-sufficiency of similarity forms to satisfy the actual conditions in the flow field. We should remember that the solution which he assumes at the beginning *is* the similarity law. He supposes that the flow is affine and has similarities. We put these similarities into a differential equation which we force, by imposing conditions on the coefficients, to accept such a solution. We come out with results that tell us how the length and the characteristic velocity should vary, and so forth. It is true that experiments do show that the predicted type of behavior is nearly correct. But we still have some difficulties. Some experimentalists have had difficulties in finding an appropriate characteristic velocity or characteristic length, not only for correlating the various results in their own experiments but also for correlating their results with those of other experimenters. If an experimenter doesn't come up with the fact that some particular length should vary according to the self-preserving law, I don't think we should be too hasty to call him a poor experimenter. There have been cases, for instance, where there has been difficulty in agreeing with other experimenters on where the virtual origin should be. There have also been some difficulties with the virtual origin obtained from the length scale, since it doesn't necessarily correspond to the virtual origin obtained from the velocity scale. Of course the natural indication is that it's not a self-preserving flow. We should really consider a self-preserving flow as a model that we propose, and which we hope to approach as closely as possible with our experiments. I don't think we should say that all types of flow must ultimately obey the simple similarity rules that have been presented here. We assume that there is no memory in the flow, that the fluid has forgotten all its past history; all it knows about is just its immediate history so that it can adjust itself subsequently. In reality, there are a lot of effects that still remain from the origin.

B. G. Newman

Yes, I hope that the eddy-migration idea will provide some guide on how far downstream you have to be in a self-preserving flow before you can expect reasonable agreement with Townsend's hypotheses. As far as the x_0 varying from one flow situation to another, I entirely agree. For example, x_0 in a still jet is quite dependent on the internal boundary layers in the slot. For external boundary layers also, the wake generated by a body is very much dependent upon the shape of the body and whether or not separation occurs on it. However, if we do eventually reach constant-momentum-increment or constant-momentum-deficit conditions at some downstream location in either of these types of self-preserving flow, then this is a necessary condition that the velocity and the length scale must both have the same x_0.

T. B. BENJAMIN (*Cambridge University, England*)

I have just one practical question, which probably can be answered easily. I wonder whether the results of jet experiments such as you have described are very sensitive to the condition of the jet upon entry? What you said seems to suggest that, at least, the position of the virtual origin would be affected by the level of turbulence in the jet at the start.

B. G. NEWMAN

   Yes.

S. J. KLINE (*Stanford University, Stanford, California*)

Can I ask a question about that same thing. Some experiments suggest, I think some of Dr. Rouse's people have measured this particularly, that the turbulence level just behind a wake-generating body tends to swamp what happens upstream; it tends to wipe out the history Dr. Benjamin is asking about. I think this shows up in your own data. What is important is the ratio of velocities across the mixing layer, from the maximum to the minimum; i.e., your U_0/U_1. This ratio affects the coefficient and this is what we saw in your data. For a small perturbation you had to have quite a different coefficient than for the large one. I wonder whether (a) you have examined the turbulence production in the back of the layer and (b) whether you have tried to correlate the data on the basis of a velocity *ratio* anywhere.

B. G. NEWMAN

   Are you talking about a jet or a wake?

S. J. KLINE

   Both.

B. G. NEWMAN

In the case of a jet, we have in a sense explored the retention of jet values since we found that the R_T for a still-air jet gives a fairly good prediction of Bradbury's measurements in this region. To answer Dr. Benjamin's question, evidence is fairly clear that at some distance downstream what has gone on in the slot isn't too important from the point of view of dL_0/dx. What *is* important is that $(U_0/U_j) [(x + x_0)/b]^{\frac{1}{2}}$ is also a constant but it is equal to 2.56 for a Gaussian profile if it is assumed that the full momentum at the slot is without internal boundary layers. Values of this parameter are indicated in Table 1. It is apparently sensitive to the slot conditions, and doesn't get up to the ideal value of 2.56. It varies in a random sort of manner from one series of experiments to another and that, I think, is due to slot conditions. But if you are only concerned with dL_0/dx, R_T and such things in the final self-preserving flow, then I don't think the slot conditions matter a great deal.

Now, as far as a wake is concerned, you really do have to go a tremendous distance downstream before you get a self-preserving condition—500 to 1000 body widths. This illustrates an interesting point which I did not bring out in the lecture but which is relevant to this question; that is, the significant non-dimensional downstream distance is not $x/|\theta|$ but rather x/b. If we look at Table 2 and consider Silverstein's measurements which were made on an aerofoil of low drag, we see that even at 17 body widths downstream the value of $x/|\theta|$ was very large because θ was small. Despite this enormous $x/|\theta|$, the value of $L_0/(x + x_0)^{\frac{1}{2}}|\theta|^{\frac{1}{2}}$ was 0.394, which is not close to the final asymptotic value. This illustrates Townsend's point that body width is very important, and it is against Spalding's idea of jet forgetfulness—that θ is the only relevant parameter for a wake.

R. E. KRONAUER (*Harvard University, Cambridge, Massachusetts*)

I would like to raise a question. If you look at photographs of the wakes of projectiles (which have been made visible, say, by temperature differences) and watch a particular part of the wake for a long time, it appears to grow in bursts. It grows rapidly for a while and then appears to sit there, the interface between the clearly turbulent core and the outer part not seeming to move. Later, a wave of some multiple length appears and the diameter grows much more rapidly again; then again it sits there. It takes a fairly long wake to see this, many of your settling times. I wonder if, in the measurements you have made, you see any evidence of this sort of periodicity as you proceed downstream, i.e., that the structure doesn't grow in a uniform fashion as the theory idealizes.

B. G. NEWMAN

Such evidence would presumably be obtained by taking a look at the spectrum for intermittency in the outer part of the turbulent wake; we haven't made any measurements of that. However, measurements of intermittency have been made by Gartshore. If he would like to comment on them, on how he made them and the difficulties in doing this, I would appreciate it.

I. S. GARTSHORE (*McGill University, Montreal, Canada*)

The way they were made was to simply construct a delta signal that tells the condition of the flow. You put a conventional hot wire into the intermittent region, and when the flow exhibits large, high-frequency fluctuations of velocity, you construct a signal which has a unit value; when the frequency or the level of fluctuations drops below a certain value, you have a zero in your delta signal. This gives a square pulse coming through. This is one technique that we used and it requires a lot of electronic equipment, filtering, smoothing and that sort of thing. It is very convenient once you have it working, but you are never quite sure that all the choices you have made on the way through give you the right answer, or whether you have been affected by a subjective desire to get the right answer. Realizing that this is the case and that you can't eliminate the subjective element, it seems just as well to put a hot wire into the intermittent region and display its output as a trace on a piece of paper where you can look at it, and save yourself all the electronic gear. In analyzing the trace you pose the question: if there are two processes going on here, how would I differentiate between them? You can give this to somebody who has never looked at intermittency before and who doesn't know what you are talking about and ask him, "if you had to distinguish two different processes going along here how would you do it? Take a pencil and mark off one process from the other." It turns out that any two people will give roughly the same answer here. It is a subjective thing, yes, but you apparently can't avoid subjectiveness in this part of the analysis so I think this procedure is the simplest, most direct and probably most satisfactory method for measuring intermittency of the flow. Both of these techniques were used in our measurements of intermittency.

B. G. NEWMAN

What sort of accuracy do you think you achieve for a local value of intermittency?

I. S. GARTSHORE

I would not like to quote it as a percentage, since the intermittency factor varies between 0 and 1 by definition, but rather as an absolute error. I would say that the error with this technique is probably in the order of ± 0.025 no matter where you are across the flow. It isn't extremely accurate; we can't claim that because it is a subjective evaluation.

G. B. SCHUBAUER (*National Bureau of Standards, Washington, D.C.*)

Do I understand that in your theory the turbulent viscosity is based on the large eddies, that it comes from the stretching of the large eddies? I am asking whether I am interpreting you correctly.

B. G. NEWMAN

No, the only assumption that is made is that the large eddy contains a certain proportion of the total $\overline{uv}$.

G. B. SCHUBAUER

I see. Well, then that brings up the question I had in mind—whether someone should not measure shear stress as a function of frequency or get a spectrum of shear stress and find out where it is coming from?

B. G. NEWMAN

Yes, I entirely agree with you.

H. W. LIEPMANN (*California Institute of Technology, Pasadena, California*)

I am rather unhappy about the random nature of turbulence research, with its random samplings of experiments and random assumptions for theories. It seems to me that it doesn't help terribly much to check any one set of experiments with some theory, or to take an average over experiments which have been made for different purposes and which have had entirely different aims and different accuracy levels. I think you can deduce from yesterday's Bureau of Standards paper that important research on turbulent-structure has to be carried on for a long time. It cannot be done by one Ph.D. student followed by another Ph.D. student followed by another Ph.D. student, because they'll never agree. I would feel a little better if the evaluation of experiments could be done in a somewhat more rational way. If a question is raised from some plausibility assumption (I hate to call it a theory), it can then be followed up by measurement. But measurement and theory must have something in common. Otherwise, the impression a general reader gets from some turbulence books, not Townsend's of course, is that in turbulence research anything goes. It's a free-for-all: make any assumption and you will check *an* experiment. That impression, I think, one ought to try to dispell as much as possible, by being extremely careful in the selection of experiments to quote and how they are followed up with what one calls theory.

B. G. NEWMAN

I agree with Dr. Liepmann that it is essential to encourage government laboratories to undertake definitive detailed work on turbulent flows. The NBS is doing this; the NPL is also doing it under Bradshaw. I find his remarks, however, a trifle superficial in relation to Gartshore's work; that is, if his remarks are intended to apply to Gartshore's work. Gartshore, of course, didn't fully explore this flow but he did do more than I have said. He did measure the turbulence stress tensor and he did measure $\overline{uv}$ as well as $\overline{u^2}$ and $\overline{v^2}$. It seems to me that this theory by Bradbury–Gartshore could be considered as the first step along the line to something more respectable. Table 3 shows values of the turbulence-stress ratio $-\overline{uv}/\overline{u^2}$ at $y = L_0$. You would expect, if this approach is reasonable, that this ratio would tend to be constant from one flow to another. Gartshore's measurement is not too much different from the 0.4 that Townsend gets from uniform distortion and stretching of homogeneous turbulence. The other values are not in particularly good agreement. The extent to which all these measurements are and are not in agreement is, I suppose, a commentary on the accuracy of the approach, but there is certainly some evidence here on the universality of turbulent structure.

E. O. MACAGNO (*University of Iowa, Iowa City, Iowa*)

You have reduced the jet and wake problems to this simple procedure. I wonder if the superposition of a jet and a wake would be amenable to the same thing.

B. G. NEWMAN

That is, you mean we blow a jet?

E. O. MACAGNO

Yes.

B. G. NEWMAN

First of all, I suppose the assumption of a Gaussian velocity profile would no longer be applicable and we would have to invent a new shape. Furthermore, it's a bit difficult to decide upon a characteristic point in the flow at which to work out R_T and hence the shearing stress. This is a difficult case. We have done something towards it by considering an asymmetric jet (figure 12). There is a still-air jet on one side and a moving-air jet on the other side. Gartshore, in his Ph.D. thesis, does attempt to predict this flow but without too much success. The prediction of the growth on the still-air side is not too bad but on the other side it's not satisfactory.

E. O. MACAGNO

Do I understand that you assume a profile shape that is realistic and then you determine the parameters of these curves?

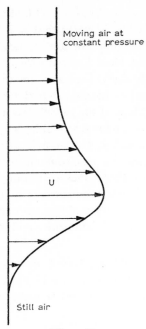

Figure 12.

B. G. NEWMAN

Yes, but you have to have cases in which the shapes are all the same in order to apply this integral method.

M. H. BLOOM (*Polytechnic Institute of Brooklyn, Farmingdale, New York*)

I would like to re-emphasize once again what was brought out yesterday in connection with Dr. Rotta's paper. It is advisable to separate questions about the experimental measurements and their accuracy from the particular calculation procedures used to relate the data to the derived constants of the diffusion and mixing. In constructing these deductions from data, it would be desirable to make full use of all the computational accuracy given to us by the available modern numerical techniques, recognizing of course the limitations of the experimental data itself.

H. W. EMMONS

We have had a discussion of another of the very difficult problems of turbulent flow. It is quite clear that when we have a problem that is as difficult to treat in a really fundamental way, we open innumerable questions, which questions differ considerably in the minds of one person and another. One person can be concerned with experimental techniques, another with the detailed mechanisms which cocur, and another with describing overall phenomena; there are many inconsistencies between these. While one person may think that these are random assumptions and random theories which are being used, another feels that this is getting *at* the basic problem from the point of view of making practical calculations. As a matter of fact, as we stand in our present ignorance who is to say whether we are making progress forward or backwards in a given attempt to understand the phenomena? So, we thank Prof. Newman for giving us this review of where things now stand from the overall point of view of trying to calculate the phenomena in these complex flows.

Critical Review and Current Developments in Three-Dimensional Turbulent Boundary Layers

P. N. JOUBERT, A. E. PERRY AND K. C. BROWN

University of Melbourne, Australia

SUMMARY

The literature has been reviewed for the case of highly skewed turbulent boundary layers. It was found that the important measurements of pressure gradient and wall shear stress were lacking from most experiments. The applicability of a similarity defect equation as proposed by Perry & Joubert has been tested by analysis of the results of Johnston, and flow close to the wall has been analysed using regional similarity arguments. The results look encouraging.

NOTATION

A	a universal constant
A'	a parameter
C	a universal constant
C'_f	local skin friction coefficient $= \tau_0 / \frac{1}{2}\rho U_0^2$
f	vector law of the wall
k	roughness scale
K	a universal constant
p	static pressure
s	suffix for streamline co-ordinates
U_0	velocity in main stream
u	velocity in boundary layer
U_τ	shear velocity at x, y
U_{τ_1}	shear velocity at upstream reference profile
U_∞	main-stream velocity at upstream reference profile
U_1	velocity in boundary layer at upstream reference profile
U_0	magnitude of main-stream velocity vector

u_s component of boundary layer velocity in the direction of U_0

v_s component of boundary layer velocity normal to u_s but in plane parallel to wall

u, v, w mean components of boundary layer velocity in directions of x, y and z respectively

U_d developed velocity

W Coles' wake function

x co-ordinate in direction of unyawed upstream flow

y co-ordinate normal to x but in plane of wall

z co-ordinate normal to wall

α kinematic pressure gradient $= (1/\rho)|\nabla p|$

α' free stream turning angle measured from reference direction x

γ yaw angle

γ_w wall yaw angle

δ boundary layer thickness

Δu_1 slip velocity at wall of extrapolated half-power law

Δu_2 decrement in slip velocity due to surface roughness action

θ angle between wall shear-stress vector and pressure-gradient vector

$\varkappa$ universal constant

ν kinematic viscosity

$\boldsymbol{\Pi}'$ vector function.

π vector function of Coles' wake component

ρ fluid density

τ_0 wall shear stress

ϕ function symbol

1. INTRODUCTION

Knowledge of two-dimensional turbulent boundary layers is incomplete. Even less is known about the three-dimensional boundary layer. However, in practice, it is more often found that turbulent boundary layers behave three-dimensionally and it is necessary for engineers and scientists to predict their behaviour and, if possible, make calculations of skin friction, pressure drop, etc. for these more complicated flows. It is therefore necessary to advance our knowledge in this direction. In this paper it is proposed to confine the main part of the discussion to the type of three-dimensional turbulent boundary layers which have large angles of yaw and are found, for example, on the end walls of curved internal flow passages of rectangular cross-section.

References p. 226

2. PAST WORK

There have been two general lines of approach to the problem of yawed turbulent boundary layers.

(1) The first approach involves representation of the main-flow and the cross-flow components by some general polynominal Pohlhausen-type functions. The boundary conditions at the wall and the edge of the layer are satisfied and the results fed into the equations of motion to predict the boundary layer development.

Prandtl (1946) was an early worker in this field and his model was the three-dimensional counterpart of the power-law approach to two-dimensional boundary layers. His approach has been extended using momentum-integral equations, and the results of other workers using these techniques are referred to in the review by Cooke (1963).

This approach has not met with much success. Too many unchecked assumptions need to be made.

(2) The second approach has been confined mainly to a study of the velocity profile and attempts to describe it in terms of fundamental parameters such as wall shear stress, pressure distribution, fluid properties and boundary layer thickness.

Coles (1956) extended his own model for two-dimensional flow to the three-dimensional case and proposed that

$$\frac{u}{U_\tau} = f\left(\frac{zU_\tau}{\nu}\right) + \pi \cdot W\left(\frac{z}{\delta}\right)$$

where f is the logarithmic law of the wall, W is Coles' universal wake function, and π is a vector function of x and y. That is, the profile is made up of the vector addition of two plane profiles having the shape of the logarithmic law of the wall and of the wake function respectively.

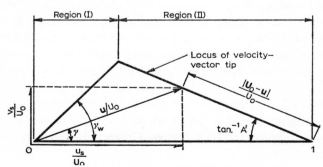

Figure 1. Johnston's triangular model.

(3) Johnston (1960) proposed a model, based on his own experimental results and those of Gruschwitz (1935) and Kuethe, McKee & Curry (1949), which specifies that in a polar plot of the mean-velocity profile (velocity vs. yaw angle γ), the tip of the velocity vector follows two straight lines (see figures 1 and 2).

The results of Mager (1952), and Squire & Winter (1951) were used by Johnston to show that a parameter A' was related to the free-stream turning angle α' by the relation,

$$A' = -2\alpha'$$

where $v_s/U_0 = A'(1-u_s/U_0)$

and $\quad v_s \quad$ = component of boundary layer velocity normal to u_s

$\quad u_s \quad$ = component of boundary layer velocity in direction of U_0

$\quad U_0 \quad$ = main-stream velocity magnitude.

He also suggested that the vertex of his triangle was within the viscous region.

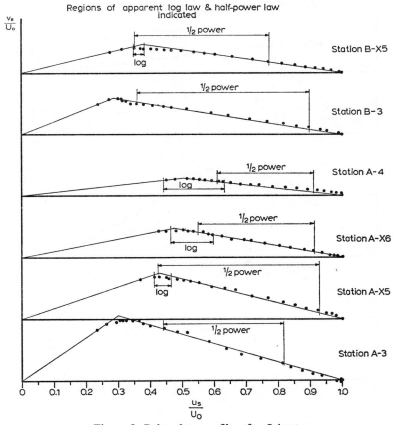

Figure 2. Polar plots, profiles after Johnston.

Johnston was the first worker to measure pressure distributions and to attempt to evaluate the wall shear stress.

(4) Hornung & Joubert (1963) carried out a detailed experimental investigation of the three-dimensional boundary layer using a slightly different configuration to that of Johnston. They used the pressure field generated by a circular cylinder standing upright on a flat plate as the means for yawing the fully turbulent two-dimensional boundary layer which had developed over the plate. A typical plot of the velocity vectors is shown in figure 3 and it is seen that the triangular model of Johnston is confirmed by these experimental results up to yaw angles of 60°. The dependence of the defect direction (i.e. parameter A') on the turning angle α' as proposed by Johnston was found to be true only for small values of A'. The value of

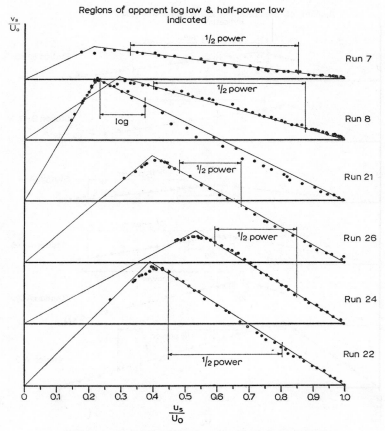

Figure 3. Polar plots, profiles after Hornung & Joubert.

zU_τ/v at the vertex of the triangle was found to range up to 150 whereas Johnston gave the highest value as about 16.

It was also proposed that the "law of the wall" applies to three-dimensional boundary layers in the same form as it does to two-dimensional layers up to the point where the boundary layer becomes yawed.

The model proposed by Coles did not apply to flow of the kind investigated in this experiment. It was thought that Coles' model might apply when the flow is subjected to a transverse pressure field right from the beginning of the layer such as in the experiments of Kuethe, McKee & Curry.

(5) Perry & Joubert (1965) were looking for some simple universality of the mean-velocity profiles and some general facts which could be stated about them. The paper was confined to the situation where an incompressible, fully developed, two-dimensional boundary layer underwent a sudden yawing which could be large. This situation is exemplified by the experiments of Johnston and Hornung & Joubert. The paper was divided into two parts, the first dealing with the outer flow and the second with the inner flow.

For the outer flow it was shown by a first-approximation analysis that the triangular model of Johnston was mainly a consequence of the geometry of the apparatus used. Further, it was shown that the outer part of the profile could be described by a single vector-similarity defect equation.

As mentioned by Taylor (1959), the linearised inviscid analyses of Squire & Winter and of Hawthorne (1951) appear to be valid only for small angles of turn α'. In Perry & Joubert's analysis however, an "inviscid boundary layer" approach has been used which is theoretically valid only for small velocity defects but applies to arbitrarily large values of α'. Experimental data appears to follow the theory over a larger range of velocity defects than might be expected from the analysis.

The flow close to the wall was treated as an equilibrium layer and using local similarity arguments developed by Townsend (1961) for two-dimensional layers, a three-dimensional version of the "law of the wall" was derived. The theory related the mean-velocity-vector distribution to the pressure-gradient vector and wall-shear-stress vector and explained how the profile skewed near the wall. When applied to two-dimensional layers the general expression simplified to agree with Townsend's equations.

This analysis led to the idea that the significant quantity to deal with was not the distribution of the velocity magnitude but rather the length of arc on the curve of the Johnston plot. That is, the "developed" velocity distribution should be used. It should also be pointed out that in the view of the authors, the Johnston triangle is not really a triangle. Two sides are straight lines, while the region close to the wall only asymptotes to a straight line.

References p. 226

Subsequently the authors have had a few further thoughts and a further small experiment has been conducted. These will now be elaborated.

3. SIMILARITY DEFECT EQUATION

If an approaching two-dimensional velocity profile is yawed suddenly and only small boundary layer thickening occurs, a defect equation of the following form can be deduced:

$$\frac{U_0 - u}{U_\tau} = \left(\frac{U_{\tau_1}}{U_\tau}\right) \boldsymbol{\Pi}'(x, y) \, \phi\left(\frac{z}{\delta}\right) \tag{1}$$

This vector defect falls in one plane and corresponds to one side of the Johnston triangle. The quantities are shown in figure 4, and U_{τ_1} corresponds to the shear velocity of the upstream reference profile while U_τ is the local shear velocity of the profile in question. Some general statements can be made about the various terms in the equation.

The vector $\boldsymbol{\Pi}'$ is influenced only by the free-stream velocity field and is governed by differential equations which have been derived. The function $\phi(z/\delta)$ corresponds to the defect distribution of the upstream profile, i.e. $(U_\infty - U_1)/U_{\tau_1}$, and the effects of surface roughness and fluid viscosity enter through the variable U_{τ_1}/U_τ.

The form of equation (1) has been verified to some extent by comparing the velocity defects at the same values of z/δ for all profiles with an arbitrarily chosen reference profile. For the method of plotting adopted, straight lines should result and these are shown in figure 5 for the experimental results of Hornung & Joubert.

The experimental results of Johnston (1957) have now been analysed in this way by the authors and the result is shown in figure 6. Good agreement can be seen. It

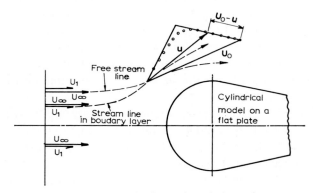

Figure 4. Definitions of symbols used.

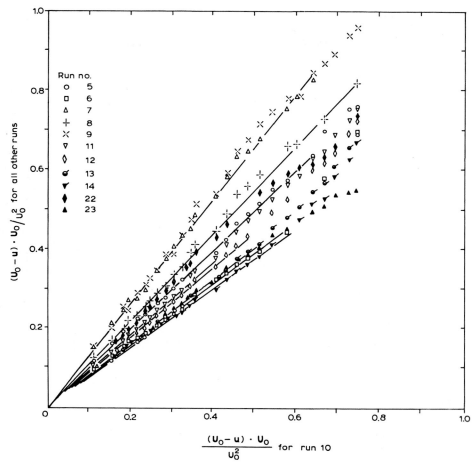

Figure 5. Comparison of velocity defects for the same values of z. Profiles after Hornung & Joubert. (δ remained constant.)

should be pointed out, however, that the boundary layer thickness δ was chosen carefully to ensure that the lines went through the origin in figure 6. This thickness corresponded to about 99.5 % of the free-stream velocity; as is well known, δ is a rather unsatisfactory concept.

An experiment was devised to test the assumption that the approaching profile needed to be two-dimensional to produce a plane defect law. The model of Hornung & Joubert was used but the upstream reference profile was distorted transversely. A hill was built on one side of the flat plate on which the boundary layer was developing. A photograph of the experimental arrangement is shown in figure 7.

References p. 226

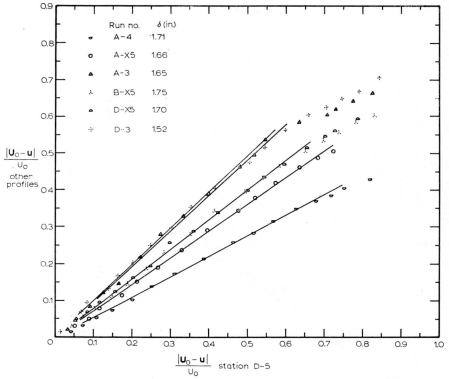

Figure 6. Comparison of vector velocity defects for the same values of z/δ. Profiles after Johnston.

A few typical Johnston plots resulting from this experiment are shown in figure 8 and it can be seen that a plane defect region does not appear to be valid.

4. WALL FLOW

Recent experimental and theoretical work carried out by A. E. Perry on two-dimensional layers in adverse pressure gradients show results which cast serious doubts on the assumptions involved in arriving at the three-dimensional law of the wall. The assumption most seriously affected is that momentum transport depends on a local gradient-type diffusion mechanism (the Boussinesq concept). This difficulty has been overcome for two-dimensional layers by the use of what could be referred to as "regional similarity" arguments. A paper along these lines is under preparation. The regional similarity analysis will also be found in a paper by Perry, Bell & Joubert (1966).

Figure 7. Hill on the flat plate in the University of Melbourne wind tunnel and located upstrea
of cylindrical model. View is in downstream direction.

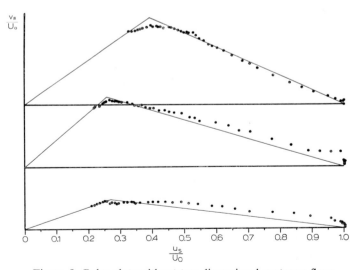

Figure 8. Polar plots without two-dimensional upstream flows.

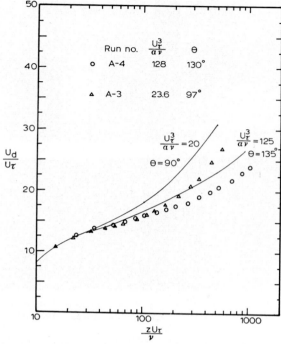

Figure 9. Comparison of Perry & Joubert's wall equation with profiles of Johnston.

In these above papers it is assumed that beyond the viscous sublayer, relative motions are independent of viscosity. For regions close to the wall, the relative motions are dependent on τ_0 while $(1/\rho)(dp/dx)$ has no influence. This enables the logarithmic law of the wall to be deduced. Further from the wall, a different flow structure exists where relative motions are independent of τ_0 but depend on $(1/\rho)(dp/dx)$. This enables the half-power law to be deduced. The two regions have velocity profiles expressible respectively as

$$\frac{u}{U_\tau} = \frac{1}{\varkappa} \ln\left(\frac{zU_\tau}{v}\right) + A - \frac{\Delta u_2}{U_\tau}\left(\frac{kU_\tau}{v}\right) \tag{2}*$$

$$\frac{u}{U_\tau} = K\left(\frac{\alpha z}{U_\tau^2}\right)^{\frac{1}{2}} + \frac{\Delta u_1}{U_\tau}\left(\frac{U_\tau^3}{\alpha v}\right) - \frac{\Delta u_2}{U_\tau}\left(\frac{kU_\tau}{v}\right) \tag{3}*$$

where $\alpha = (1/\rho)(dp/dx)$ and K is a universal constant. For sufficiently large values of $U_\tau^3/\alpha v$ the function $\Delta u_1/U_\tau$ (the slip function) is given by

* The brackets after $\dfrac{\Delta u_1}{U_\tau}$ and $\dfrac{\Delta u_2}{U_\tau}$ denote a functional dependence.

$$\frac{\Delta u_1}{U_\tau} = \frac{1}{\varkappa} \ln \left(\frac{C U_\tau^3}{\alpha v} \right) + A \qquad (4)$$

The function $\Delta u_2 / U_\tau$ is a roughness function and k is the scale of roughness.

If $\varkappa = 0.41$, $A = 5.1$, $C = 0.19$ and $K = 4.16$, then experimental data of two-dimensional layers from a wide variety of sources correlate quite well with these equations. Some of the sources are Schubauer & Klebanoff (1951), Perry & Joubert (1963) (who tested a rough wall) and Bell (1965). Also, mean-flow inertia forces near the wall do not seem to affect the results significantly provided the boundary layer is sufficiently thick.

An interesting point is that the logarithmic law of the wall appears to join on to the half-power law (equation (3)) almost tangentially and this occurs at $\alpha z / U_\tau^2 = 1.41$. Townsend's theory on the other hand gives a result which is asymptotic to the log law (equation (2)) at low values of $\alpha z / U_\tau^2$ and asymptotic to the half-power law at large values of $\alpha z / U_\tau^2$, with a large blending region between the laws. The assumed

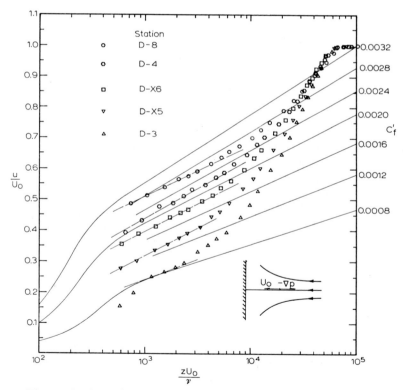

Figure 10. Plane-of-symmetry profiles after Johnston on Clauser's chart.

mechanism adopted by Townsend may have been too restrictive since only one adjustable constant appears in the theory. A relationship exists between K and C which prevents the theory from fitting the data. The authors have used the combination of $K=4.16$ and $C=0.19$; for $K=4.16$, Townsend's equation requires $C=0.80$. Also the theory implies that the half-power law is applicable only to layers close to separation, while data examined to date shows that it has a wider application.

The original wall theory of Perry & Joubert for three-dimensional layers has now been compared with the experimental data of Johnston and poor correlation was found. This comparison is shown in figure 9 for two typical profiles. Inaccuracies in pressure-gradient measurements do not explain the discrepancy completely. The current thoughts of the authors are that the use of regional similarity concepts may be more fruitful and preliminary attempts at correlation have been made along

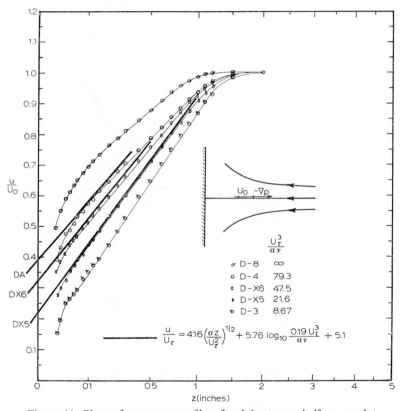

Figure 11. Plane-of-symmetry profiles after Johnston on half-power plot.

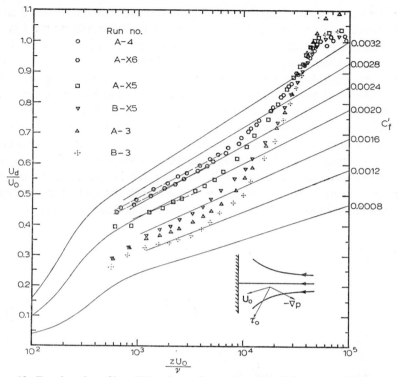

Figure 12. Developed profiles off the plane-of-symmetry after Johnston on Clauser's chart.

these lines. One assumption in the original analysis which will be retained is that the developed velocity profile is the significant one with which to work.

One result obtained from regional similarity arguments applied to two-dimensional layers is that if the parameter $U_\tau^3/\alpha v$ is less than 20 (very strong adverse pressure gradients), no logarithmic law exists and that the half-power law joins onto the viscous zone. Also, for $U_\tau^3/\alpha v$ less than 20 equation (4) is no longer applicable, while for $U_\tau^3/\alpha v$ approaching zero another law can be deduced (see Stratford (1959) who considered layers with zero wall-shear-stress). Johnston's three-dimensional layers have been examined in the light of these findings. It was found that for the profiles along the plane of symmetry a logarithmic law existed provided the above criterion was satisfied, and the profiles fitted reasonably well on the Clauser chart. When $U_\tau^3/\alpha v$ was less than 20, a dip in the profile occurred (see later; figures 11 and 13) and no sensible log law resulted. These profiles are shown in figure 10. It is believed that some of the profiles of Hornung & Joubert also fit into this scheme provided one carefully chooses which part of the profile is logarithmic and which is not. The authors may have been choosing the wrong region in past work.

References p. 226

The pressure gradient along the axis of symmetry in Johnston's experiment could be calculated with reasonable accuracy and the resulting half-power law, using constants from two-dimensional layers, was compared with these results. The comparison is shown in figure 11 and agreement is encouraging.

The same general behaviour was found for the skewed boundary layers of Johnston provided the developed profiles were used. The Clauser-chart plots are shown in figure 12. The value of α was rather difficult to determine accurately off the plane of symmetry and so the slope of the linear region of the profiles on a half-power plot was adopted to determine α. These values compared reasonably well with the magnitude of $(1/\rho)\nabla p$ although the authors suspect that for these skewed layers some component of this quantity should really be used. The resulting half-power law and slip function agreed reasonably well for these profiles provided $U_\tau^3/\alpha v$ was greater than 20. These results are shown in figure 13. However the slip

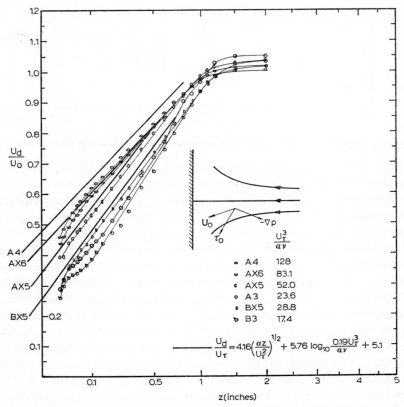

Figure 13. Developed profiles off the plane-of-symmetry after Johnston on half-power plot.

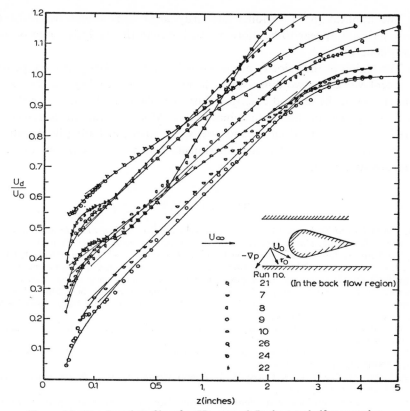

Figure 14. Developed profiles after Hornung & Joubert on half-power plot.

function is consistently low (approximately 5–10%). It is conjectured that either more slip occurred at the wall than is indicated by the Johnston triangles or else the effect of skewing was to reduce the slip. However the data is not sufficiently accurate to warrant further theorising on this point.

Hornung & Joubert's profiles have been plotted on a half-power chart and extensive linear regions can be seen in figure 14. However the authors have not as yet calculated the slip function or checked the slopes because of the difficulties in obtaining reliable values of ∇p from the experimental contours of static pressure.

5. CONCLUSIONS

(1) Further analysis of data confirms the similarity defect in the form proposed by Perry & Joubert provided the necessary features of the flow are fulfilled.

References p. 226

(2) The application of regional similarity arguments found from the two-dimensional case appear to be more promising than the analysis based on eddy-viscosity concepts.

(3) The region of the velocity profiles which shows similarity of the type found from recent work on two-dimensional layers extends well beyond the skewing region. However, the method described fails to explain the skewing near the wall.

(4) Existing experimental data is inadequate. More accurate measurements are required of pressure distribution and wall shear stress, including its direction. It might be wise to carry out more experiments before any extensions of present theories are attempted.

REFERENCES

Bell, J. (1965) *Forced Turbulent Convective Heat Transfer from a Flat Plate in Adverse Pressure Gradients*. M. Eng. Sc. Thesis, University of Melbourne (in course of preparation).

Coles, D. (1956) *The Law of the Wake in the Turbulent Boundary Layer*. J. Fluid Mech. **1**, 191–226.

Cooke, J. C. (1963) *Three-Dimensional Turbulent Boundary Layers*. Aero. Res. Counc. C.P. 635.

Gruschwitz, E. (1935) *Turbulente Reibungsschichten mit Sekundärströmungen*. Ing. Arch. **6**, 355–65.

Hawthorne, W. R. (1951) *Secondary Circulation in Fluid Flow*. Proc. Roy. Soc. **206**, 374–87.

Hornung, H. G. & Joubert, P. N. (1963) *The Mean Velocity Profile in Three-Dimensional Turbulent Boundary Layers*. J. Fluid Mech. **15**, 368–84.

Johnston, J. P. (1957) *Three-Dimensional Turbulent Boundary Layer*. Sc. D. Thesis, Massachusetts Institute of Technology.

Johnston, J. P. (1960) *On the Three-Dimensional Boundary Layer Generated by Secondary Flow*. Trans. ASME, Series D, **82**, 233–48.

Kuethe, A. M., McKee, P. G. & Curry, W. H. (1949) *Measurements in the Boundary Layer of a Yawed Wing*. NACA T.N. 1946.

Mager, A. (1952) *Generalisation of Boundary Layer Momentum Integral Equations to Three-Dimensional Flows Including those of Rotating Systems*. NACA Report 1067.

Perry, A. E., Bell, J. B. & Joubert, P. N. (1966) *Velocity and Temperature Profiles in Adverse-Pressure-Gradient Turbulent Boundary Layers*. J. Fluid Mech. (to be published).

Perry, A. E. & Joubert, P. N. (1963) *Rough-Wall Boundary Layers in Adverse Pressure Gradients*. J. Fluid Mech. **17**, 193–211.

Perry, A. E. & Joubert, P. N. (1965) *A Three-Dimensional Turbulent Boundary Layer*. J. Fluid Mech. **22**, 285–304.

Prandtl, L. (1946) *On Boundary Layers in Three-Dimensional Flow*. M. A. P. Volkenrode (Rep. and Trans. 64).

Schubauer, G. B. & Klebanoff, P. S. (1951) *Investigation of Separation of the Turbulent Boundary Layer*. NACA Rep. 1030.

Squire, H. B. & Winter, K. G. (1951) *The Secondary Flow in a Cascade of Airfoils in a Non-Uniform Stream*. J. Aero. Sci. **18**, 271–7.

Stratford, B. S. (1959) *The Prediction of Separation of the Turbulent Boundary Layer*. J. Fluid Mech. **5**, 1–16.

Taylor, E. S. (1959) *The Skewed Boundary Layer*. Trans. ASME, Series D, **81**, 297–304.

Townsend, A. A. (1961) *Equilibrium Layers and Wall Turbulence*. J. Fluid Mech. **11**, 97–120.

Discussion

E. A. EICHELBRENNER (*Laval University, Quebec, Canada*)

I would like to comment on a generalization of Johnston's triangular plot that we have made jointly at the Universities of Syracuse (New York) and Poitiers (France). In certain flow circumstances, we observed at Syracuse that the crossflow above certain points of the surface of a three-dimensional body could change sign (figure 15). The data of Hansen & Herzig and the theoretical considerations of laminar flow by Cooke have previously indicated such a phenomenon. In three-dimensional laminar and—as experiments in Poitiers showed—turbulent flow, the crossflow velocity does not always have the same sign but may have one or even more changes in sign at a given point. In a thesis at Syracuse, Shanebrook showed that this happens downstream of an inflection point on the streamlines of the outer

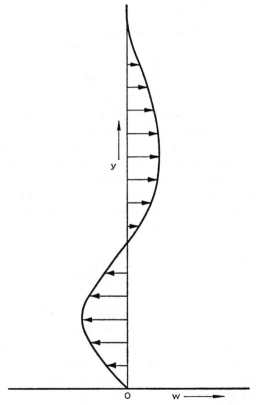

Figure 15. Reversal of the crossflow velocity in a turbulent, three-dimensional boundary layer.

flow around the body. This condition is a necessary but not a sufficient condition, because a well-developed strong crossflow will resist the action of a reversed transverse pressure gradient after the inflection point.

Now, in the case which Prof. Joubert investigated there is a very heavily skewed flow inside the boundary layer upstream of the cylinder, but the inflection point of the outer-flow streamlines only occurs downstream of the region of observation. A change in the sign of the crossflow velocity might not therefore have been noticed.

At Poitiers we studied the flow around an ellipsoid of revolution and a flattened ellipsoid at sufficiently large Reynolds number that natural transition took place in the first third of the body. The large Reynolds numbers were achieved by using bodies with an overall length of 6 feet and employing a tunnel speed of 150 to 180 ft/sec. Boundary layer separation occurred in the turbulent flow region and on the rear part of the body. Consequently, there was a very extended region of attached turbulent flow where the outer-flow streamlines had an inflection point. This made it possible to experimentally find crossflow-velocity profiles of the multiple-sign type a little above the flank of the ellipsoids at approximately two-thirds of their length. The question of interest was, how far could Johnston's triangular scheme be conserved in this case and what would be the correct profile parameter to use?

The experimental results, partly reproduced in AGARDOgraph 97 (AGARD meeting on "Recent Developments in Boundary Layer Research", Naples, May 1965), indicated the following fact: The curvature, $\partial^2 (w/u_e)/\partial(u/u_e)^2$, of Johnston's "polar" plot (crossflow w/u_e versus longitudinal flow u/u_e) is—to the degree of precision of the measurements—equal to zero at the outer edge of the boundary layer and at the wall not only for single-signed crossflow-velocity profiles but for multi-signed ones as well. Conserving these conditions, we can express w/u_e in the form of a 5th degree polynomial as a function of u/u_e, with the other conditions being $w/u_e = 0$ at the wall and at the outer edge. The two parameters are B (the tangent of the polar-plot angle at the wall) and C (the tangent of the polar's angle at the outer edge, called A by Johnston).

One of these two parameters may be left unknown to be determined by a global condition; the other has to be determined by the outer flow. The latter parameter should be C since it is prescribed by conditions at the outer edge; the problem is to express it along a curved surface in a curvilinear coordinate system like the one introduced by Hayes (1952) in his famous NAVORD Report number 1313.

The problem can indeed be solved and the solution is given in the previously mentioned AGARDOgraph 97. It is based on the following considerations:

If we accept the Navier–Stokes equations as they appear after application of Prandtl's simplifications, we may try to make a limiting process towards the outer edge of the boundary layer for

$$C = \frac{w}{u - u_e} = \frac{\partial w/\partial n}{\partial u/\partial n} = \frac{\partial^2 w/\partial n^2}{\partial^2 u/\partial n^2} = \frac{\partial^3 w/\partial n^3}{\partial^3 u/\partial n^3}$$

after having isolated numerator and denominator, respectively, from the transverse and longitudinal momentum equation. This limit can be executed and leads to a differential equation for C, with respect to the coordinate s along streamlines of the outer flow, which has the form

$$\frac{\partial C}{\partial s} = C \left(\frac{1}{u_e} \frac{\partial u_e}{\partial s} - \frac{1}{e_2} \frac{\partial e_2}{\partial s} \right) + \frac{2}{e_1} \frac{\partial e_1}{\partial z}$$

e_1 and e_2 being scale factors from Hayes' curvilinear coordinate system and given with the outer flow. C may thus be obtained by integration of this equation along outer streamlines (using a simple quadrature) when the outer flow is given and if Prandtl's simplifications hold.

The outer flow is well-known in the case of ellipsoids and the corresponding C has been calculated at Poitiers by Bernard. It is tempting to try an experimental determination of C and compare it with the calculated values, in particular for the case of crossflow profiles with changes in sign; such a change of sign is indicated by a change in the sign of C.

This is even of philosophical interest: If the calculated result is confirmed by the tests, everything is fine and B can then be determined from the global crossflow equation. If the calculation is *not* confirmed, the only reason for this failure must reside in Prandtl's assumptions. In this case it would have been proved that a second-order approximation of the turbulent boundary layer would be required in three-dimensional flow!

A conclusion could not be reached using the ellipsoids because of the relative weakness of the crossflow on the geometries considered. The skewness angle inside the boundary layers was only of the order of ± 3 to ± 5 degrees. Even careful measurements of such angles can easily give a wrong sign; as a matter of fact, a small error in the positioning of the traversing gear with respect to a normal to the local body surface is sufficient to cause a change in sign. To resolve the question, it would be necessary to make crossflow measurements in more heavily skewed configurations, such as those considered by Prof. Joubert, but farther downstream of inflection points on the outer-flow streamlines. I wanted to make this comment in order to ask Prof. Joubert whether his group has observed such changes in sign and, if so, how they envisaged taking the presence of such a phenomenon into account in their theory.

P. N. JOUBERT
    The answer is no.

J. P. JOHNSTON (*Stanford University, Stanford, California*)

I would like to speak briefly on heavily skewed flows. I have prepared slides of some polar plots which demonstrate that there is quite a variety of shapes, other than a simple triangle, for the polar plot. Some of the slides were made from Prof. Eichelbrenner's report with his permission. They show, in addition to the data, curves generated from his fitting formula; the formula gives a very good representation, in my opinion, of the variation of w with respect to u in the peak region of these polar plots. Consider the first figure (figure 16) which shows some data from Poitiers. It shows that his formula gives a good fit to the data for weakly skewed flows. The next figure (figure 17) gives profiles from Gruschwitz's developing boundary layer on a channel wall; the skewing goes from very small to very large. The formula appears to fit this data quite well, much better I think, than the straight-line triangular fit. The next figure (figure 18) shows the data of Kuethe *et al.* for moderate skewing. Finally, figure 19 presents some of my own data fitted with Prof. Eichelbrenner's formula. Here, as in Kuethe's data, the cases with heaviest skew demonstrate that the fitting formula works quite nicely in the region of the peak, but not too well in the outer region of the layer. Furthermore, the formula doesn't, in these cases, correspond to Joubert's outer-flow model.

The next figure (figure 20) is a selection of some data by Gardow (obtained at the

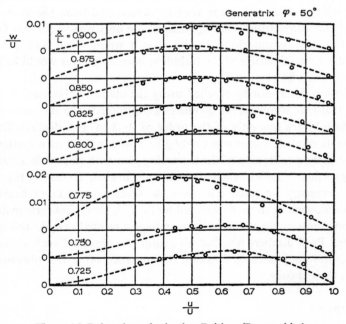

Figure 16. Polar plots obtained at Poitiers (Bousgarbies).

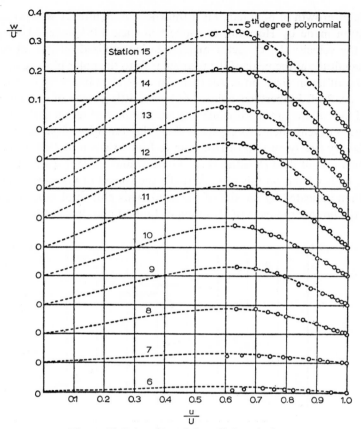

Figure 17. Polar plots of data of Gruschwitz.

M.I.T. Gas Turbine Lab) that has not been analyzed by Prof. Eichelbrenner. It is an interesting set of data which should, I believe, be used more extensively by people working in this area. Gardow's data is for a turbulent boundary layer on one wall of an axisymmetric, vaneless diffuser with swirling inlet flow. The sample shown represents six profiles taken at increasing radial distance as you go from number 1 to number 6 (about equally spaced in radius as you march out through the diffuser). They indicate that skewing becomes very heavy, very early in the diffuser, but then stays at about the same magnitude as you move further out in radius. Also note that the tip of the polar triangle rounds as you go out. The viscous effects seem to propagate out through the layer from the wall and restrain the excess overturning of the flow.

Now, I think, we can see something about the history effect in skewed turbulent boundary layers; that is, the effects of history on rate-of-growth of skew as compared to rate-of-growth of boundary layer thickness, δ. Figure 21 was prepared from a suggestion made by Hornung & Joubert in their 1963 paper. They suggested plotting the velocity defect-vector magnitude, normalized on the velocity defect-vector magnitude at the peak of the triangular fit to the polar plot, against distance from the wall normalized on δ. All their data correlate in a very narrow band on this plot. As Prof. Joubert has pointed out here, little growth of δ occurred in their layer and thus all the profiles became very heavily skewed rather early in the history of the layer's development. As expected, from the similarity of our experiments, my data falls very nearly on that of Hornung & Joubert when plotted in this manner. Three other sets of data (Kuethe *et al.*, Gardow and Jansen) scatter throughout a different, higher band on this plot. Actually the spread of Gardow's data is much smaller than indicated by the size of the band. This plot emphasizes the difference between the boundary layers of Hornung & Joubert and those of Kuethe, Gardow

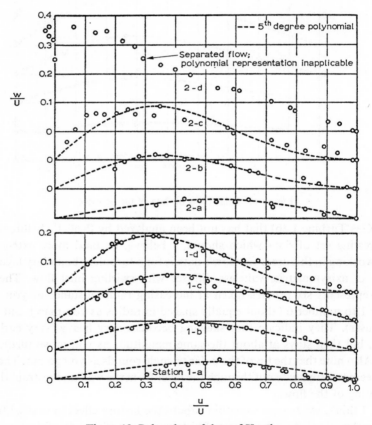

Figure 18. Polar plots of data of Kuethe.

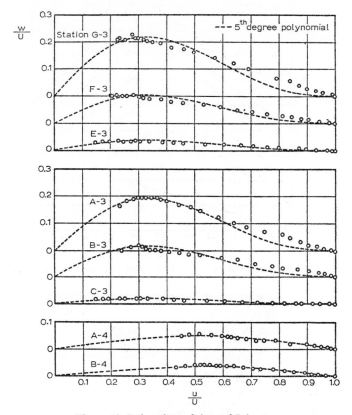

Figure 19. Polar plots of data of Johnston.

and Jansen which have substantial growth of layer thickness with only moderate or no change of skew in the downstream direction. The Gruschwitz band falls between the others. Physically it is an intermediate case since the flow starts with no skewing, and has steady growth of both skewing and thickness in the downstream direction. The bottom line of the Gruschwitz band corresponds to the upstream profile, where the skewing is very small; the top line of the band corresponds to his downstream profile, where the skewing is large and the layer has grown considerably thicker. In conclusion, it is felt that this type of plot may help to characterize, at least qualitatively, the skewing and growth history of a particular three-dimensional turbulent boundary layer.

References

Bousgarbies, J. L. (1963), Thesis, Université de Poitiers.

Eichelbrenner, E. A. (1963) *Theoretical Investigation and Control by Measuring Tests on the Behavior of the Three-Dimensional Turbulent Boundary Layer on an Annular Wing at Various*

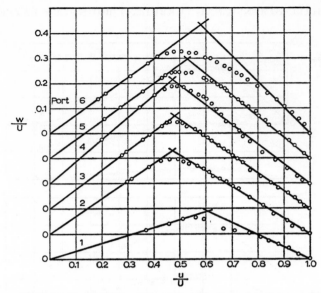

Figure 20. Polar plots of data of Gardow. Velocity polar plots run B-59.6.

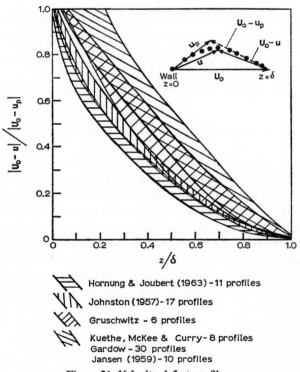

Hornung & Joubert (1963) - 11 profiles

Johnston (1957) - 17 profiles

Gruschwitz - 6 profiles

Kuethe, McKee & Curry - 8 profiles
Gardow - 30 profiles
Jansen (1959) - 10 profiles

Figure 21. Velocity-defect profiles.

Incidences. Final Report Sept. 15, 1963 to ONR, Air Programs Branch, Washington, D.C.

Gardow, E. B. (1958) *The Three-Dimensional Turbulent Boundary Layer in a Free Vortex Diffuser*. M.S. Thesis, Mass. Inst. of Tech.; also M.I.T. Gas Turbine Lab. Rep. No. 42.

Gruschwitz, E. (1935) *Turbulente Reibungsschichten mit Sekundärströmungen*. Ing. Arch. **6**, 355–65.

Hornung, H. G. & Joubert, P. N. (1963) *The Mean Velocity Profile in Three-Dimensional Turbulent Boundary Layers*. J. Fluid Mech. **15**, 368–84.

Jansen, W. (1959) *Incompressible Fluid Flow in a Radial Vaneless Diffuser*. M.I.T. Gas Turbine Lab. Rep. No. 52.

Johnston, J. P. (1957) *Three-Dimensional Turbulent Boundary Layer*. Sc.D. Thesis, Mass. Inst. of Tech.; also M.I.T. Gas Turbine Lab. Rep. No. 39.

Kuethe, A. M. McKee, P. B. & Curry, W. H. (1949) *Measurements in the Boundary Layer of a Yawed Wing*. NACA Tech. Note 1946.

E. S. TAYLOR (*Massachusetts Institute of Technology, Cambridge, Massachusetts*)

The report of Gardow that Prof. Johnston referred to is available at the Gas Turbine Laboratory.

I just have a couple of remarks. One of them is on the universality of the triangle in the polar plot. If you look in Schlichting's book you will find a solution by Bödewadt for the problem of a semi-infinite fluid rotating with wheel-type rotation

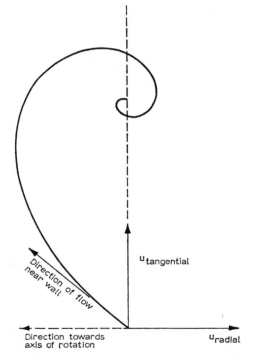

Figure 22. Polar plot of velocities in a swirling laminar flow with wheel-type rotation near a stationary wall, after Bödewadt.

against a stationary plane. This laminar flow has a rather interesting polar plot (figure 22). Now you may think that this particular polar plot is just a mathematical solution of an idealized problem, but while working on the movie Secondary Flow we took some pictures of a situation somewhat similar to that studied by Bödewadt. We had a rotating tank which was rotated for a long time to get wheel-type rotation of the fluid inside it; we then stopped the tank and looked at the velocity profiles. They were not altogether steady, but if you picked an appropriate

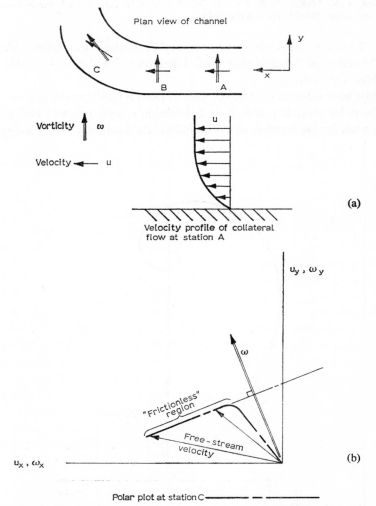

Figure 23. (a) Boundary layer flow on the end wall of a curved, two-dimensional channel; (b) Polar plot of the boundary layer.

velocity profile it almost exactly fitted Bödewadt's polar form. Unfortunately, calculations indicated a discrepancy of about 4 in the z-direction. I have been unable to resolve this discrepancy. Nevertheless, this spiral form of the polar certainly occurs and therefore the triangular plot is, as you would expect, not exactly universal.

In making the movie, I also ran across a sufficient condition for the part of the polar plot which represents the outer part of the boundary layer to lie on a straight line. Assume we have a flow in a straight channel which has developed a boundary layer on the bottom; assume further that the straight part of the channel is followed by a bend. The situation is as in figure 23a. The flow entering the bend then has horizontal vorticity perpendicular to the streamlines. If we assume the flow is inviscid, and that vertical velocities are negligible, the vortex lines (which are fluid lines) must turn opposite to the streamlines, which are also fluid lines, to preserve zero vertical vorticity. With a little manipulation it is not difficult to show that under these conditions the polar plot must appear as a straight line perpendicular to the vorticity vector (figure 23b). Very near the wall the frictionless assumption is very poor. Because of local friction, the part of the polar plot representing the inner part of the boundary layer departs from the straight line and must pass through zero at the wall.

If you consider a collateral boundary layer flowing around a bend, you will always get a straight-line polar plot of the outer (essentially frictionless) part of the layer. This is similar to what actually happened in Johnston's original experiment; however, it is not very similar to what happens in flow over an ellipsoid and therefore you wouldn't expect it to follow necessarily in that case.

J. H. HORLOCK (*University of Liverpool, England*)

I am very surprised that the angle A' in the polar plots is twice the turning angle. This is really just a statement of the Squire & Winter secondary vorticity if you neglect the variation in the flow normal to the main streamlines. I would have thought that this is not a very good approximation in the Johnston experiments and in the flow around the cylinder. My second point is just a statement of experimental fact. We have put a flat plate perpendicular to the axis of a free-vortex flow where the streamlines are circular; there is no pressure gradient along the streamlines, but there is a strong pressure gradient across the streamlines. In this case, the Johnston plot doesn't look so good and the Cooke plot looks very much better.

H. W. EMMONS (*Harvard University, Cambridge, Massachusetts*)

I want to thank the author very much for this careful consideration of the accumulated experimental data and an attempt to make some sense out of where three-dimensional boundary layers are headed.

The Applicability of Secondary Flow Analyses to the Solution of Internal Flow Problems

W. R. HAWTHORNE

Cambridge University, Cambridge, England

SUMMARY

The value of inviscid flow theory in internal aerodynamics is greater than may at first sight appear. In the flow through compressors and turbines, round bends and through screens there are large regions in which the flow, although non-uniform, may be assumed to be frictionless. This paper divides the approximate solutions to the problem of three-dimensional, inviscid, steady flow into three types. First there are problems in which the disturbance and the gradient of stagnation pressure (or shear) are both small. In this case the disturbance is shown to be an irrotational flow or, for a compressible perfect gas, a family of flows derivable from an irrotational flow. Examples include the shear flows upstream and downstream from a wire screen or row of blades. In the second type of approximation the disturbance is large, but the shear is small. It is shown that this flow consists of an irrotational primary flow convecting the vortex filaments, which in turn induce the secondary flow. Solutions have been applied to the flow in bends, cascades and around cylinders and spheres. In the third class the disturbance is small, but the shear is large. The disturbance is then a rotational flow superimposed on a primary rotational flow. This approximation is applicable to flow past thin airfoils and slender bodies, to cascades of small deflection and to flow through screens and blade rows when the shear is large.

Some experimental results are compared with the theories and the effects of viscosity are discussed. Experimental results from the flow in bends are used to illustrate the limitations of the linearising approximations described above.

NOTATION

A constant, gradient of velocity in simple shear flow
a radius of sphere, cylinder

b semi-width of channel
b $\sqrt{2C_pT_0}$
C_L local lift coefficient
C_{L0} lift coefficient in plane irrotational flow
C_p specific heat at constant pressure
c chord of airfoil
k ratio of specific heats
l semi-height of channel
p pressure
s $\frac{1}{2}$ shear layer thickness
s distance along streamline
T temperature (absolute)
t drift function $= \int \mathrm{d}s/V$ along a streamline
U upstream velocity
U' upstream velocity gradient
u velocity component (x)
V velocity
v velocity component (y)
W reduced velocity $= V/b$
w velocity component (z)
x Cartesian co-ordinate
y Cartesian co-ordinate, spanwise
z, Z Cartesian co-ordinate
α geometrical angle of attack
α angle between principal normal to streamline and normal to Bernoulli surface
θ angle of streamline
ρ density
ϕ scalar function (potential function)
ψ stream function
Ω vorticity

Subscripts
o stagnation conditions, initial conditions
s streamwise component

INTRODUCTION

A survey of the usefulness and promise of any part of the theory of fluid flow ought perhaps to start with a reminder of the objectives of any such theory. One such

References p. 263–265

objective is the aesthetic one—the satisfaction afforded by an enlightening description of some natural phenomenon. From the utilitarian point of view theories
are of greatest assistance when they can be used to optimize the design of engineering equipment. However, the degree of refinement with which such optimizations
can be performed, even with the assistance of well correlated experimental data, is
often disappointing to engineers designing equipment in which fluid mechanics
plays a significant role. In many instances the theory is incomplete and the theoretical procedures appear to be too complicated and their results too uncertain to
be worth the effort of a genuine process of optimization. On the other hand the use
of theory to interpret and correlate experimental data from which overall performance can be estimated, although a less ambitious objective, has been more useful,
even though the theoretical basis of such correlations is often no more complicated
than dimensional analysis.

One should not neglect the contribution made by theoretical analysis to the
understanding of new phenomena or in overcoming unexpected difficulties, not
the least of which are vibrational effects introduced by unsteadiness in the flow.
In fact many of the results of research in fluid mechanics which are of most value in
engineering, are those which offer a new insight into hitherto unexplained or un-
recognised effects and thereby give forewarning of likely troubles or suggest means
of overcoming them.

Our general understanding of the problems of internal flows has been growing
steadily in the last twenty years, but no one will claim that it has reached a great
degree of refinement. The development of computer programmes for use in the
design of turbo-machinery and for other flow equipment has in fact shown up the
unsatisfactory state of much of our knowledge, which too often lacks the precision
expected by the computer. The theoretical work which is the subject of this paper is
no exception, as this account of its present state will show.

The term secondary flow has been used to describe several different phenomena.
It was used by Prandtl (1952), Goldstein (1938) and others to describe the flow in
the corners of straight ducts of non-circular cross-section. This flow is transverse
to the axis of the duct and is caused by an asymmetry in the turbulent shear stresses
(this type of secondary flow does not occur when the flow regime is laminar). The
same authors also used the term to describe the spiralling flow in bent ducts and
pipes.

In his classical papers on the design of axial compressors Howell (1942) described
the losses near the ends of the blades, where the boundary layers on the walls of the
annulus flow through them, as secondary losses. The flow in these regions transverse to the mean flow, and at one time thought to be somewhat similar to the flow
behind the tips of aircraft wings, came to be known as secondary flow. A theory of
these flows was first introduced by Squire & Winter (1951) who showed that the

transverse flow could be accounted for by the presence of a velocity gradient in the flow approaching the blades. Although the velocity gradient in the flow approaching the cascade or bend is produced by frictional effects far upstream, the theory does not require the existence of shear stresses or friction to predict the secondary flow. It is in fact a theory of the rotational flow of an inviscid fluid and, as such, an application of classical hydrodynamic theory. Because of the presence of vorticity it is inevitable that non-trivial exact solutions of three-dimensional flows of this kind are virtually unattainable, and approximate methods are necessary. As we shall see later, Squire & Winter's method is one such approximation suited particularly to the flow in bent ducts. Lighthill (1957a) has discussed the relation between Squire & Winter's approximation and other approximate solutions to inviscid rotational flow problems, of which one presented by von Kármán & Tsien (1945) for the flow of a sheared parallel stream over an aerofoil represented by a lifting line is an important historical example.

TRANSITION FLOWS

In external aerodynamics the use of the concept of the boundary layer as a thin region of viscous flow close to the walls of a body, which is immersed in an otherwise inviscid fluid, has been so successful that it is only natural that every effort should be made to make the same approach in internal aerodynamics. At first sight this possibility is not promising. In flows bounded by walls, as for instance in long, straight pipes, the region of flow affected by viscosity covers the entire width of the passage and there is no region in which viscous or turbulent shear stresses may be neglected. However on closer examination of practical problems of interest to the engineer it becomes apparent, especially in equipment in which there is a premium on weight and space, that there are many cases in which the frictional effects of the walls may not extend far into the flow. For instance at the entry to a straight pipe there is a transition region of considerable length in which there is a gradual growth of boundary layer on the walls. In the flow through a cascade of turbine or compressor blades there is a characteristic boundary layer development on the blades. In pipe bends the influence of the walls only gradually extends inwards as the flow passes round the bend. More than 360 degrees of pipe bend may be required to establish fully developed curved flow, i.e. the equivalent in a continuous bend of fully developed flow in a straight pipe (Hawthorne 1963), and in most equipment the bends and pipes do not normally extend so far. Hence the value of inviscid flow theory and of boundary layer theory in internal aerodynamics may be greater than at first sight appears, largely because the flow in steam and gas turbines, internal combustion engines and their associated equipment is rarely "fully developed".

References p. 263–265

It almost always consists of a turbulent non-uniform flow leaving one part of an apparatus and entering another. This type of flow may be described as entry or transition flow. It occurs for example when fluid passes from a straight pipe into a bend or from a bend into a straight pipe, from an annular duct into a row of turbine nozzles, at entry to or exit from a bank of heat exchanger tubes. In another class of transition flows we may include the flow between rows of blades in compressors and turbines, in pump and compressor impellers, the flow between screens in the settling chamber of a wind tunnel, and the flow on either side of a flame front.

THEORETICAL APPROACHES

Our basic objective is to evaluate the usefulness of inviscid theory in internal aerodynamics. The first step is then to find inviscid solutions to the equations of motion which can be compared with experimental results. Unfortunately there are available only very few exact solutions of the inviscid flow equations, so that approximations are required. It turns out that more than one type of approximation is possible, so that before discussing the usefulness of the inviscid theory it will be necessary to examine the modes in which it has been used and the types of flow problems for which each mode is suited. For the sake of simplicity the discussion will be restricted to steady flows in the absence of body forces and either to incompressible fluids or to perfect gases. Fortunately these conditions are not too restrictive because there are many practical examples to which they may be applied.

For steady, compressible flow the inviscid assumption of classical theory is extended to include the assumption of negligible heat transfer or diffusion from one fluid particle to another. Hence all stagnation properties, i.e. stagnation enthalpy, temperature, pressure and density, remain constant along a streamline as does the entropy. We then find that it is possible to classify the approximate solutions in terms of the magnitude of the gradient of the stagnation pressure and the degree of disturbance of the flow from some known pattern. It should be noted that any variation of the stagnation temperature from one streamline to another has little effect, since the geometrical configuration of the streamlines of a steadily flowing perfect gas is dependent only on the stagnation pressure gradient and not on the stagnation temperature gradient.

In many examples the upstream flow, or the undisturbed flow pattern, is parallel, although such a restriction is by no means essential.

The approximate solutions may be divided into three types*:
(1) Flows with small shear, i.e. small stagnation-pressure gradient, and small disturbances from a known flow pattern

---

* Rotational flows with constant stagnation pressure, i.e. Beltrami flows, are a special case not included in this classification.

Shear	Disturbance	
	Small	Large
Small	1. Irrotational disturbance. Bernoulli surfaces undistorted. Flow through screens, actuator discs, and behind shocks. Viscous effects normal.	2. "Secondary flow approximation". Primary flow irrotational, convects Bernoulli surfaces. Flow in bends, cascades, about struts and spheres. Viscous effects close to wall and at blunt leading edges.
Large	3. Disturbance is rotational, Bernoulli surfaces are distorted. Flow about slender bodies, airfoils, through actuator discs. Flow distortion affects boundary layer.	4. Restricted two-dimensional and axisymmetric solutions. Flow past bodies and through actuator discs.

Figure 1. Scheme of approximate solutions to inviscid shear-flow problems.

(2) Flows with small shear but large disturbances

(3) Flows with large shear but small disturbances.

We note that there are

(4) A limited number of exact solutions for flows which are two-dimensional or axi-symmetrical.

A brief summary of the theory supporting these conclusions will be found in the Appendices.

A diagrammatic representation of these different approximations is given in figure 1.

Small-Shear, Small-Disturbance Flows

These flows fall into the category of the first and simplest approximation listed above. It may be shown that when the fluid density is constant all such flows consist of the known, undisturbed shear flow plus a disturbance flow *which is irrotational* (Hawthorne 1965). When the fluid is a compressible perfect gas the disturbance flow has the geometrical properties of an irrotational flow (Appendix II). The theoretical treatment of such flows is therefore comparatively simple. In many examples, such as for instance the flow about bodies and airfoils which must by assumption be slender and thin, the solutions are trivial being simple additions of well-known potential flows to the undisturbed shear flow. There are however several examples in which this simple inviscid flow theory has been found to be of more value.

In the flow through a wire screen, which is either intended to remove non-uniformities (variations in stagnation pressure) or to introduce shear, the use of this approximation to describe the flow on either side of the screen has shown good agreement with experimental results.* The screen is regarded as an actuator disc across which there is a pressure drop and a small change of flow direction. At the walls forming the boundaries of the flow there are, of course, viscous effects but the main portion of the flow is satisfactorily accounted for by the inviscid theory.

Another example of the use of this approximation together with an actuator disc assumption is in the flow through rows of compressor and turbine blades. It is assumed that the blade row consists of a large number of blades of very small chord and may be replaced by an actuator disc across which there is a change of stagnation pressure (and density when the flow is compressible) and a flow deflection. The theory is fully presented by Marble (1965). Hawthorne & Horlock (1962) and Hawthorne & Ringrose (1964) have presented experimental results which support the use of this approximation in the flow on either side of or between actuator discs representing the blade rows. In this case the undisturbed shear flow is a swirling annular flow to which is added the potential-flow disturbance caused by the changes introduced by the blade-row actuator disc.

This theory has also been applied to the flow across flame fronts (Hawthorne & Banks 1961), and there is no reason why it should not be used in determining the flow approaching and leaving heat exchanger matrices or honeycombs, although I have not been able to find experimental results supporting its usefulness in the literature.

Another application of this approximation is in the flow through shock waves. Examples, together with a review of small-perturbation theory in rotational compressible flow, are given by Sears (1954).

One of the features of this approximation is that the disturbance normally vanishes both upstream and downstream of the disturbing body. An exception is the case of a thin airfoil of finite span immersed in a weakly sheared flow, which will have the trailing vorticity associated with airfoils of finite span in an irrotational flow. Even in this case the disturbance does not alter the distribution of vorticity in the flow, which remains that in the undisturbed stream. In many practical examples of shear flows, therefore, this approximation does not predict the disturbances which have been found to extend far downstream from bodies of revolution, actuator discs, and bends nor the distortion of the shear-flow distribution associated with them.

The imperfections of the theory because it is inviscid are no greater than in corresponding attempts to use potential-flow theory in irrotational flow problems.

---

* References include: Taylor & Batchelor (1949), Elder (1959), G. de V. Davis (1963).

Small-Shear, Large-Disturbance Approximation

It can be shown that in this approximation the flow consists of a primary flow which is an irrotational flow satisfying the boundary conditions and which convects the vorticity found in the approaching shear flow. The vortex filaments are stretched and twisted by the primary flow. The flow induced by these vortex filaments is the rotational portion of the total flow extending from the approaching shear flow to a more complex flow around and downstream of the disturbance. The portion of this induced flow transverse to the main primary-flow stream direction is the secondary flow defined by Squire & Winter (1951). Hence this approximation is known as the "secondary flow" approximation.

The approximation has been applied to the flow in bends and cascades of airfoils, around thick struts, cylinders and spheres.

As the vortex filaments are assumed to be convected by the primary potential flow, any distortion of the vorticity by the secondary velocity is of second order and is neglected. This implies that the distribution of stagnation pressure downstream of a body or bend retains its upstream form (or at least is a comparatively simple variation of it). In practice it is found that the stagnation-pressure distribution is often considerably distorted by the secondary flow.

In general viscosity appears to reduce the development of secondary flow, and there are several examples in which allowance has to be made for its effects.

Large-Shear, Small-Disturbance Approximation

In this approximation it is possible to linearise the equations of motion because the disturbance is assumed to be small. We then find that the flow consists of the original undisturbed shear flow on which is superimposed a small rotational flow. The disturbance flow in effect distorts the original vorticity and stagnation-pressure distribution, and the effects of the body cause the disturbance to extend far downstream in a fashion different to that found in approximation (2) discussed above. As the disturbance is assumed to be small the theory does not allow for the presence of stagnation points; all airfoils must be thin and all bodies slender.

The theory has been applied to thin airfoils, struts and to bodies. It has also been applied to cascades of small deflection.

Another interesting application of this approximation is to the flow through actuator discs. We have already discussed a number of uses of the actuator disc concept for problems of small shear. When the shear is large but the disturbance introduced by the actuator disc is still small, the equations of motion for the flow on each side of the actuator disc are linear. The equations for swirling flow with large shear in an annular duct, which are used in the actuator disc representation of the flow through rows of axial compressor and turbine blades, have been given by Rannie (1954) and Marble (1965). For the large-shear case the disturbance, as

References p. 263–265

shown clearly by Hawthorne (1965), is not irrotational. In another respect it may differ from the result of the first small-shear approximation; namely, the disturbance need not necessarily vanish far downstream. For high enough swirl angles the disturbance may appear as a standing wave, extending downstream from the actuator disc, although Marble (1965) dismisses this as unlikely to occur in practical turbomachinery. By passing air through a rotating honeycomb Denton (1965) has recently obtained such wavy flows.

The flow behind shocks may also require the use of this approximation when the shear is large, Sears (1954).

Because the disturbance is small the effects of viscosity are likely also to be small, although some special cases will be noted later.

Exact Solutions

The only exact solutions available are for two-dimensional or axially symmetric flows. The two-dimensional solutions are somewhat restrictive in that a particular vorticity distribution is assumed. For instance examples given by Tsien (1943), James (1951), Jones (1959) and Murray & Mitchell (1957) assume linear (first two references), hyperbolic and sinusoidal velocity profiles respectively.

More realistic exact solutions for axially symmetric flows deal with the actuator disc representation of flow through compressors and turbines. Examples are given by Bragg & Hawthorne (1950), Hawthorne & Horlock (1962).

These examples provide useful checks of the accuracy of approximate methods.

COMPARISON BETWEEN THEORY AND EXPERIMENT

After this discussion of the various theoretical approaches and their limitations let us now turn to a more detailed examination of the applicability of the theories in practice. To do this effectively it is necessary to select examples which will afford the greatest help in the application of the theory or throw up problems which can provoke useful further development.

The summary already given suggests that approximation (1), figure 1, is perhaps most suitable for use in actuator-disc type problems. References have already been given to the work in which the theory is developed and compared with experimental results and it is not intended to discuss further this application of the theory.

Approximation (2) appears to be most useful in its application to flow in bends and cascades. A first limitation will arise from viscous effects close to the walls of a bend. It is also the only theory which can be applied to bodies such as spheres and thick struts or airfoils which have stagnation points or large thickness. Attempts to apply it to bluff bodies lead also to the need to make some allowance for viscous effects.

Thin airfoils and cascades of small deflection are best dealt with by approximation (3). Its value for flows through actuator discs when the shear is large has already been noted.

There may be examples in which it is possible to use either approximation (2) or (3). For instance, in the flow through cascades there are borderline cases where the cascade may be considered either as a series of passages or as an array of thin aerofoils.

Where possible, examples will be selected in which a comparison between theory and experiment can be made, but there are many well developed theoretical solutions which have not yet been tested experimentally and there are also experimental results which have so far defied theoretical analysis.

Applications of the Secondary Flow Approximation

The approximation was first applied to the flow in bent ducts by Squire & Winter (1951). The technique is to calculate the change in the component of vorticity in the direction of the primary flow, as the fluid passes round the bend. It may be shown that this secondary or streamwise vorticity component varies approximately linearly with the angle of the bend. It is then possible to compute the secondary flow by a Trefftz-plane type of approximation, i.e. by assuming that the flow in a plane transverse to the main flow is a two-dimensional flow possessing the computed secondary vorticity distribution and satisfying the boundary conditions on the duct walls. Figure 2 shows the results of Squire & Winter's original computation for the flow in one of the channels formed by a cascade of corner vanes in the return circuit of a large wind tunnel. The channel was of width $2b$ and height $2l$ and de-

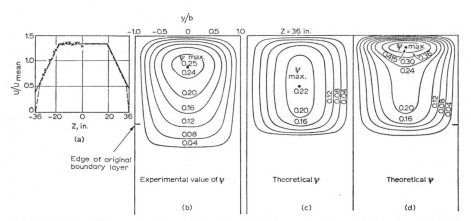

Figure 2. Secondary-flow stream functions for flow downstream of a bent rectangular duct. Deflection 94.8°; $l/2b = 7.5$. From Squire & Winter (1951), by permission Chief Scientist Ministry of Aviation; British Crown Copyright reserved.

References p. 263–265

flection of 94.8°. The upstream flow is shown in figure 2(a), in which the crosses show experimental points. The theoretical secondary flow streamlines in figure 2(c) are calculated from the assumed upstream velocity profile shown by the full lines in figure 2(a). The measured secondary flow streamlines are shown for comparison in figure 2(b). There are flows up and down the walls, $y = \pm b$, and evidence of strong overturning by the transverse flow at the end wall $Z = 36$ in. The secondary flow is found outside the original boundary layer whose edge is at $Z = 20$ in. (fig. 2(a)) and produces a weak under-turning there.

At this point we must describe one of the major limitations in applying the inviscid flow theory to real flows, which were presaged in the introduction. The secondary vorticity produced in a flow around a bend depends on the vorticity in the approaching flow. In normal pipe flow this vorticity reaches its maximum at the wall of the inlet duct. The closer this flow is to the duct walls the larger the fluid shear and the more likely, first, that the small-shear assumption becomes invalid, but secondly, and more importantly, that viscous effects become significant. Squire & Winter (1951) recognised the inadequacy of the inviscid theory by neglecting a portion of the approaching velocity profile, upon which the secondary vorticity and velocity depend. They assumed that the approaching velocity profile was "cut off" at 45% of the mean velocity, figure 2(a). The effect of taking into account the whole velocity profile is shown in figure 2(c) which shows the secondary flow streamlines calculated by Armstrong (1954) on the basis of the inlet velocity profile shown by the broken line in figure 2(a).

The same problem was met by Detra (1953) in a theoretical and experimental study of the flow in a bent pipe in which it was found necessary to cut off the upstream velocity profile at the wall at 65% of the mean velocity. The theory is clearly in an unsatisfactory state with regard to the problem of cut off. Possible approaches to a solution have been discussed by Hawthorne (1965) based on the idea of a boundary layer subjected to a sudden lateral pressure gradient (Mager 1955). It is however clear that much more work is required if the matching of inviscid-flow bend theory to the boundary layer theory on bend walls is to be of maximum use.

Another application of the secondary flow approximation is to flows which are weakly sheared and which pass over bodies such as thick struts, airfoils and spheres. When the upstream velocity is parallel and varies only in the direction of the span of the strut or airfoil, the primary flow becomes a simple two-dimensional flow. The vortex filaments are convected downstream by this flow and become permanently bent and stretched in the process. The secondary vorticity far downstream from struts of various shapes has been calculated by Hawthorne (1954) and Lighthill (1956a). Lighthill (1956a) has shown how to compute all the vorticity components throughout the field of flow and has calculated the secondary velocities for the case of a circular cylinder in a linear velocity gradient. For this simple case the only component of secondary velocity which exists is in the spanwise direction. Lighthill's solution is reproduced in figure 3. The magnitudes of the secondary velocity and vorticity on the stagnation streamline tend to infinity, and it has been shown that this applies to all bodies in whose primary flows there are stagnation points.

In this approximation the secondary flows persist far downstream and their energy may be considered as a source of drag. When the strut has a blunt or rounded leading edge it may be shown (Hawthorne 1954) that whatever the spanwise variation of shear the drag is infinite. If the leading edge is wedge shaped the drag is finite. Infinite velocities and vorticities are avoided and the least drag is obtained by the use of a cusp-shaped leading edge.

The large velocities near the stagnation point predicted by this theory present an obvious limitation to the analysis. Toomre (1959) has shown that this limitation may be overcome by introducing a boundary layer close to the surface of the body. Toomre has studied the flow close to the leading-edge stagnation point of a circular cylinder and an infinitely long flat strip or plate placed normal to the flow. He assumes that the upstream flow is the simple, linear velocity profile assumed by Lighthill in the derivation of the results shown in figure 3. In spite of the assumption of this artificial velocity profile the results are an important contribution to the development of the theory and show how the stagnation pressure at the leading edge could be estimated. Unfortunately there are no experimental results available to support Toomre's calculations.

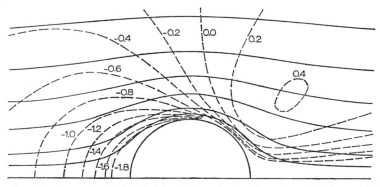

Figure 3. Primary and secondary flow about a circular cylinder of radius a, with axis the y-axis, when the upstream velocity is $(U+Ay, 0, 0)$.
—— Streamlines of the primary flow (note that the velocity components in the x and z directions follow these streamlines even when the secondary flow is included).
- - - Contours of constant v/Aa (note that the negative values, which predominate, denote secondary flow in the direction of decreasing primary flow velocity).
(Flow is from left to right and only the upper half is shown.) Lighthill (1956a).

The most remarkable application of the secondary flow approximation is Lighthill's (1956a, b; 1957b) calculation of the stagnation-point pressure on a sphere. The vorticity components are first calculated (Lighthill 1956a), then the downwash velocity on the dividing streamline (1957b). The correct boundary conditions are obtained by reflecting the vortex elements in the sphere, Lighthill (1956b). If the sphere were used to measure the stagnation pressure in a uniformly and weakly sheared flow, the calculations show that its reading for the velocity would be increased above the correct value by $90(aU'/U)^2\%$, where U and U' are upstream velocity and velocity gradient respectively and a is the radius of the sphere. This purely inviscid solution has not yet been checked experimentally, and there may still be some need to introduce a viscous boundary layer as Toomre has done for the cylindrical strut.

Another criticism of the work of Lighthill and Toomre is that the choice of a linear velocity profile (see figure 3) in the upstream flow is too unrealistic. It leads to difficulties in the estimation of effects far from the body, and is for instance particularly troublesome when the total downwash of the Bernoulli surfaces from far upstream to the leading edge of the body is to be calculated. Results such as that already quoted for the correction to the stagnation pressure on a sphere are too large. Toomre comments on the lack of realism in the assumption of an unbounded shear layer. The extra work required to obtain solutions for bounded shear layers can now be handled by computers, and such solutions are clearly required in the future development of the analysis. So also are the associated experimental results for both the cylinder (or bluff body) and the sphere.

The discussion of the application of this approximation to the flow in cascades will be left to a later section in which solutions by both approximation (2) and (3) will be considered.

As in the secondary flow approximation the distortion of the Bernoulli surfaces by the secondary flow is of second order; we shall for the moment leave consideration of such distortions in bends. We note however that Lighthill's result for the change in stagnation pressure on a sphere has been obtained from an estimation of this distortion.

Thin Airfoils and Slender Bodies

A prime application of approximation (3) is to the flow about thin airfoils, and the earliest example of its use was given by von Kármán & Tsien (1945). Analysis of the flow close to the airfoil or body shows that when the length of the body or the chord, c, of the airfoil is small compared to the thickness of the shear layer (or $(U'c/U) \ll 1$), the pressure distribution close to the surface is the same as that obtained in a potential flow.

For a thin strut in a parallel shear flow the pressure distribution at any section is the same as that in a potential flow about the section with the same upstream velocity. For instance, for the strut orientation and upstream flow distribution similar to that shown in figure 4 the pressure distribution close to and on the surface of a strut is proportional to U^2 (provided the strut is of the same section at all values of y) and is the same as that in the potential flow about the strut with upstream velocity U. To obtain the same pressure distribution everywhere it would be necessary to vary the thickness distribution of the strut with y inversely as U^2.

When the airfoil has lift, the surface pressure distribution is still an irrotational one but the angle of attack at any spanwise section is changed from the geometrical one by an amount which can only be estimated from a knowledge of the whole field of flow. There is some similarity here to the problem of the flow over a wing of finite span for which a lifting-line type of solution is adequate when the aspect ratio is large. A lifting-line theory for the shear flow over an airfoil of infinite span was given by von Kármán & Tsien (1945). More recently Kotansky (1965) has computed lifting-line solutions for airfoils spanning a duct for various velocity profiles and has also presented numerous experimental results. In the theory a Trefftz-plane assumption is made, viz. that the pressure far downstream is uniform and equal to the pressure far upstream. As a sheet of vorticity trails downstream from the airfoil and secondary vorticity appears distributed throughout the field of flow, this assumption is no more valid than in the theory of wings of finite span. Never-

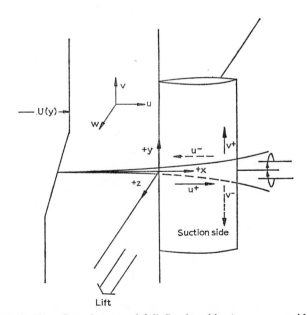

Figure 4. Shear flow about an airfoil. Suction side, $+z$; pressure side, $-z$.

theless Kotansky (1965) finds just as good correlation between experiment and theory, and the results of his experiments are of such interest as to warrant further discussion.

Kotansky's experiments were done with symmetrical airfoils with NACA 0012 profiles. A free shear layer was used, that is a shear layer which was bounded on either side not by walls but by regions of uniform flow. The arrangement is shown diagrammatically in figure 4. A shaped honeycomb was used to produce the stepped linear velocity distribution shown upstream of the airfoil. The flow was bounded in the y and z directions by walls forming a rectangular duct which was spanned by the airfoil. Figure 5 shows the spanwise variation of lift ($\propto U^2\,C_L$). The broken lines show the lift which would be obtained if lift were simply proportional to U^2. The full lines show the results of using the third approximation and the lifting-line theory. It will be noted from figure 5 that the local lift coefficient C_L and the angle of attack on the low-velocity side of the shear layer are larger than the geometrical values. On the other hand, angle of attack and C_L are smaller on the high-velocity side. This result is also shown up clearly in figures 6 and 7 which are curves of the local lift coefficient versus geometrical angle of attack at various spanwise positions. In two-dimensional flow the airfoil stalled at a lift

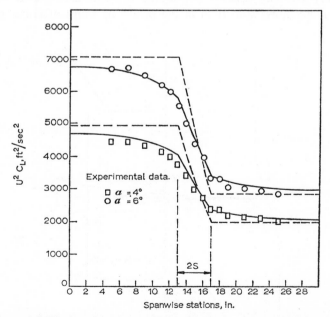

Figure 5. Lift on airfoil in free shear layer. NACA 0012, 3 in. chord with 0.006 in. trip wires at 10% chord; C_L = local lift coefficient; C_{L0} = lift coefficient for two-dimensional flow at geometrical angle of attack α. Full curve is lifting-line theory, broken curve is $U^2 C_{L0}$. Kotansky (1965).

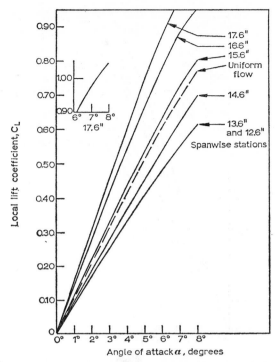

Figure 6. Local lift coefficient at various spanwise positions for airfoil in free shear layer. NACA 0012, 6 in. chord with 0.010 in. trip wires at 10% chord. Shear layer extends from 13 in. to 17 in. spanwise stations. Curves are obtained from average of pressure distribution measurements at $\pm\alpha$, the geometrical angle of attack. Kotansky (1965).

coefficient of approximately 0.8 so that it is rather unexpected to see lift coefficient curves reaching values of 1.0 without showing signs of stall. Kotansky investigated the flows on the suction surface under these conditions and found that spanwise flows were occurring in such a way as to thin the boundary layer in this region. This is perhaps the first clear example of a case where the secondary flow has a favourable effect on the boundary layer.

Figure 8 shows Kotansky's results for an airfoil of larger chord (i.e. 6″ instead of 3″). The lift is everywhere larger than that predicted by lifting-line theory(full lines). The ratio of chord to shear-layer thickness is now 3:2 and the conclusion that the pressure distribution is that of a two-dimensional potential flow is no longer applicable. The lifting-line theory therefore breaks down as does the assumption that the lift is proportional to the circulation at any one spanwise position. The effect is due to the spanwise displacement of the surfaces of constant stagnation pressure (Bernoulli Surfaces) on either side of the airfoil, see figure 4. The applica-

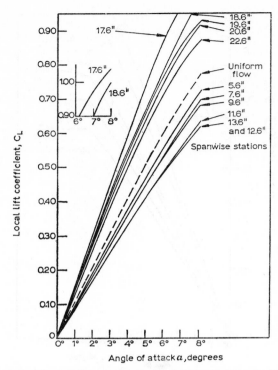

Figure 7. Continuation of figure 6 showing local lift coefficients outside shear layer.

tion of the third approximation to the flow round a thin airfoil of large chord has been presented by Honda (1960) who also assumes that the pressure far downstream is uniform and equal to the pressure far upstream. Honda's solution is naturally more complicated than the lifting-line theory. Kotansky (1965) has shown that the effect is to increase the lift above the value obtained in the lifting-line theory and estimates that the increase in the lift is approximately $16.7 \, (U'c/U)^2 \%$ for the velocity distribution shown in figure 4. The correction is shown by the broken lines in figure 8 and is of the right order.

Cascades

One approach to the problem of shear flow through a cascade of airfoils is to use the secondary flow approximation and Squire & Winter's (1951) application of it as already described. It is possible to determine the strength of the trailing vortex sheet leaving each blade by calculating the upwash and downwash velocities at $y = \pm b$, figure 2. Owing to the bending and stretching of the vortex filaments by the primary flow a portion of the trailing vortex sheet consists of vorticity from the upstream flow. This portion may be determined theoretically and subtracted from the total strength of the vortex sheet to give the bound vorticity shed off the blade and hence the change of circulation and lift produced by the secondary flow. Such a calculation is presented by Hawthorne & Armstrong (1955) and compared with the results of measurements on a cascade of impulse turbine blades of 72° deflection. The variation of lift was obtained from static pressure measurements on the blade surface. The boundary layer in the flow approaching the cascade was artificially thickened. The experimental results were in satisfactory agreement with the theory.

Honda (1961) has developed the third approximation for thin airfoils in cascade. The work is an extension of the theory for a single, thin airfoil of large chord (Honda 1960). A uniform pressure is assumed far downstream from the cascade, and the continuity condition far downstream is satisfied by averaging the spanwise displacement of the Bernoulli surfaces over a blade pitch.

Although Honda's theory is strictly only valid for cascades with small deflection, he has applied it to Hawthorne & Armstrong's (1955) experimental results. In figure 9 Honda's estimate of the variation of local lift coefficient (curve a) is com-

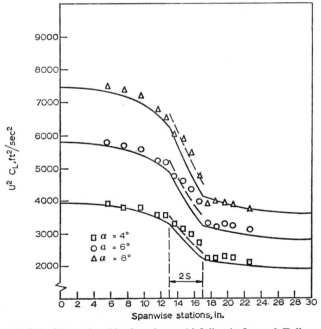

Figure 8. Lift on airfoil of large chord in shear layer. Airfoil as in figure 6. Full curve is lifting-line theory; broken curve is correction to allow for spanwise displacements.

pared with the experimental results. Figure 9 also shows (curve b) the results of applying the secondary flow approximation i.e. using Hawthorne & Armstrong's (1955) basic approach. The curve (b) has been obtained by a different calculation procedure from that used by Hawthorne & Armstrong (1955). The procedure has been to determine the contribution of the flow passing through the cascade to the pitchwise momentum change; this flow is obtained from the pitchwise secondary velocity. The results shown in figure 9, curve (b), were computed by Rowe (1965). Both theoretical curves (a) and (b) in figure 9 were obtained for upstream velocity profiles which were approximations to the experimental profile. As might be expected the secondary flow approximation affords the better correlation with experimental results, but Honda's small-deflection theory is surprisingly good.

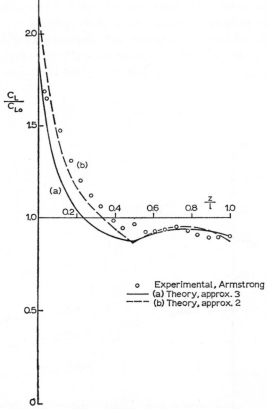

Figure 9. Variation of local lift coefficient in impulse turbine cascade; deflection 72° (approx.). Two-dimensional $C_{L0} \simeq 2.97$. Curve (a), Honda's (1961) theory based on approximation (3). Curve (b), theory based on approximation (2). Data points from Armstrong (1954) for thick shear layer.

In the application described above, the shear layer, which was artificially produced, was attached to the end wall of the cascade and it was found necessary to cut off the velocity at about 0.35 of its midspan value. There are however a number of results for free shear layers (generally in the form of wakes) passing through a cascade. Hawthorne & Armstrong (1956) presented some results and compared them with a theoretical solution in which the cascade was treated as a series of bent passages; the deflection caused by the secondary flow, found from the pitchwise components of secondary flow in the passage and the spanwise displacement of the Bernoulli surfaces upstream and downstream of the cascade, was estimated from the actuator disc representation of the blade row using approximation (1). Other experimental results are available in the literature. It seems as though the solution of problems of the flow of free shear layers over thin airfoils or through cascades can be satisfactorily obtained by the inviscid theory in one approximation or the other.

On the other hand the flow of attached shear layers about bodies such as airfoils projecting from walls or through cascades with end walls introduces viscous effects which must be accounted for. Cascades of compressor blades in particular exhibit stall or separation regions near the trailing edge on the suction side of the blades close to the wall. In two-dimensional cascade wind tunnels the separation accounts for a contraction of the main flow stream away from the walls (recognised by Howell 1942) and reduces the pressure rise. The NACA avoided this effect of wall stall by using extensive wall boundary layer suction in their cascades.

The prediction of stall or its effects in these circumstances is not at all satisfactory and is even less so in the axial compressor itself.

Limitations of the Theory

Although the secondary flow approximation has given a real insight into the behaviour of the flow in bends, the approximation fails in several respects. In the first place the theory does not predict the distortion of the Bernoulli surfaces which is found in practice. It is however possible to make a second-order calculation which predicts the distortion fairly satisfactorily in simple bends but not so successfully near the end-wall regions of cascades.

In the second place, owing to the distortion of the Bernoulli surfaces by the secondary flow the conclusion that the secondary vorticity and velocities grow approximately linearly with bend angle is limited to bend angles not exceeding about $\sqrt{d/R}$ radians, where d is the diameter or width of the duct and R is the bend radius. In fact for bends of prolonged curvature the secondary flow develops in an oscillatory fashion as may be shown by very approximate methods, Hawthorne (1951). Experimental evidence for this oscillatory secondary flow was given by Joy (1950), Eichenberger (1953) and Squire (1954) and summarised by Hawthorne (1963).

References p. 263–265

Figure 10 reproduces the experimental results of Joy (1950) on a bent rectangular duct 5 in. × 10 in. Screens upstream produced the symmetrical velocity distribution shown by the contour plot for station (1) in the straight duct 6 in. upstream of the bend. Stagnation pressures were measured with a Pitot tube inserted through slots in the wall, static pressures were measured with a static probe and wall taps. The results shown in figure 10 are given as velocity contours, but the variation of static pressure is relatively so small that the Bernoulli or stagnation-pressure contours are almost coincident. As the fluid moves round the bend the Bernoulli surfaces are gradually moved from a horizontal to a vertical position, each pair joining up and the higher-stagnation-pressure particles moving towards the outside of the bend, stations (1) and (4). Between stations (3) and (4) there appears to be a separation from the wall of the low-stagnation-pressure particles represented by the contour marked 40 ft/sec (the growth of contour 35 is probably the result of local wall-

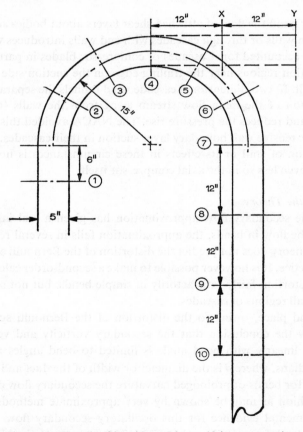

Figure 10a. Details of bent duct, 5 in. × 10 in. cross section.

Figure 10b. Distortion of Bernoulli surfaces in flow round a bend, Joy (1950). Duct 5 in. × 10 in., bent on 15 in. mean radius. Velocity contours (ft/sec).

References p. 263–265

friction effects in the bend itself). As the rotation at the top and bottom of the duct proceeds the lower-stagnation-pressure fluid separates into two regions, station (5). Between stations (5) and (6) the direction of the secondary flow is reversed and the contours shown at the outlet station (7) are beginning to take on the appearance of those at station (3) but with the opposite direction of rotation. In the straight duct downstream the reversed rotation continues until at station (9) the stagnation-pressure distribution has the same form as that at station (1), i.e. high stagnation pressure at the center and low values at the top and bottom walls. The rotation continues between stations (9) and (10) showing a tendency for the low-stagnation-pressure contours to spread along the outer wall. If there were no viscous effects damping the secondary flow, presumably the reverse rotation would continue until the low-stagnation-pressure fluid separated into two islands as at stations (5) and (6).

Measurements were also made on a 90° bend, with similar results up to station (4). In the straight pipe downstream a measurement at station X shows the secondary rotation continuing in the normal direction and dividing the low-stagnation-pressure fluid into two islands. This process continues, as is shown in the contours at station Y, 12 in. further downstream from station X.

These and other results indicate that the flow in bent pipes is extremely complicated and that the assumption made in handbooks that the bend losses are some simple function of bend angle or radius is likely to be wrong. Upstream and downstream conditions exert large effects, and the losses are also likely to depend on the degree to which fluid of high stagnation pressure is brought close to the walls.

The secondary flow in turbine nozzles and blades often shows somewhat similar effects to those just described (Armstrong 1955). The deflection is large and when the vorticity is large, i.e. the boundary layer is not artificially thickened, the low-stagnation-pressure surfaces are swept quickly onto the convex surface of the blade and separate from it. Often two cores of low stagnation pressure appear downstream, one rotating in the direction of the passage vortex and the other in the opposite direction containing a low-loss region from the wake.

CONCLUSION

This brief survey of the applicability of inviscid theory to the problems of internal flow has had to consider first the limitations of the theory. Three types of approximations are in general use and have some degree of applicability. Considerable experimental work has been done to check the theory but there is need for more and for the development of boundary layer approximations which will be complementary to the inviscid flow solutions. In many practical problems the behaviour of the flow has so far defied analysis.

APPENDIX I

USEFUL EQUATIONS IN THE THEORY OF SHEAR FLOWS

For an inviscid, incompressible fluid flowing steadily in the absence of body forces we have Lamb's equation

$$V \times \Omega = \operatorname{grad} p_0/\rho \tag{1}$$

where $\Omega = \operatorname{curl} V$, V is the velocity vector, p_0 the stagnation pressure and ρ the density. The vortex filaments and streamlines lie in surfaces of constant stagnation pressure (Bernoulli surfaces).

Helmholtz' equation is obtained by taking the curl of equation (1) and using the continuity condition

$$\operatorname{div} V = 0 \tag{2}$$

i.e.

$$(V \cdot \nabla)\Omega = (\Omega \cdot \nabla)V \tag{3}$$

Useful formulations for the velocity are:

(a)
$$V = \operatorname{grad} \phi + \operatorname{curl} \Psi \tag{4}$$

where $\operatorname{div} \Psi = 0$

or

(b)
$$V = \operatorname{grad} \phi - t \operatorname{grad} p_0/\rho \tag{5}$$

where
$$V \cdot \operatorname{grad} t = 1. \tag{6}$$

i.e. t is the drift function used by Lighthill (1956). The surfaces $t = $ constant contain the same fluid particles.

The change of secondary circulation about a stream tube is given by (Hawthorne 1951)

$$(\Omega_\mathrm{s}/V)_2 - (\Omega_\mathrm{s}/V)_1 = -2 \int_1^2 \frac{|\operatorname{grad} p_0/\rho|}{V^2} \sin \alpha \, d\theta \tag{7}$$

where Ω_s is the streamwise component of vorticity, α is the angle between the direction of the principal normal to the streamline and the normal to the Bernoulli surface, and $d\theta$ is the angle between tangents to the streamline an elementary arc length apart. When the secondary flow approximation is made for flow in a bent duct we obtain Squire & Winter's (1951) result,

$$\Omega_\mathrm{s} \doteqdot -2\Omega_0 \theta \tag{8}$$

References p. 263–265

where Ω_0 is the vorticity in the approaching flow, which is assumed to be normal to the velocity.

Reduced Equations for Compressible Flow

When the fluid is a perfect gas we may define a reduced velocity

$$W = V/\sqrt{2C_pT_0} \tag{9}$$

where T_0 is the stagnation temperature which remains constant along a streamline, but may vary from one streamline to another, and C_p is the specific heat at constant pressure. Equations equivalent to (1), (3), (5) and (7) are

$$W \times \text{curl } W = \frac{k-1}{2k}\left(\frac{T}{T_0}\right)\text{grad}(\log_e p_0) \tag{10}$$

$$\left[\left(\frac{p_0}{p}\right)\text{curl } W \cdot \nabla\right]\left(\frac{T_0}{T}\right)W = \left[\left(\frac{T_0}{T}\right)W \cdot \nabla\right]\left(\frac{p_0}{p}\right)\text{curl } W \tag{11}$$

$$W = \text{grad } \phi^* + \frac{k-1}{2k}\left(\phi^* - t\sqrt{2C_p T_0}\right)\text{grad}(\log_e p_0) \tag{12}$$

$$\left[\frac{\Omega_s}{(\rho/\rho_0)V}\right]_1^2 = -\frac{k-1}{k}\int_1^2 \frac{|\text{grad}(\log_e p_0)|}{(\rho/\rho_0)W^2}\sin\alpha\,d\theta \tag{13}$$

where k is the ratio of specific heats, t is the drift function and ϕ^* a scalar. Note that p/p_0, T/T_0, and ρ/ρ_0 are functions of W.

These equations demonstrate Munk and Prim's (1947) conclusion that flows of this type with the same distribution of p_0 have the same geometrical pattern of streamlines regardless of the distribution of T_0.

APPENDIX II

APPROXIMATE METHODS OF SOLUTION

1. *Small Shear, Small Disturbance*

We consider equations (5) and (12) where grad p_0 is of order ε. We write in equation (12)

$$\phi^* = \phi_0^* + \phi_1^*, \; t = t_0 + t_1, \; b = b_0 + b_1, \text{ etc.} \tag{14}$$

where $b = \sqrt{2C_pT_0}$ and subscripts o give the value in the undisturbed flow. Subscripts 1 denote terms for the disturbance, which are of order ε. Hence the reduced velocity to order ε becomes

$$W = \text{grad}(\phi_0^* + \phi_1^*) + \frac{k-1}{2k}(\phi_0^* - b_0 t_0)\text{grad}(\log_e p_0) \tag{15}$$

Subtracting the terms representing the undisturbed flow, we find for the reduced disturbance velocity

$$W_1 = \text{grad } \phi_1^*$$

Hence the reduced disturbance flow is irrotational and its streamlines have the same configuration as an irrotational flow. Note that the disturbance to grad p_0 is of order ε^2 so that p_0 retains its upstream value throughout the field of flow.

2. Small Shear, Large Disturbance

When the disturbance is large the terms with subscript o in equation (14) are no longer functions for the undisturbed stream only. We then find that the expression for the reduced velocity becomes

$$W = \text{grad } \phi_0^* + \varepsilon\left(\text{grad } \phi_1^* + \frac{k-1}{2k}(\phi_0^* - b_0 t_0)\,\text{grad}\,(\log_e p_0)\right) + O(\varepsilon^2) \quad (16)$$

Hence we deduce that the primary flow of order unity is irrotational (in the reduced sense) and convects the vortex filaments.

3. Large Shear, Small Disturbance

In this case the equation for the reduced velocity becomes

$$W = \text{grad } \phi_0^* + (\phi_0^* - b_0 t_0) P_0^* + \varepsilon\,\{\text{grad } \phi_1^* + (\phi_0^* - b_0 t_0) P_1^*$$
$$+ (\phi_1^* - (b_0 t_1 + b_1 t_0)) P_0^*\} + O(\varepsilon^2) \quad (17)$$

where

$$\frac{k-1}{2k}\,\text{grad}\,\log_e p_0 = P_0^* + \varepsilon P_1^*$$

and P_1^* is the perturbation due to the disturbance. The solution requires the derivation of expressions for P_1^*, b, and t_1 which are linear in ϕ_1^* to order ε. The continuity equation may then be used to obtain ϕ_1^*.

The above results for incompressible flow were given by Hawthorne (1965).

REFERENCES

Armstrong, W. D. (1954) *The Non-uniform Flow of Air Through Cascades of Blades*, Ph. D. thesis, Univ. of Cambridge.

Armstrong, W. D. (1955) *The Secondary Flow in a Cascade of Turbine Blades*. British Aero. Res. Counc. Rep. and Mem. 2979.

Bragg, S. L. & Hawthorne, W. R. (1950) *Some Exact Solutions of the Flow through Annular Cascade Actuator Discs*. J. Aero. Sci. **17**, 243–9.

Davis, G. de V. (1963) *The Flow of Air Through Wire Screens*. Proc. First Australasian Conf. on Hydraulics and Fluid Mechanics 1962. Pergamon Press, Oxford.

Denton, J. (1965), Private Communication, Dept. of Engineering, Univ. of Cambridge.

264   W. R. HAWTHORNE

Detra, R. W. (1953) *Secondary Flow in Curved Pipes*. Mitt. Inst. Aerodynamik, E.T.H. Zürich, No. 20.

Eichenberger, H. P. (1953) *Secondary Flow within a Bend*. J. Math. and Phys. **32**, 34–42.

Elder, J. W. (1959) *Steady Flow through Uniform Gauzes of Arbitrary Shape*. J. Fluid Mech. **5**, 355–68.

Goldstein, S. (1938) *Modern Developments in Fluid Dynamics*, Vol. II. Oxford Univ. Press.

Hawthorne, W. R. (1951) *Secondary Circulation in Fluid Flow*. Proc. Roy. Soc. A, **206**, 374–87.

Hawthorne, W. R. (1954) *The Secondary Flow about Struts and Airfoils*. J. Aero. Sci. **21**, 588–608 and 648.

Hawthorne, W. R. & Armstrong, W. D. (1955) *Rotational Flow through Cascades*, Part II: *The Circulation about the Cascade*. Quart. J. Mech. and Appl. Math. **8**, 280–92.

Hawthorne, W. R. & Armstrong, W. D. (1956) *Shear Flow through a Cascade*. The Aero. Quart. **7**, 247–74.

Hawthorne, W. R. & Banks, P. J. (1961) *The Effect of a Sudden Density Change on a slightly Non-uniform Flow*. J. Fluid Mech. **11**, 385–99.

Hawthorne, W. R. & Horlock, J. H. (1962) *Actuator Disc Theory of the Incompressible Flow in Axial Compressors*. Proc. Inst. Mech. Eng. **176**, 789–814.

Hawthorne, W. R. (1963) *Flow in Bent Pipes*. Proceedings of Seminar in Aeronautical Sciences, 1961, National Aeronautical Laboratory, Bangalore, India, pp. 305–33.

Hawthorne, W. R. & Ringrose, J. (1964) *Actuator Disc Theory of the Compressible Flow in Free-Vortex Turbo-machinery*. Proc. Inst. Mech. Engrs. **178**, Part 31(ii), 1–13 (1963–64).

Hawthorne, W. R. (1965), Chapter I, Research Frontiers in Fluid Dynamics, editors R. J. Seeger and G. Temple. Interscience, New York.

Honda, M. (1960) *Theory of a Thin Wing in a Shear Flow*. Proc. Roy. Soc. A, **254**, 372–94.

Honda, M. (1961) *Theory of Shear Flow through a Cascade*. Proc. Roy. Soc. A, **265**, 46–70; also published in Rep. Inst. High Speed Mech. Japan **16**, 85–118 (1964–65).

Howell, A. R. (1942) *The Present Basis of Axial Flow Compressor Design*, Part I: *Cascade Theory and Performance*. British Aero. Res. Counc. Rep. and Mem. 2095.

James, D. J. (1951) *Two-Dimensional Airfoils in Shear Flow*, Part I. Quart. J. Mech. and Appl. Math. **4**, 407–18.

Jones, E. E. (1959) *The Elliptic Cylinder in a Shear Flow with Hyperbolic Velocity Profile*. Quart. J. Mech. and Appl. Math. **12**, 191–210.

Joy, W. (1950) *Experimental Investigation of Shear Flow in Rectangular Bends*. M.Sc. thesis, M.I.T., Cambridge, Mass.

Kármán, Th. von & Tsien, H. S. (1945) *Lifting Line Theory for a Wing in Non-uniform Flow*. Quart. Appl. Math. **3**, 1–11.

Kotansky, D. R. (1965) *Thin Airfoils in Rotational Flow*. Sc. D. thesis, M.I.T., Cambridge, Mass.

Lighthill, M. J. (1956a) *Drift*. J. Fluid Mech. **1**, 31–53. Note also Corrigenda to Drift (1957) J. Fluid Mech. **2**, 311–2.

Lighthill, M. J. (1956b) *The Image System of a Vortex Element in a Rigid Sphere*. Proc. Camb. Phil. Soc. **52**, 317–21.

Lighthill, M.J. (1957a) *The Fundamental Solution for Small Steady Three-Dimensional Disturbances to a Two-dimensional Parallel Shear Flow*. J. Fluid Mech. **3**, 2, 113–44.

Lighthill, M. J. (1957b) *Contributions to the Theory of the Pitot-Tube Displacement Effect*. J. Fluid Mech. **2**, 493–512.

Mager, A. (1955) *Thick Laminar Boundary Layers under Sudden Lateral Perturbation*. 50 Jahre Grenzschichtforschung, Friedrich Vieweg und Sohn, Brunswick, 21–33.

Marble, F. E. (1965) *Aerodynamics of Turbines and Compressors*. High Speed Aerodynamics and Jet Propulsion, Vol X. Editor W. R. Hawthorne, Princeton Univ. Press.

Munk, M. & Prim, R. C. (1947) *On the Multiplicity of Steady Gas Flows having the Same Streamline Pattern*. Proc. Nat. Academy of Sci. U.S. **33**, No. 5, 137–41.

Murray, J. D. & Mitchell, A. R. (1957) *Flow with Variable Shear past Circular Cylinders*. Quart. J. Mech. and Appl. Math. **10**, 13–23.

Prandtl, L. (1952) *The Essentials of Fluid Dynamics*. Blackie & Son Ltd., London.

Rannie, W. D. (1954) *Three-Dimensional Flow in Axial Turbo-machines with Large Free Stream Vorticity*. Proceedings of the Traveling Seminar, June 1954, Advisory Group for Aeronautical Research and Development, NATO, Paris.

Rowe, M. (1965), Private Communication, Dept. of Engineering, Univ. of Cambridge.

Sears, W. R. (1954) *General Theory of High Speed Aerodynamics*. High Speed Aerodynamics and Jet Propulsion, Vol. VI, Section 6. Princeton Univ. Press.

Squire, H. B. & Winter, K. G. (1951) *The Secondary Flow in a Cascade of Airfoils in a Non-uniform Stream*. J. Aero. Sci. **18**, 271–77.

Squire, H. B. (1954) *Note on Secondary Flow in a Curved Circular Pipe*. Unpublished British Aeronautical Research Council Report No. 16,601.

Taylor, G. I. & Batchelor, G. K. (1949) *The Effect of a Wire Gauze on Small Disturbances in a Uniform Stream*. Quart. J. Mech. and Appl. Math. **2**, 1–29.

Toomre, A. (1959) *The Viscous Secondary Flow ahead of an Infinite Cylinder in a Uniform Parallel Shear Flow*. J. Fluid Mech. **7**, 145–55.

Tsien, H. S. (1943) *Symmetrical Joukowski Airfoils in Shear Flow*. Quart. Appl. Math. **1**, 130–48.

Discussion

J. B. Jones (*Virginia Polytechnic Institute, Blacksburg, Virginia*)

I think that perhaps we need a new term to distinguish between the two different kinds of secondary flow. The one we have been talking about this morning is a secondary flow which is brought about by a transverse pressure gradient that produces a deflection of the mean flow outside the boundary layer; it occurs in either a laminar or a turbulent flow. But, we also use the term secondary flow to refer to what goes on in the corners of non-circular channels. This does not occur in laminar flow; it is tied up with the turbulent structure. While it's risky to assign cause and effect roles in this case, by and large the pressure gradient probably *results* from the secondary flow rather than being the cause of it.

W. R. Hawthorne

I agree. I am not too keen on using secondary flow as a universal description of the flow produced when a shear flow is disturbed. But as you see, it does end up with flows transverse to the main stream and, of course, people have called this secondary flow. Even Goldstein describes both types of flow as secondary flow, so the confusion at least dates back to 1938.

E. S. Taylor (*Massachusetts Institute of Technology, Cambridge, Massachusetts*)

In connection with the filming of the ESI movie, Secondary Flow, I had the problem of defining this type of flow and came to the following conclusion. Secondary flow obviously involves a first approximation called a primary flow. Therefore, it is in the mind of the person who is analyzing the flow; it is not a physical thing.

It is merely evidence of a stepwise approximation process and that's all it is. Presumably it's completely logical to refer to any second-approximation correction as secondary flow.

J. H. HORLOCK (*University of Liverpool, England*)

I would like to make several comments. First of all, I think that Prof. Hawthorne's division of these flows into four types is extremely useful. It is a stimulating paper altogether, and I would agree that the small-shear, small-perturbation work is probably in a satisfactory state. I would be less pessimistic than Prof. Hawthorne about the small-shear, large-disturbance work. I think this is in pretty good shape as long as you obey the rules. There are now 4 sets of experiments on the shear flow through a cascade, all of which look pretty good. These are due to Armstrong (as shown in the paper), Louis, Soderberg and Lakshminarayana. The only reservation I would have now about the analytical description of Armstrong's experiments is the combination of the Class I flow with the Class II flow that resulted from placing the actuator disk at the trailing edge. We now know that it shouldn't be at the trailing edge and I think that the shift in the velocity, which Armstrong described as an actuator-disk effect, may very well have been due to a viscous effect, i.e. to viscous decay.

Prof. Hawthorne mentioned that with shear flows close to a wall we are in trouble with separation. This is certainly true in cascades but I am never really convinced that it is always there in machines. In a machine you have streamwise vorticity at entry and this may swamp out the secondary flow produced by the cascade, and cancel it out entirely in some cases. The tip clearance may also modify the separation and I think we might do quite well in the machine by tracing the vorticity through the blade rows, row by row. It seems to me that the real challenge in this problem, particularly insofar as cascades are concerned, is the question of predicting the losses. We really haven't the faintest idea of what these losses are and we are reduced to guessing the loss distribution radially, putting it into the three-dimensional programs that most of the engine companies have and seeing whether it comes out right.

I think the most exciting part of the paper is the survey of the large-shear, small-disturbance approximation. This is entirely new and I haven't got it entirely clear. (There is an appendix in the paper to which I can refer anyone who fancies himself a vector analyst.) I am not clear, in the work that was described and the experiment that was quoted which produced a lee wave, whether or not the aerofoil pressure distribution is unchanged when you have no lee wave. When you have this rotating flow which produces lee waves, is the pressure distribution on the aerofoil what you would expect from just taking a cut across the flow or does it change when the lee waves develop?

The last point I would make is that the three-dimensional calculation programs which most of the engine companies are now using should presumably show up some of these things. They have the same equations of motion which Prof. Hawthorne has used so that presumably we shouldn't be too surprised in some cases if out of these programs (such as those of Smith at GE and the Wu analyses) you get a few of these lee-wave patterns. Whether or not you could distinguish them from the sinusoidal shift of the streamlines that also takes place from stage to stage I don't know.

W. R. HAWTHORNE

I think the only comment that I want to make is that the lee-wave phenomenon I was describing is not much related to the experiments on the thin aerofoil by Kotansky. The lee-wave case occurs when you have a rotating fluid passing down an annulus and the speed of rotation divided by the axial velocity is sufficient to produce such lee waves. It is important to note that the pressure distribution on an aerofoil in such a flow is no longer a two-dimensional pressure distribution; that, I think, is the point. It would take another paper to discuss the work we have done in connection with the remark I made in passing about lee waves. It is a kind of shear-flow problem, but a rather special kind.

T. B. BENJAMIN (*Cambridge University, England*)

I wonder if Prof. Hawthorne could make any suggestions as to a general criterion by which one might justify neglecting the turbulence—or rather neglecting the direct effects of turbulence—in secondary-flow analyses of the present kind? What, in effect, his analysis does is to follow the experiences of the mean-flow vorticity, which of course owes its existence originally to the turbulence field, but the analysis neglects any subsequent effect of the turbulence when the mean flow is distorted. Now, in applications of secondary-flow analyses to *laminar* flows, a definite argument in support of neglecting viscous effects can generally be made on the following lines: For most problems one may readily define a viscous length-scale, which may be interpreted as the typical length necessary for viscous effects to spread across the flow (e.g., the "entry length" for laminar flow along straight pipes). Then if, for example, the radius of the pipe bend, or the dimensions of the aerofoil that might be in question, were very much smaller than the viscous length, one could reasonably assume that the flow will behave in an inviscid way throughout most of the vicinity of the bend or the aerofoil. My question to Prof. Hawthorne refers to the possibility of some corresponding formal basis for justifying the application of the simple inviscid theory to turbulent flows.

W. R. HAWTHORNE

Well, as a matter of fact, it was while listening to Prof. Joubert that I also began to wonder whether something shouldn't be done about this. Why take the flow around a cylinder jutting through a boundary layer on a wall and then say that the three-dimensional boundary layer effects extend out to the edge of the two-dimensional boundary layer? If they don't extend as far, which I don't think they do in a thick boundary layer, then you *can* regard some of the flow as inviscid for the purposes of the immediate disturbance around the nose. How much of it can be so regarded and what are the limitations involved? I think this is a very interesting question because if we have to carry a three-dimensional boundary layer analysis all the way across bent ducts we haven't a hope of simplifying internal flow problems. If we can't regard part of the flow as inviscid, we shall have to do for every conceivable piece of equipment just what we have done for long straight pipes. We will only be able to proceed by empiricism.

H. W. EMMONS (*Harvard University, Cambridge, Massachusetts*)

I would like to add to that. I think that you (Dr. Benjamin) have essentially answered your own question, when you described the laminar flow criterion. It seems to me that we need to regard the presence of any boundary layer of a given thickness at a particular location not as the result of the immediately adjacent surface at that location but as the consequence of that local surface *and* the surface all the way back upstream. The boundary layer has grown along the surface. If you do something locally to this surface, the effect again propagates (as a first crude approximation) as a leading-edge situation. It propagates at a rate that depends upon the length that is required to propagate the effect a given distance into the stream. So, if you apply a pressure gradient in a region which is small compared to the region required to build a layer of the existing thickness, all of the region affected by that pressure gradient (i.e., beyond the position of *its* leading edge) is essentially a perfectly new flow which is carrying along miscellaneous turbulent eddies. Like all the "theories" that we have had during the symposium this no doubt is only a qualitatively correct one, but it does hold some usefulness in giving a feel for when you have to do it one way and when you ought to do it another. It is very difficult for me, after listening to Profs. Joubert and Hawthorne, to know just how much overlap there was in their two treatments. These treatments certainly emphasize very different things and I somehow have the feeling that they were both talking about the same thing, at least in some regions, although it is quite obscure at the moment.

B. S. STRATFORD (*Rolls Royce Ltd., Derby, England*)

The other point that Prof. Hawthorne raised was where one should take the cutoff point. Is it not connected with Johnston's triangle (which was obtained by considering the simplest of flows in which you have a straight approach and a single sharp turn)? The outer part of the flow in this triangular representation is associated with the type of analysis Prof. Hawthorne has been discussing and perhaps more or less defines the region where that sort of analysis is applicable. The inner part of the triangle is that region which is dominated by the viscous or turbulent viscous forces and it is that part of the flow where one should not apply Prof. Hawthorne's type of analysis.

W. R. HAWTHORNE
  It is difficult, but I get the idea.

P. N. JOUBERT (*University of Melbourne, Australia*)
  I would like to make one point here. The one difficulty that I did see with Prof. Hawthorne's earlier theory was that it only applied to small yaw angles.

W. R. HAWTHORNE
  Approximation number 2 applies to a large yaw angle.

Experimentally Determined Optimum Geometries for Rectilinear Diffusers with Rectangular, Conical or Annular Cross-Section

GINO SOVRAN AND EDWARD D.KLOMP

General Motors Research Laboratories, Warren, Michigan

SUMMARY

The measured performance characteristics of uncurved diffusers of the three common types are analyzed and compared. Systematic data for two-dimensional and conical units is obtained from the published literature while that for the annular configuration was developed in an investigation conducted by the authors. In each case, optimum geometries are defined for two frequently occurring design problems in which either the magnitude of the diffuser length or the area ratio is prescribed as an initial condition. With the appropriate selection of non-dimensional length in each case, these optimum geometry lines for the different diffuser types are shown to have a significant degree of similarity.

The large reduction in diffuser pressure-recovery which occurs with increased thickness of the turbulent inlet boundary layer is also considered. For geometries on the particular optimum line for which diffuser length is specified, a single correlation is developed which gives the quantitative effect for diffusers of all three types. This correlation is based on the area blockage which occurs in internal flows because of non-uniformities in velocity over the cross-sections of the systems.

NOTATION

A	cross-sectional area
A_B	blocked area, $A - A_E$
A_E	effective area, $\int^A \dfrac{u}{U}\,\mathrm{d}A$
AR	area ratio, A_2/A_1

B	blocked-area fraction, A_B/A
$\bar{C}_P$	pressure-recovery coefficient based on $\bar{q}_1$, $\Delta P/\bar{q}_1$
$\bar{C}_{P,i}$	pressure-recovery coefficient for an ideal, one-dimensional flow, $\Delta P_i/\bar{q}_1 = 1 - 1/AR^2$
C_P^*	the locus of maximum pressure-recovery coefficient at prescribed non-dimensional length
C_P^{**}	the locus of maximum pressure-recovery coefficient at prescribed area ratio
E	effective area fraction, A_E/A
$\bar{\mathscr{E}}_0$	overall effectiveness, $\Delta P/\Delta P_i = \bar{C}_P/\bar{C}_{P,i}$
H	shape factor
L	wall length
$\bar{L}$	average wall length for annular diffusers
$\hat{L}$	non-dimensional wall length for conical, 2-D and annular diffusers; L/R_1, L/W_1, $\bar{L}/\Delta R_1$
N	diffuser axial length
$\hat{N}$	non-dimensional axial length for conical, 2-D, and annular diffusers; N/R_1, N/W_1, $N/\Delta R_1$
P	static pressure
P^0	stagnation pressure
P_m^0	stagnation pressure at point of maximum velocity
$\mathscr{P}$	wall perimeter
ΔP	actual pressure rise
ΔP_i	pressure rise for an ideal, one-dimensional flow
Q	volume flow rate, $\int^A u\,dA = \bar{u}A$
$\bar{q}$	dynamic head based on mass-averaged velocity, $\frac{1}{2}\rho\bar{u}^2$
R	radius of axisymmetric diffuser
Re	Reynolds number; $\bar{u}D_1/v$, $\bar{u}W_1/v$, $\bar{u}\Delta R_1/v$
(R_H/R_T)	radius ratio for annular diffuser
ΔR	annulus height, $(R_T - R_H)$
u	velocity at a particular point in a cross-section
U	maximum velocity in a cross-section
W	two-dimensional diffuser width in diverging direction, or local width of control volume used for plane boundary layer flows
α	kinetic-energy-flux velocity-profile parameter, $\dfrac{1}{A}\int^A\left(\dfrac{u}{\bar{u}}\right)^3 dA$
δ	boundary layer thickness
δ_{pl}^*	plane-boundary-layer displacement thickness, $\displaystyle\int_0^\delta\left(1 - \dfrac{u}{U}\right)dy$

δ_{ax}^{*} axisymmetric-boundary-layer displacement thickness, $\int_{0}^{R}\left(1-\dfrac{u}{U}\right)\dfrac{r}{R}\,\mathrm{d}r$

δ^{*} physical displacement thickness for axisymmetric flows, $A_{B}=\pi[R^{2}-(R-\delta^{*})^{2}]$

δ_{pl}^{**} plane-boundary-layer energy thickness, $\int_{0}^{\delta}\left[1-\left(\dfrac{u}{U}\right)^{2}\right]\dfrac{u}{U}\,\mathrm{d}y$

δ_{ax}^{**} axisymmetric-boundary-layer energy thickness, $\int_{0}^{R}\left[1-\left(\dfrac{u}{U}\right)^{2}\right]\left(\dfrac{u}{U}\right)\dfrac{r}{R}\,\mathrm{d}r$

θ_{pl} plane-boundary-layer momentum thickness, $\int_{0}^{\delta}\left(1-\dfrac{u}{U}\right)\dfrac{u}{U}\,\mathrm{d}y$

θ_{ax} axisymmetric-boundary-layer momentum thickness,
$\int_{0}^{R}\left(1-\dfrac{u}{U}\right)\left(\dfrac{u}{U}\right)\dfrac{r}{R}\,\mathrm{d}r$

ν kinematic viscosity
ρ fluid density
τ_{w} wall shear stress
ϕ divergence half-angle
ω_{m} loss coefficient along streamline of maximum velocity
$\bar{\omega}$ loss coefficient for the whole diffuser

Subscripts
H   hub (annular)
i   inner or ideal
m   maximum or mean
o   outer
T   tip (annular)
1   inlet condition
2   exit condition

Superscript
⁻   average value

INTRODUCTION

The diffuser represents a very old and geometrically simple fluid-mechanical device. In spite of a rather voluminous literature, its basic characteristics are still not clearly understood. In a broad sense it is a device which produces both a reduction in the velocity level of a fluid stream and an increase in its static pressure. Which of these is the primary objective is dependent on the particular diffuser installation.

By starting with the premise that it is nearly always desirable to minimize the internal losses of a diffuser, attention can be focused on the velocity-decrease or pressure-increase objective in various applications. In many internal flow systems it is desirable to reduce the velocity level in some components so that large losses will not occur. Diffusers are used for such purposes and a common example is found in closed-circuit wind tunnels. In these systems it is desirable to reduce the velocity level at the test-section discharge so that the fluid stream can be returned to the test-section inlet with as low a power requirement as possible. Diffusers are also used between the compressor and burner of gas turbine engines, and some-times between the two turbines in a free-turbine arrangement of these engines. In the first case the objective is to reduce the velocity level of the stream to avoid blowing out the flame while in the second it is to produce a velocity level that coin-cides with the efficient operating regime of the downstream turbine. The rotating and stationary blade passages in the compressor of such engines are also diffusers since they produce an overall reduction in the relative velocity of the working medium. The amount of energy that can be transferred to the fluid is determined by the magnitude of the velocity reduction which can be produced in the rotor; the maximum reduction is often sought so as to minimize the number of stages re-quired for a particular work input.

The use of a diffuser downstream of a turbine is an example of an application where the pressure rise produced is the primary objective. In this instance it serves the same function as a condenser in a steam power plant, i.e., to reduce the back pressure on the turbine, thereby increasing the expansion ratio across it and in-creasing its work output.

FLOW REGIMES

There are instances where the uniformity or steadiness of the diffuser discharge-flow is of as much importance as the velocity reduction or static-pressure rise that is produced. This is particularly true when a turbomachine (especially a compressor) is located near the diffuser discharge since the performance of such a device is sensitive to velocity non-uniformities in its inlet flow.

The occurrence of unsteady and/or non-uniform discharge flow in two-dimen-sional diffusers has been correlated by Kline, Abbott & Fox (1959). Based on an extensive and systematic test program, these conditions have been related to the overall geometric characteristics of the units (figure 1). Four different flow regimes exist, three of which have steady, or reasonably steady flow. The region of no-appreciable-stall is steady and uniform; the region of transitory stall is unsteady

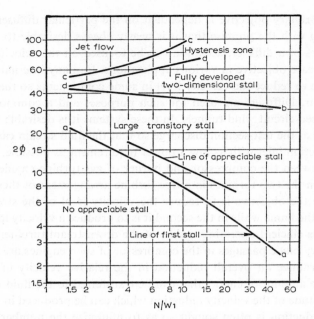

Figure 1. Flow-regime chart for two-dimensional diffusers (Stanford University).

and non-uniform, while the fully-developed and jet-flow regimes are reasonably steady but very non-uniform. The line of demarcation between the first two regions is one of interest in some diffuser applications. A sharply marked transition does not exist and the definition of an appropriate line therefore involves a certain degree of arbitrariness and subjectivity. This is particularly evident when attempts are made to define it for other geometric types of diffusers. Two demarcation lines are shown, a line of "first stall" and a line of "appreciable stall"; both lines were defined by flow-visualization tests using a water table.

A flow-regime chart of this type is not available for diffusers with conical or annular cross-sections, although McDonald & Fox (1965) have defined a line of "first stall" for conical units. However, the same general type of behavior is to be expected. An awareness of these possible flow regimes is necessary for a complete understanding of diffuser performance characteristics.

PERFORMANCE PARAMETERS

There is at present no satisfactory method for predicting the quantitative performance of a diffuser with arbitrary shape and inlet flow. The only recourse is to systematic experimental tests of particular geometric types, and such data is not very plentiful in the literature. Before considering the information that is available it is worthwhile to consider the criteria that can be used to evaluate diffuser performance. All the considerations that follow are restricted to the subsonic flow of an incompressible fluid.

A number of different parameters have been proposed for and used in diffuser investigations. Most of them are measures of the static-pressure rise that is produced. This pressure rise can usually be unambiguously defined and easily measured since experience shows that, in the absence of swirling flow or streamline-curvature effects, the static pressure is essentially uniform over any cross-section of a diffuser. On the other hand, any attempt to use the reduction in velocity produced by a diffuser encounters considerable difficulty in evaluation since the velocity generally varies over diffuser cross-sections.

Relative measures of pressure-producing capability are obtained by comparing the measured pressure rise with either the "maximum" value that could be theoretically obtained at the particular flow rate or with the "ideal" pressure rise that it was possible to achieve with the particular diffuser geometry. In each case an inviscid flow process is presumed, with the first also implying the use of an infinite area ratio to produce complete diffusion (i.e., essentially zero exit velocity). This, however, is not sufficient to prescribe these reference pressure-rises unless the inlet flow to the diffuser is uniform, i.e., one-dimensional. The pressure rise produced in the absence of losses is determined by the reduction in kinetic-energy flux that occurs in the diffuser. With non-uniform inlet flow the kinetic-energy flux entering a diffuser is greater than it would be if the same flow rate entered under uniform conditions and a knowledge of the inlet profile is therefore required in order to determine the maximum pressure rise that can be achieved. For the ideal pressure rise to be determined, the ideal exit-velocity profile must also be established. This presents difficulty in both definition and evaluation and the non-uniform ideal process does not, therefore, lend itself to convenient usage in diffuser performance parameters.

A more convenient, though possibly less meaningful, reference process can be defined on the basis of uniform flow conditions. This permits a simple evaluation of the decrease in kinetic-energy flux which takes place in an ideal diffuser and therefore of the corresponding increase in static pressure. Only the mass-averaged velocity at the inlet and outlet are required and both are readily obtained from the flow rate and the particular geometric areas, quantities which are usually known in diffuser applications. The performance parameters that will be considered, and the notations that will be used, are therefore defined as follows:

The pressure-recovery coefficient relates the actual pressure rise of a diffuser to the maximum attainable at the particular flow rate with one-dimensional flow, i.e.,

$$\bar{C}_P = \frac{\Delta P}{\bar{q}_1} \tag{1}$$

where

$$\bar{q}_1 = \frac{\bar{u}_1^2}{2}\rho \tag{2}$$

and $\bar{u}_1$ is the mass-averaged inlet velocity.

The overall diffuser effectiveness relates the actual pressure rise to that achievable from the same geometry with ideal, one-dimensional flow at the same flow rate, i.e.,

$$\bar{\mathscr{E}}_0 = \frac{\Delta P}{\Delta P_i} = \frac{\Delta P/\bar{q}_1}{\Delta P_i/\bar{q}_1} = \frac{\bar{C}_P}{\bar{C}_{P,i}} \tag{3}$$

where the ideal pressure-recovery coefficient can be readily shown to be a function of only the geometric area ratio of the diffuser, i.e.,

$$\bar{C}_{P,i} = 1 - \frac{1}{AR^2} \tag{4}$$

The term effectiveness has been used to describe the parameter of equation (3) rather than efficiency, as is often found in the literature. Efficiency implies losses and, as will be discussed later, this parameter is more representative of the effectiveness with which the geometric area ratio of a diffuser is used for diffusion purposes than it is of the amount of loss which occurs within the device.

Because of the assumption of uniform flow for the reference diffuser process it is possible, though not very probable, for $\bar{\mathscr{E}}_0$ to exceed unity. No violation of energy principles would be involved; it would just reflect the fact that the one-dimensional reference process does not represent the maximum pressure rise that a particular diffuser can produce at a given flow rate.

PERFORMANCE CHARACTERISTICS

Two-Dimensional Diffusers

Extensive and systematic testing is required to develop a performance chart for any geometric type of diffuser. Such an investigation for two-dimensional diffusers has recently been reported by Reneau, Johnston & Kline (1964). Testing was done in an air rig and covered a range of inlet turbulent-boundary-layer thicknesses. Contour plots of $\bar{C}_P$ as a function of area ratio, AR, and non-dimensional length, N/W_1, were made for four of these thicknesses. A typical plot is shown in figure 2. The geometry of this type of diffuser is completely defined by two parameters. Since AR and N/W_1 are used on the coordinate axes, the third (ϕ) enters the figure

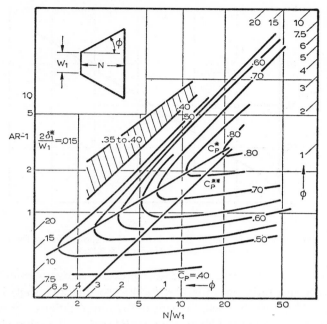

Figure 2. Performance chart for two-dimensional diffusers (Reneau, Johnston & Kline).

as a dependent parameter. With the choice of logarithmic coordinates and the use of $AR-1$ on the ordinate, lines of constant half-angle ϕ appear as a series of parallel, straight lines. This type of plot has been used extensively by the Stanford group and it has the convenient characteristic that the geometry line for any particular value of ϕ can easily be drawn by utilizing the small hash marks around the perimeter of the figure in the upper-right and lower-left regions. In addition, since area ratio must always be greater than unity, the use of $AR-1$ on the ordinate stretches the scale in the region of smaller area ratios where the units of greatest practical interest lie.

Two optimum diffuser lines that are very useful for design purposes have been added to the figure. One of them (line C_P^*) is the locus of points which define the diffuser area ratio producing maximum pressure recovery in a prescribed non-dimensional diffuser length. The other line (C_P^{**}) is the locus of points which define the diffuser non-dimensional length producing maximum pressure recovery at a prescribed area ratio. It can be shown that the C_P^{**} line must lie below line C_P^*. Although the diffuser angle varies along the C_P^* line, it is very nearly equal to 3.5° all along the C_P^{**} line. This provides a convenient method for defining the functional relationship between AR and N/W_1 that exists along the latter. However, the

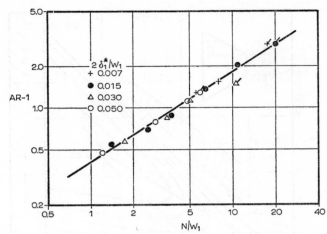

Figure 3. Effect of inlet-boundary-layer thickness on optimum geometry for two-dimensional diffusers (Reneau, Johnston & Kline).

location of the line is not critical since the pressure-recovery contours are very nearly constant-area-ratio lines for $2° < \phi < 4.5°$ so that any angle in this range would define C_P^{**} reasonably well. In many diffuser applications, either the diffuser length or its area ratio are fixed by broader considerations than those involving the diffuser alone. A design must therefore often be made under the restriction of one of these conditions and the optimum lines prove very useful for this purpose.

In the investigation of Reneau, Johnston & Kline, contour plots were obtained for four different inlet-boundary-layer thicknesses; these were generated by varying the extent of the constant-cross-section entrance length upstream of the diffuser throat. These thicknesses were characterized by the ratio of displacement thickness to throat width. The C_P^* lines obtained with each of them are compared in figure 3. The indicated points were taken from smoothed curve-fits of the data and do not represent specific test geometries. It can be seen that the data is adequately represented by a single straight line. This fortuitous result means that, within the thickness range investigated, the optimum two-dimensional-diffuser *geometry* for a large range of area ratios can effectively be chosen without regard for the inlet-boundary-layer conditions. The flagged symbol for each thickness represents the particular geometry on the C_P^* line that produces maximum recovery. In order to avoid unsteadiness, Reneau, Johnston & Kline have recommended that diffuser geometries for any particular inlet-boundary-layer thickness should not be any longer than 125% of the N/W_1 value at the corresponding flagged symbol.

Conical Diffusers

An extensive and systematic experimental investigation similar to that of Reneau,

Johnston & Kline has been made for conical diffusers by Cockrell & Markland (1963). However, this data is not presented in the form of $\bar{C}_P$ contour plots and it has therefore been necessary to generate them using performance numbers read from the curves of their paper. Although a considerable amount of data was taken, the number of cone angles investigated was not sufficient for producing good contour plots without some technique for interpolating and extrapolating the measured results. A procedure has been developed by the present authors and involves the use of a triangular plot for presenting diffuser data. Such a plot is shown in figure 4. It has $\bar{C}_P$ plotted against $\bar{C}_{P,i}$; effectiveness contours are therefore represented by a family of straight lines passing through the origin and having numerical values corresponding to their intercept at the right-hand edge of the figure. A single point on this plot permits both the $\bar{C}_P$ and the $\bar{\varepsilon}_0$ of a diffuser to be shown. Since an effectiveness of unity is represented by a 45° line, essentially all data points will fall in the triangular area formed by this line and the horizontal axis. With $\bar{C}_{P,i}$ being a function of area ratio (i.e., $\bar{C}_{P,i}=1-1/AR^2$) the horizontal scale is also an area-ratio scale. Because of its non-linearity, this scale expands the area-ratio range of most interest (from 1.0 to 4.0) at the expense of that of less interest (from 4.0 to ∞). It can readily be seen that area ratios larger than 4.0 afford little potential for increased pressure recovery.

The data of Cockrell & Markland at one particular turbulent-inlet-boundary-

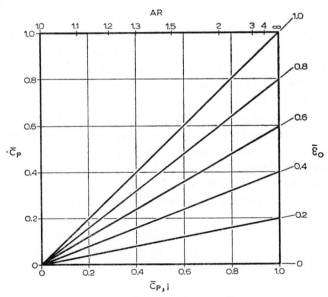

Figure 4. Triangular-plot coordinates.

References p. 307

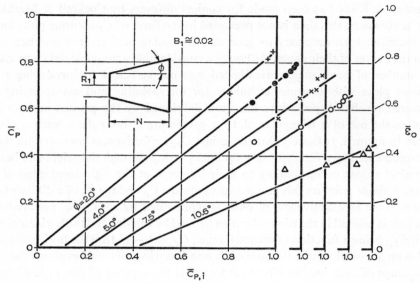

Figure 5. Triangular plot for conical diffusers (based on data from Cockrell & Markland).

layer thickness is shown on a triangular plot in figure 5. Twenty-six different geometries were investigated. The plot for each half-cone angle has been horizontally displaced by an incremental amount in order to separate the data and make the trends more readily apparent. Except for the larger cone angles, it can be seen that the data for a given angle is fairly well represented by a line of constant effectiveness. This characteristic is also displayed by the annular-diffuser data to be presented later. Curves of constant non-dimensional length, N/R_1 can readily be drawn on this figure since the area ratio corresponding to any point on a constant ϕ line can be determined from its indicated value of $\overline{C}_{P,i}$.

In generating a contour plot from this data it was assumed that effectiveness was constant for each cone angle. The particular value used for each angle was selected by an iterative procedure that required simultaneous fitting of the data with respect to half-cone angle, diffuser length, and inlet-boundary-layer thickness. This procedure represents a better approach to the handling of a small amount of data than does individual curve fitting since it establishes consistent trends with respect to all three parameters.

The contour plot that was generated and the C_P^* optimum line obtained from it are shown in figure 6. This is the same type of plot used for the two-dimensional units. The C_P^* line should not be seriously affected by the constant-effectiveness assumption used in obtaining it since it lies in a range of cone angles for which this was a good approximation.

Plots similar to figure 6 were generated for three of the seven inlet conditions for which data was reported. These represented thin, medium and thick inlet boundary layers, the thickest one being fully-developed pipe flow. The C_P^* lines obtained at these thicknesses are compared in figure 7. Even though a large range of inlet-boundary-layer thickness is involved, the line is nearly independent of thickness; this is the same general characteristic demonstrated by the two-dimensional data of Reneau, Johnston & Kline. In view of the relatively small amount of data on which they were based, it is probably not meaningful to attempt to rationalize the small differences between the lines, and an average curve for all thicknesses should be used. In contrast to the two-dimensional case, the reported data was not sufficient for prescribing the limits for steady flow along this line.

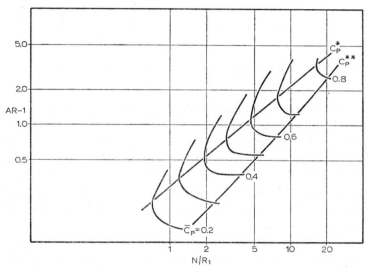

Figure 6. Performance chart for conical diffusers, $B_1 \simeq .20$ (based on data from Cockrell & Markland).

A less extensive systematic study of conical diffusers was made by McDonald & Fox (1965). This involved 17 different geometries and was conducted with only a single inlet condition. The details of the inlet flow were not reported but, considering the layout of the test facility and the performance results obtained, the boundary layer thickness must have been small. This data has been processed by the same technique used on that of Cockrell & Markland and a C_P^* line defined. It is different than the one obtained by McDonald & Fox, being nearly linear while the line reported by those investigators has a small curvature. However, the difference between them is not large at any point in the test range; the linear curve

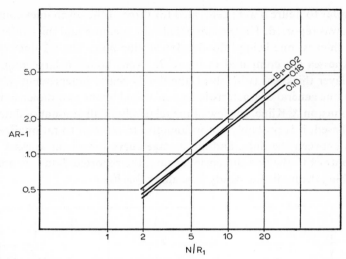

Figure 7. Comparison of C_P^* lines for conical diffusers with various inlet blockages (based on data from Cockrell & Markland).

compares very favorably with those obtained from the Cockrell & Markland data and has essentially the same slope.

Since small as well as large cone angles were used in this study it was possible to also obtain a C_P^{**} line. As has been indicated, the location of this line is not well defined; however, this is not critical since the $\bar{C}_P$ contours are relatively flat in its immediate neighborhood. A geometry line of $\phi = 2.5°$ adequately approximates a reasonable curve and this has already been seen to be consistent with the Cockrell & Markland data (figure 6).

Another systematic investigation was made by Rippl (1956). Both the C_P^* and C_P^{**} optimum lines were obtained and they are very close to the ones that have just been indicated.

Annular Diffusers

Diffusers of the annular type occur quite naturally in turbomachines because of the necessity for a fluid stream to flow over and around a central shaft and bearings. An extensive investigation of such units has been carried on for several years at the General Motors Research Laboratories. The type of configuration that has been considered and the nomenclature used for defining its geometric characteristics are shown in figure 8. Four parameters are required to specify the relative geometry of such straight-walled units and a convenient set is indicated on the figure. It contains the two wall angles, the inlet radius-ratio and a non-dimensional length. This number is two more than is required in the case of two-dimensional and conical units and greatly increases the difficulty involved in any attempt to generalize the performance characteristics of annular diffusers.

These geometric parameters were divided into two groups, those expected to have the greatest influence on diffuser performance and those expected to produce only second-order effects. Since the overall *diffusion* being attempted in a diffuser is prescribed by its geometric area ratio, the area ratio was an obvious choice as one of the primary variables. Some form of non-dimensional length was a logical selection for another since, in combination with the area ratio, it prescribes the overall *pressure-gradient* which is the principal factor in boundary layer development. However, the particular length dimension that should be used to characterize the geometry and the appropriate reference length with which it should be normalized need to be prescribed. The average wall length, $\bar{L}$, and the inlet annulus height, ΔR_1, have proved to be suitable choices.

Diffuser axial length, N, is an important dimension in diffuser applications and was used as the characteristic length during part of the investigation. For small angles, the difference between diffuser length, N, and wall length, L, is not very great. Since good diffusers of the two-dimensional and conical types usually have small angles, either length can successfully be used to correlate their performance. The diffuser axial length was chosen in the previous developments because it is usually the more critical dimension as far as space limitations are concerned. With annular diffusers, however, good performance is also possible with large wall angles since an inner surface is present to guide the flow radially outward. The wall length of such geometries can become significantly different from the diffuser length.

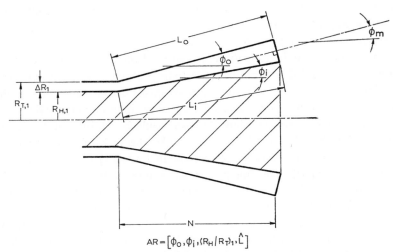

$$AR = [\phi_o, \phi_i, (R_H/R_T)_1, \hat{L}]$$

Figure 8. Geometric characteristics of straight-walled annular diffusers.

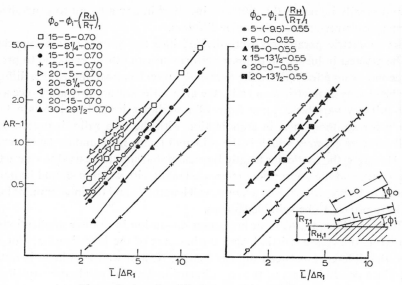

Figure 9. Annular-diffuser geometries tested.

Since the most pertinent overall pressure gradient is that which is dependent on the length of the wall, this has been chosen as the characteristic length for correlating purposes.

The choice of ΔR_1 as the normalizing factor was initially based on the fact that the resulting expression for area ratio became similar to that for conical units when the inlet radius-ratio approached zero, and similar to that for two-dimensional units when it approached unity. This made it possible to plot the performance characteristics of all three types of diffusers on a single set of coordinate axes. The subsequent results of the investigation also showed that this choice permitted the annular geometries at different radius ratios to be brought to a common basis.

The primary purpose of the testing was to investigate a sufficient number of diffuser configurations in a systematic way so that optimum-geometry lines that are useful for selecting diffusers in design situations could be established. In view of the multiplicity of geometric combinations possible, the task of generating *general* information from a finite number of tests is an imposing one. For each AR–$\hat{L}$ combination, for example, two free parameters are possible. For a meaningful investigation to be practical it is therefore mandatory that test geometries be judiciously selected and their performance results carefully analyzed.

The approach taken was to initially select several rather-arbitrary combinations of wall angle and radius ratio and then use their performance results as the basis for selecting other combinations which had potentially good characteristics. The primary emphasis was placed on diffusers of good performance so that the greatest amount of useful *engineering* information would be produced.

More than one hundred diffuser geometries were tested, ninety-three of which are shown in figure 9. A fixed combination of wall angles and radius ratio was called a diffuser family. The nomenclature system used is shown in the figure. Particular members of any given family were specified by prescribing their non-dimensional wall length.

The diffusers were made of wood and tested in the facility shown in figure 10. Although turning vanes were available for introducing swirl into the diffuser inlet flow, all the results reported in this paper were obtained with non-swirling inlet conditions. The outer radius of the inlet annulus was 7.55 inches. Testing was done under free-discharge conditions so that the selection of test geometries would not be unduly restricted by compatibility requirements with a discharge system. This permitted a simple measurement of diffuser pressure recovery to be made and easy access to the diffuser discharge for flow-visualization purposes. Its disadvantage was that it presented a problem in defining the magnitude of the discharge area. A general method for defining the discharge area of annular diffusers with arbitrary wall angles in a manner that is self-consistent and also compatible with that used for two-dimensional and conical geometries is difficult to conceive. The particular definition used in this investigation is shown in figure 8.

The experimental program was conducted with an inlet Mach number less than 0.30, a Reynolds number of 4.8×10^5 to 8.5×10^5 and essentially a single inlet-velocity profile. The turbulent boundary layer on both inlet-annulus walls was reasonably small. The tabulated experimented data is given in appendix A.

In order to permit definition of the C_P^* and C_P^{**} lines, diffuser pressure-recovery was plotted against area ratio at a fixed non-dimensional length, and against non-

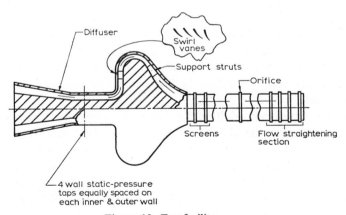

Figure 10. Test facility.

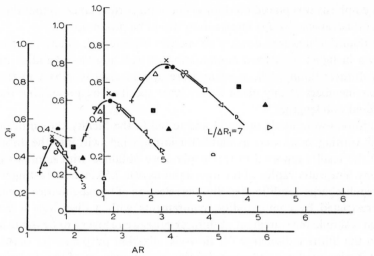

Figure 11. Variation of pressure-recovery coefficient with area ratio for annular diffusers at constant non-dimensional length, $B_1 \cong .02$.

dimensional length at a fixed area ratio. The results are shown in figures 11 and 12, respectively for a Reynolds number of 6.0×10^5.

Curves at three different non-dimensional wall lengths are shown in figure 11. The points indicated do not represent actual data points since, with the number of variables involved, it was not feasible to maintain $\hat{L}$ at constant values during the testing. The points shown were obtained by interpolation of measured results.

At each length the area ratio was varied by changing the diffuser family, i.e., the $\phi_o-\phi_i-(R_H/R_T)_1$ combination. The groups of points connected by curves represent cases where ϕ_o and the inlet radius-ratio were held constant while ϕ_i was systematically varied in order to change the area ratio. This represents the initial type of testing that was performed. A radius ratio of 0.70 and two outer wall angles of 15° and 20° were used. At each length it can be seen that the 15° and 20° curves blend together and form a well-defined peak. This suggests that the area ratio for maximum recovery might be relatively independent of the particular wall-angle combination used.

To check this hypothesis, additional diffuser pieces were fabricated so that area ratios corresponding to the vicinity of the curve-peaks could be achieved with combinations involving greater outer-wall angles and smaller inner-wall angles than had previously been used. Furthermore, some geometries with an inlet radius-ratio of 0.55 were tested so that the influence of this variable could be determined. Since the area-ratio schedule with length is different for each diffuser family, combinations which are near the peak at one non-dimensional length may be slightly off the peak at others, thereby offering an additional opportunity for evaluating the hypothesis.

Although the evidence is not clear-cut, a close examination of these curves shows that the recovery coefficient was high for combinations having area ratios corresponding to those near the peaks of the curves, and was lower for those off the peaks. This included the effect of the change in radius-ratio as well as that of wall angles. It was possible to assemble some geometric combinations which were well off the peaks and, as expected, their performance was poor.

All factors being considered, the test results indicate that the optimum geometry at fixed wall length (i.e., the C_P^* line) occurs at an area ratio that is reasonably independent of the combination of wall angles and radius-ratio employed. This generalization significantly simplifies the treatment of annular diffuser geometries. The radius-ratio range covered was from 0.55 to 0.70, and a survey of annular diffuser installations (appendix B) indicates that this covers most cases of practical interest.

In figure 12, the curve-peaks which determine the C_P^{**} line are not so pointed and well-defined as are those in figure 11 which define the C_P^* optimum line. First of all, this is a general characteristic of the C_P^{**} line and was observed in the previous treatments of two-dimensional and conical data. Furthermore, there are not many points defining the peak region of the curves. This is the consequence of inten-

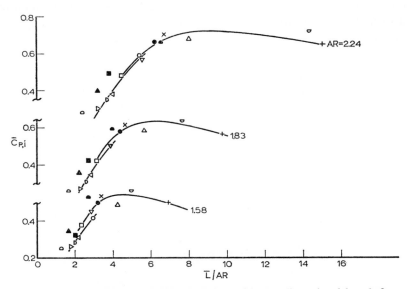

Figure 12. Variation of pressure-recovery coefficient with non-dimensional length for annular diffusers at constant area ratio, $B_1 \cong .02$.

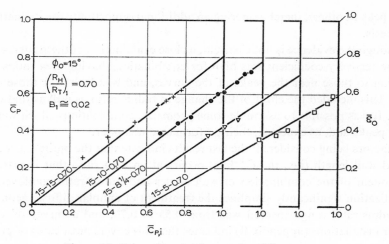

Figure 13. Triangular plot for annular diffusers.

tionally selecting geometries so as to adequately define the generally more useful and more critical C_P^* line. Most of the geometries therefore fall to the left of the peaks in figure 12. For each curve, there appears to be a consistent variation of the pressure-recovery coefficient with outer-wall angle at the optimum non-dimensional length. Large angles produce lower recovery, the effect being greatest for small area ratios, and this may be a consequence of the large streamline curvature required to make the transition from the axial direction to the mean angle of the diffuser walls.

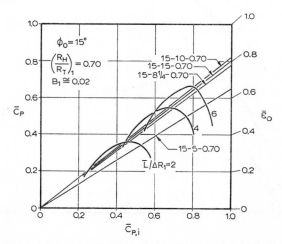

Figure 14. Triangular plot for annular diffusers with lines of constant non-dimensional length, $B_1 \cong .02$.

The C_P^* and C_P^{**} lines defined by the curve-peaks in figures 11 and 12, respectively, are shown in figure 15.

The qualitative variation of recovery away from the neighborhood of the optimum lines was established by generating pressure-recovery contours for the families having a 15° outer wall and a radius-ratio of 0.70. The data for these families is presented on triangular plots in figure 13. It is apparent that each diffuser family had approximately constant effectiveness over the area-ratio range tested. This is particularly true for the more effective families. The previously described technique for establishing diffuser performance trends from a limited amount of data was applied and the non-dimensional length contours of figure 14 developed. This permitted extrapolation of the data to diffuser lengths other than those actually tested.

The $\bar{C}_P$ contours that can be developed from figure 14 are shown in figure 15. The optimum lines obtained from figures 11 and 12 are also shown and are seen to be very consistent with the contours just developed. This indicates that the assumption of constant effectiveness for each diffuser family represents a good approximation for the better families. The error that results for the poorer families only affects the contours outside the neighborhood of the optimum lines. The 15–10–.70 family graphically demonstrates the constant-effectiveness characteristic of good annular-diffuser families. Figure 16 shows the performance of 17 of its individual members. This earlier data, obtained with a different inlet condition than that presently being considered, shows that the effectiveness is almost constant. Further-

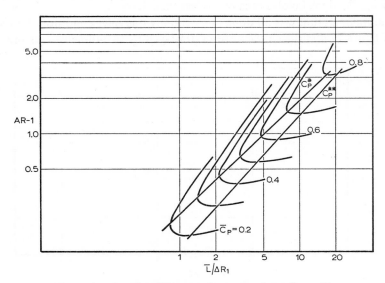

Figure 15. Annular-diffuser performance chart, $B_1 \cong .02$.

more, this characteristic does not appear to be dependent on the presence of an inviscid core at the diffuser exit.

Although the recovery contours of figure 15 were developed from the performance results of particular diffuser families, the hypothesis made with respect to the independence of the optimum lines from the detailed characteristics of the AR–$\hat{L}$ combinations on them would imply that they could also be used for a range of other diffuser families.

A partial confirmation of the validity of the optimum lines has been obtained from a survey of annular diffusers reported in the literature and found in the advertising brochures of turbine-engine manufacturers. In most cases a complete description of the units was not given and it was necessary to measure geometric parameters from small cross-sectional drawings. The units considered are listed in appendix B and a point representing each one of the overall geometries (AR and $\hat{L}$) is shown on the performance chart of figure 17. It can be seen that the points tend to be concentrated around the optimum lines, very few of the diffusers lying in a region of really poor performance. The four solid triangles denote diffusers in which splitter cones were used. These diffusers were located on the chart by using the average overall geometry of the parallel passages formed by the splitters. In three of the four cases the overall geometry without splitters would have moved the unit to the left of the optimum lines and to a region of poor performance. Three-quarters of the geometries fall within a rectangle defined by $1.4 \leq AR \leq 3.0$, $2 \leq \hat{L} \leq 10$. This re-emphasizes the point previously made, to the effect that most diffuser applications involve area ratios less than 4.

The annular testing was all done at essentially one inlet condition. However, in view of figure 17 and the characteristics displayed by two-dimensional and conical

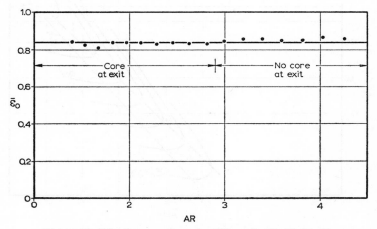

Figure 16. Effectiveness of annular-diffuser family 15–10–.70.

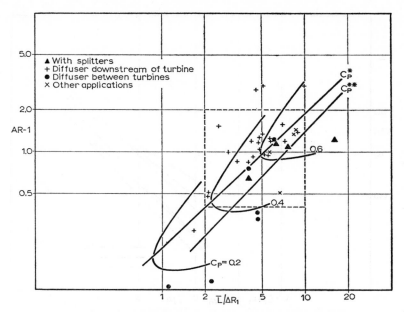

Figure 17. Survey of annular diffusers used in turbomachinery applications.

units, it would seem reasonable to assume that the optimum lines for annular diffusers are also relatively independent of inlet-boundary-layer thickness.

COMPARISON OF OPTIMUM LINES

A comparison of the optimum lines for the three different types of diffusers is shown in figure 18. The curves for the two-dimensional and conical units have been converted to the wall-length basis for comparison with the annular geometry. Considering the differences that might have existed, the relatively close grouping for each optimum line is encouraging. The general implication is that the overall geometric characteristics of area ratio and non-dimensional length are the controlling factors in determining optimum diffuser geometry, regardless of diffuser type.

EFFECT OF INLET-BOUNDARY-LAYER THICKNESS

Although the preceding considerations have indicated that the optimum *geometry* lines for two-dimensional and conical diffusers having naturally developing, turbulent, inlet boundary layers are relatively unaffected by the thickness of these

References p. 307

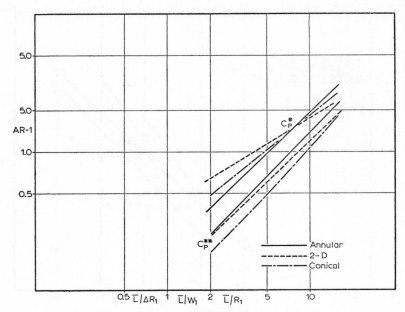

Figure 18. Optimum lines for various diffuser types.

layers, the actual *pressure recovery* produced by such optimum geometries is known to be strongly influenced by the inlet flow. Because of the large reduction in pressure rise that can result, it is important to inquire into the nature of the physical mechanism by which this deterioration takes place. In addition to qualitatively explaining the observed behavior, such an inquiry might also shed some light on the problem of how to quantitatively predict diffuser performance for any arbitrary non-uniformity of the inlet-velocity profile.

The mass-averaged stagnation pressure at any cross-section of an incompressible internal flow system is obtained by integrating over the section. If the static pressure is considered constant across the stream, a condition that very nearly exists for flow in uncurved ducts, then the average stagnation pressure can be expressed as

$$\overline{P^0} = P + \alpha \bar{q} \tag{5}$$

where α is the kinetic-energy-flux velocity-profile parameter for the arbitrarily shaped cross-section. In analytical terms,

$$\alpha = \frac{1}{A} \int^A \left(\frac{u}{\bar{u}}\right)^3 dA = \frac{\overline{u^2}}{\bar{u}^2} \tag{6}$$

Physically, α represents the ratio of the actual kinetic-energy flux at a given cross-section of an internal flow stream to the minimum kinetic-energy flux which could exist at the particular flow rate. This minimum flux would occur if the velocity were uniform across the specified section. The effect of velocity non-uniformity is to make α greater than unity, the excess kinetic-energy flux increasing as the non-uniformity increases.

Using the definition of mass-averaged stagnation pressure, the following identity relating two cross-sections of the flow stream can be written.

$$P_2 - P_1 = (\alpha_1 \bar{q}_1 - \alpha_2 \bar{q}_2) - (\overline{P_1^0} - \overline{P_2^0}) \tag{7}$$

Introducing this into the defining equation (3) for overall diffuser effectiveness and simplifying,

$$\bar{\mathscr{E}}_0 = \frac{\alpha_1 \left[1 - \dfrac{\alpha_2/\alpha_1}{AR^2} \right]}{\left[1 - \dfrac{1}{AR^2} \right]} - \frac{\bar{\omega}}{\left[1 - \dfrac{1}{AR^2} \right]} \tag{8}$$

where

$$\bar{\omega} = \frac{\overline{P_1^0} - \overline{P_2^0}}{\bar{q}_1} \tag{9}$$

and is the loss coefficient for the whole diffuser. This equation shows that effectiveness values less than unity can result from a distortion of the velocity profile (i.e., $\alpha_2/\alpha_1 > 1$) and/or from losses (i.e., $\bar{\omega} > 0$), each mechanism being expressed explicitly by a separate term. Since diffusion requires a reduction in kinetic-energy flux and since $\alpha - 1$ represents the excess of flux at any cross-section over the minimum required value at the particular flow rate, any increase in α along the length of a diffuser represents a reduction in the amount of diffusion that takes place. The first term in the above equation therefore shows the reduction in effectiveness which occurs because of *insufficient* diffusion. The second term, on the other hand, represents the integrated loss of available energy occurring within the diffuser as a result of the viscous effects in real flows and, therefore, represents *inefficient* diffusion. A determination of the proportion of the effectiveness depreciation in any particular unit that is caused by insufficient diffusion and that which can be assessed to inefficient diffusion requires the accurate measurement of both the inlet and outlet velocity profiles as well as the overall static-pressure rise. Such complete data is not often found. However, a survey of the published diffuser literature would indicate the rather commonly held concept that fluid-mechanical losses are the principal cause of poor diffuser performance.

Diffuser effectiveness can also be expressed in another manner. The stagnation pressure at the point or points of maximum velocity in any cross-section of an internal flow system is

$$P_m^0 = P + \frac{U^2}{2}\rho \tag{10}$$

where U is the maximum velocity in the section. In some cases there may be a uniform core of finite area over which the maximum velocity exists and in which there are no viscous effects. In general, however, the maximum velocity may exist at only one point in the cross-section. In the absence of curvature effects or immersed bodies and with symmetrical velocity profiles, the locus of such points at different sections along the diffuser will be a streamline.

If the static pressure is uniform across all sections of the diffuser, the pressure rise along the streamline of maximum velocity will be the same as that of the diffuser. This can be evaluated by equation (10) and used in the defining equation for diffuser effectiveness (3) which can then be written in the following form:

$$\bar{\mathscr{E}}_0 = \left(\frac{U_1}{\bar{u}_1}\right)^2 \left[\frac{1 - \left(\frac{U_2}{U_1}\right)^2}{1 - \frac{1}{AR^2}}\right] - \frac{\omega_m}{\left[1 - \frac{1}{AR^2}\right]} \tag{11}$$

where

$$\omega_m = \frac{P_{m,1}^0 - P_{m,2}^0}{\bar{q}_1} \tag{12}$$

and is the loss coefficient along the streamline of maximum velocity.

The maximum velocities at the diffuser inlet and outlet section can be related by introducing the concept of effective and blocked area. The effective area of any arbitrarily-shaped cross-section of an internal flow system is defined as that area which could pass the particular volume flow rate of the system if the velocity were uniform and of magnitude equal to that of the maximum velocity in the cross-section. Explicitly,

$$A_E U = \int^A u\,dA$$

or,

$$A_E = \int^A \frac{u}{U}\,dA \tag{13}$$

where u is the velocity at any particular point in the cross-section. It can be seen that the effective area will be equal to or less than the geometric area, being equal to it only when the local velocity is uniform across the section. The greater the non-uniformity of velocity, the smaller the effective area.

It is also convenient to define a blocked area which is the difference between the geometric and effective areas, i.e.,

$$A_B = A - A_E = \int^A \left(1 - \frac{u}{U}\right)dA \tag{14}$$

It proves useful to express both the effective and blocked areas as fractions of the corresponding geometric area, i.e.,

$$E = \frac{A_E}{A} \leq 1 \tag{15}$$

$$B = \frac{A_B}{A} \geq 0 \tag{16}$$

$$E = 1 - B \tag{17}$$

Now, the volume flow rate through any cross-section of an internal flow is

$$Q = \int^A u \, dA = \bar{u} A \tag{18}$$

where $\bar{u}$ is the mass-averaged velocity of the section.

Utilizing equations (13) and (15), we also have

$$Q = \int^A u \, dA = U \int^A \frac{u}{U} \, dA = UAE \tag{19}$$

Equating (18) and (19),

$$\frac{\bar{u}}{U} = E \tag{20}$$

These last two equations show that the velocity-profile parameter, E, of a cross-section can be obtained without actually measuring the detailed velocity profile if the flow rate and maximum velocity in the cross-section are known. For the cases where an inviscid core exists, the maximum velocity can usually be determined from a single measurement made in the core.

Used in conjunction with the continuity requirement for steady flow, equation (19) yields the relationship between the maximum velocities at two different sections of an internal flow system in terms of the geometric areas and the effective area fractions of the sections, i.e.,

$$\frac{U_2}{U_1} = \left(\frac{A_1}{A_2}\right)\left(\frac{E_1}{E_2}\right) \tag{21}$$

Introducing this into the effectiveness expression being considered,

$$\bar{\mathscr{E}}_0 = \frac{1}{E_1^2} \left[\frac{1 - \dfrac{(E_1/E_2)^2}{AR^2}}{1 - \dfrac{1}{AR^2}} \right] - \frac{\omega_m}{\left[1 - \dfrac{1}{AR^2}\right]} \tag{22}$$

This is similar to the formulation previously derived (equation 8) in that it has two terms, one of which is determined by the change in the velocity profile and the other by viscous losses. Although formally the same, there is an important difference between the equations. The loss term which appears in equation (22) concerns the dissipation which occurs only along a maximum-velocity streamline rather than throughout the whole diffuser. In view of this, it is possible to draw some conclusions concerning the relative magnitude of the two terms in the above equation. In many instances an inviscid core persists throughout the length of a diffuser and therefore $\omega_m = 0$. However, even when this is not the case ω_m is often small compared to the profile-distortion term since the core may only disappear near the discharge end of the diffuser in a region where the velocity level is low. Furthermore, the shear stresses on and in the vicinity of the maximum-velocity streamline are small since the local velocity gradients normal to the streamlines are small. It can be concluded, therefore, that the velocity-profile-distortion term in equation (22) *completely* accounts for the effectiveness of diffusers being less than unity when an inviscid core exists throughout the diffuser length, and *largely* accounts for it in many other diffuser-flow situations. On this basis, then, it can be said that the problem of many diffusers is *insufficient* diffusion rather than *inefficient* diffusion. The principal effect of flow separation, for example, is to produce a large increase in area blockage rather than a large increase in internal losses.

With the significance of the cross-sectional velocity profile being made apparent, it becomes pertinent to investigate the cause of the profile distortion generated by many diffusers. The static-pressure and velocity changes along any streamline of an incompressible flow are related by the following expression:

$$\mathrm{d}u = \frac{1}{\rho u}[\mathrm{d}P^0 - \mathrm{d}P] \qquad (23)$$

Since the static pressure is nearly constant over any cross-section of most uncurved fluid streams, all streamlines must experience the same pressure change in passing between the same two stations along the flow path. In the absence of losses, this equation indicates that the change in velocity required along each streamline will be inversely proportional to the local velocity level. In diffusing flows (i.e., $\mathrm{d}P > 0$) velocity reductions will occur and, since the magnitude of the reduction will be greatest where the local velocity is smallest, the velocity differences across the stream will be accentuated and the profile distorted. For accelerating flows the pressure forces have the opposite effect and make the velocity profile more uniform.

This picture can be modified by the presence of losses generated along the streamlines (i.e., $\mathrm{d}P^0 \neq 0$). Changes in stagnation pressure along a streamline are caused by momentum exchanges with adjacent streamlines, the magnitude depending on the local gradient of velocity across the flow stream and the local shear stress. In general, such changes will be different for each streamline and can be either positive or negative. Viscous effects alone can either accentuate velocity-profile distortion (e.g. developing flow in a constant-area pipe) or attenuate it (e.g. jets and wakes with zero pressure gradient). The actual changes in velocity profile which take place along any internal flow system will therefore depend on the relative magnitude of the pressure and viscous forces.

Equation (22) and the preceding discussion indicate that the effectiveness of a diffuser with a particular area ratio, AR, and a given inlet-flow condition, E_1, may be primarily determined by the effective-area fraction, E_2, at the diffuser exit. It is therefore suggested that the performance characteristics of diffusers with various types of inlet flow might correlate on the basis of this velocity-profile parameter. The diffuser discharge-velocity profile will be determined by the velocity profile which exists at the inlet and by the profile distortion produced by the diffuser as the flow passes through it. For geometries in which pressure forces predominate over viscous forces, the velocity-profile distortion will be primarily determined by the pressure forces. Since these are determined by the diffuser area ratio, it is suggested that the discharge effective-area fraction, E_2, in such cases might correlate with inlet blockage and area ratio. Pressure forces should predominate in diffusers of good performance which have a large pressure rise per unit length. Such diffusers are found on the C_P^* optimum line, and the hypothesis has therefore been evaluated for these geometries.

The results of both analytical and experimental studies have been used. An analytical investigation was first made in order to establish a correlation technique that might then be applied to experimental data. Conical diffusers were considered since they are the simplest of the three geometric types to deal with analytically. The flow model considered at each cross-section of the diffuser consisted of a uniform, inviscid core surrounded by a turbulent axisymmetric boundary layer. The growth of the boundary layer was determined by using an adaptation of the von Doenhoff & Tetervin (1943) plane-boundary-layer method for solving the axisymmetric form of the momentum integral equation. The von Doenhoff & Tetervin auxiliary equation was assumed to be applicable to axisymmetric boundary layers and the Ludwieg & Tillmann (1949) skin-friction relationship was employed.

In solving for the boundary layer development, it is necessary to know the streamwise velocity or static-pressure gradient that is imposed on the boundary layer. A distinguishing feature of internal flows is the interdependence between this pressure gradient and the growth of the boundary layer itself. The required relationship is developed as follows:

For an axisymmetric stream, the defining expression (14) for blockage area has the particular formulation

$$A_B = 2\pi R \left[\int_0^R \left(1 - \frac{u}{U} \right) \frac{r}{R} \, dr \right] = 2\pi R \delta_{ax}^* \tag{24}$$

The blocked area at any cross-section is determined by the boundary-layer integral parameter δ_{ax}^{**} of the axisymmetric flow. This parameter is conventionally called the displacement thickness because of the physical interpretation it can be given in plane-boundary-layer flows. However, the above equation indicates that this would not be appropriate terminology for axisymmetric flows. A displacement thickness, δ^*, which has the same physical interpretation as that used for plane boundary layers can be defined but it will not be equal to δ_{ax}^*. This δ^* is the amount by which the radius of a cross-section would have to be reduced (i.e., the amount by which the wall would have to be *displaced* radially inward) in order to reduce the cross-sectional area by the blockage area A_B, i.e.

$$A_B = \pi [R^2 - (R - \delta^*)^2]$$
$$= 2\pi R \delta^* - \pi (\delta^*)^2 \tag{25}$$

A comparison with equation (24) shows that $\delta^* \neq \delta_{ax}^*$. The physical concept of wall displacement which is valid for plane or two-dimensional boundary layers does not carry over to axisymmetric flows, the concept of a *blocked area* being more general than that of a displacement thickness. Furthermore, as will be indicated subsequently, area-type integral parameters are also more general in concept for expressing momentum-flux and kinetic-energy-flux defects in internal flow systems and boundary layers than are thickness-type parameters. Using equation (24) in (20),

$$\frac{\bar{u}}{U} = E = 1 - B = 1 - \frac{A_B}{A} = 1 - \frac{2\delta_{ax}^*}{R} \tag{26}$$

This gives the required relationship between the core velocity and the boundary layer characteristics. An interesting feature of the equation is the indication that the particular boundary-layer integral parameter can be experimentally determined without making detailed velocity-profile measurements. All that is required is a knowledge of the flow rate and the maximum velocity in a cross-section. Furthermore, this procedure should yield a more representative circumferentially averaged value than can be obtained from a detailed velocity traverse at only one or a few circumferential positions.

There are instances in the diffuser literature where erroneous expressions have been used to prescribe the core velocity corresponding to a particular boundary layer condition. In some cases the plane-wall definition of displacement thickness has been used in (26), in others the axisymmetric displacement thickness has been incorrectly used to define a blockage area by the wall-displacement method (25) and, in still others, both types of error have been made. The resulting errors in U can be quite significant when the blockage is large; this is usually the case at diffuser exits, and often at the inlets.

Calculations were made for a number of diffuser geometries on an average C_P^* line derived from the data of Cockrell & Markland (figure 7). Inlet flows composed of a naturally developing turbulent boundary layer surrounding a uniform central core were considered. Inlet-velocity profiles were characterized by the blockage fraction B_1, and a range of boundary layer thicknesses was investigated. The results of these calculations are shown in figure 19.

An attempt was made to empirically determine a set of variables which would collapse these calculations to essentially a single curve. If this could be accomplished, it would be much easier to determine whether experimental values of E_2 for optimum diffusers could actually be correlated on the basis of B_1 and AR since data at random values of B_1 would all have the same reference curve with which their trends could be compared. Furthermore, if the correlation of experimental points looked encouraging, the totality of all available data could then be used to specifically define this single curve. The objective was successfully accomplished by using the quantity $AR(B_1)^{\frac{1}{4}}$ as the independent variable.

The experimental results from conical diffuser geometries along the C_P^* lines obtained from the Cockrell & Markland data were plotted on these new coordinate axes. Values of E_2 at a given AR were determined from the measured values of $\bar{\mathscr{E}}_0$

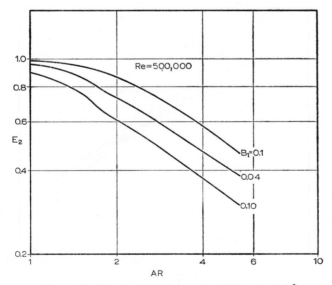

Figure 19. Calculated E_2 for conical diffusers on C_P^*.

and B_1 by using equation (22), neglecting ω_m. The results, which cover a range of inlet blockages from 0.02 to 0.18, are shown in figure 20 and it is seen that they could be reduced to a single curve reasonably well. The curve-fit for the calculated values is also shown for reference. The fact that the calculated and experimental curves do not coincide is not surprising since coincidence would require that the calculation procedure do a perfect job of predicting the diffuser performance characteristics that were used. This is unlikely. An evaluation of the accuracy of the calculation procedure was not the objective of this work. The purpose of the calculations was to suggest a set of variables which might be used to adequately correlate experimental data. The important conclusions to be obtained from the figure are (1) that the experimental data does correlate well on the postulated basis and (2) that the average curve is of essentially the same shape as that obtained from the calculations.

It should be pointed out that the effectiveness values used for determining the discharge effective-area fraction of each diffuser did not represent actual experimental data since geometries right on the C_P^* lines were not tested. The optimum line was derived from test results by a technique which involved smoothing and interpolation of both the effectiveness and inlet-blockage values. However, since the same data-treatment technique was used for each inlet condition, the qualitative behavior of the results in figure 20 should be fairly representative.

Although no other investigation of inlet-boundary-layer effects on conical diffusers that is of comparable scope to that of Cockrell & Markland can be found

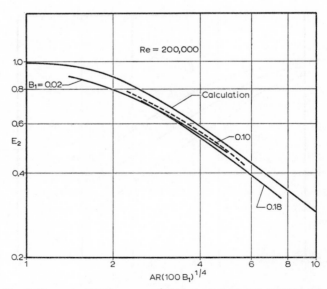

Figure 20. E_2 for conical diffusers on C_P^* (based on data of Cockrell & Markland).

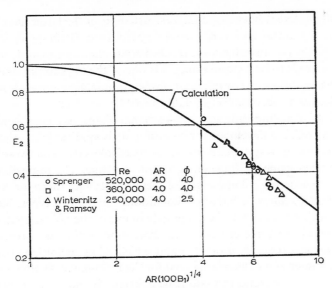

Figure 21. E_2 for conical diffusers near C_P^*.

in the literature, there are two instances where the effect on a single diffuser geometry was studied in detail. Sprenger (1959) investigated a unit with $AR=4.0$ and $\phi=4°$. This geometry falls slightly above the C_P^* line that has been used but, for comparative purposes, its performance characteristics were reduced to the form being considered here. Winternitz & Ramsay (1957) also used a diffuser of $AR=4.0$ but with $\phi=2.5°$. This geometry falls a little below the C_P^* line. In both cases the inlet turbulent boundary layers were of the naturally-developing type, different thicknesses being produced by different lengths of inlet pipe. The data from both sources is shown in figure 21, where the curve obtained by calculation has again been included for reference. The experimental points appear to follow the same general trend as the curve.

Although it looks very encouraging, this correlation does not *prove* that inlet blockage is the proper basis for evaluating inlet-profile effects on the diffuser geometries that have been considered. The inlet flows might have been characterized by δ_{ax}^* or θ_{ax} and a similar correlation could have been developed since δ_{ax}^* is proportional to B, and the ratio of θ_{ax} to δ_{ax}^* was essentially constant for the test results used, i.e., H was essentially constant. Only by changing the proportionality constant between δ_{ax}^* and B or by changing the value of the inlet shape factor in order to uncouple δ_{ax}^* and θ_{ax} can a meaningful choice be made between them. The first possibility can best be accomplished by changing the diffuser cross-sectional shape, while the second would require a method for artificially generating a range of significantly different inlet shape factors. Attempts at the latter have been made by Winternitz & Ramsay and, very recently, by Cockrell, Diamond & Jones (1965). Unfortunately, the two investigations reached contradictory conclusions. This type of experiment needs to be repeated since it is one of the keys to our understanding of inlet effects on diffusers. Optimum or near-optimum geometries should be used and a complete and consistent set of data should be obtained.

The effect of changing diffuser cross-sectional shape has been studied to see whether the correlation developed for conical units is applicable to other types. As mentioned previously, a systematic investigation of inlet effects on two-dimensional diffusers has been made by Reneau, Johnston & Kline. The immediate problem that arises in considering a comparison of these results with those for conical units is that of defining *equivalent* inlet-flow conditions for the two types. Should equivalence be made on the basis of the magnitude of one of the boundary layer integral thicknesses relative to some characteristic dimension of the inlet cross-section? If so, which thickness (i.e., δ^*, θ or δ^{**}) and which of its definitions (i.e., axisymmetric or two-dimensional) should be used for the rectangular section and to which dimension of the cross-section should it be referred? It can be seen that there are several possibilities, with no conclusive reason for selecting one over the others.

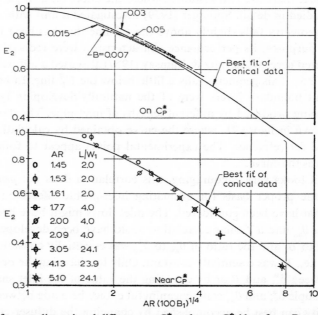

Figure 22. E_2 for two-dimensional diffusers on C_p^* and near C_p^* (data from Reneau, Johnston & Kline; Re from 80,000 to 250,000).

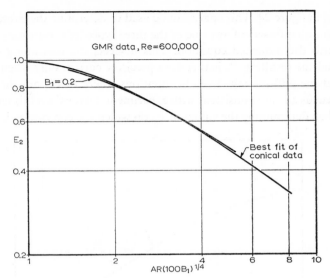

Figure 23. E_2 for annular diffusers on C_p^*.

The approach taken in the present investigation was to equate diffuser entrance conditions on the basis of blocked-area fraction. Even if nothing else, this at least provides a clear and precisely definable relationship between cross-sectional geometries of any shape. As a matter of interest the thickness equivalence that results from this correspondence is δ_{ax}^*/R to δ_{pl}^*/W. It is unlikely that this equivalence would be arrived at on the basis of relative thickness considerations since the radius or half-width of a circular section is used, while the total width of the rectangular section is employed.

The results for two-dimensional diffuser geometries located on the C_p^* line of Reneau, Johnston & Kline are shown in figure 22; the best-fit curve for conical units is also shown for reference. Although the range of inlet blockages tested ($0.007 \leq B_1 \leq 0.05$) was not as great as that used by Cockrell & Markland, the curves for the two types compare very well over the range they have in common. Also shown are particular test points for two-dimensional diffusers having geometries close to the optimum line. Some of these extend to larger inlet blockages than do the C_p^* lines.

The annular-diffuser optimum line determined in the present investigation has also been treated in the same manner. These tests were conducted at only one inlet blockage and the results are shown in figure 23. The agreement with the other geometrical types is quite favorable.

A best-fit curve has been determined for the results of all three geometrical types and is shown in figure 24. This curve can be used to determine the overall effective-ness for optimum diffusers of any one of the three types by substituting the value it prescribes into the indicated equation. This neglects the loss along the diffuser centerline and the resulting $\bar{\mathscr{E}}_0$ is therefore precisely correct only when an inviscid core exists at the diffuser exit. Even in situations where this is not the case, how-ever, it still yields a result consistent with experimental data since this term was also neglected when determining the values of E_2 on which the correlation is based.

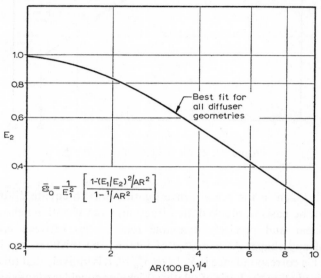

Figure 24. Effect of inlet-boundary-layer blockage on the performance of diffusers on C_P^* and near C_P^*.

Useful as it is, this correlation is still fairly restricted in its application. Although the blockage concept is general enough to include any kind of inlet-velocity profile, only non-uniformities caused by boundary layers on the duct walls have so far been considered. Furthermore, these turbulent boundary layers were basically of the flat-plate type with corresponding values of shape factor, H. Information on the validity of the correlation for different values of H is required. The stall sensitivity of optimum diffusers must also be established since sufficiently large values of shape factor can cause diffuser stall. In addition, inlet-velocity profiles containing distortions in the central portion of the stream need to be investigated. These can be caused in internal flows by wakes, curvature effects or energy gradients. The blockage concept is general enough to include this type of velocity distortion and the same line of reasoning should be applicable to it, but the type of correlation that results may well be different than that for the bound shear layers. The com-

plexity of the total problem is so great, however, that any approach which adds
even a small measure of understanding is welcome.

MOMENTUM INTEGRAL EQUATION

In the course of this investigation a generalized integral method of expressing the
momentum equation for flows with non-uniform velocity profiles has been developed. While considering internal flows of arbitrary cross-sectional shape it became
apparent that area-type integral parameters could be introduced into the momentum equation in a more general manner than could the usual thickness-type ones.
For internal flows in which dA/dx is not large, the momentum equation can be
expressed in the following manner:

$$d(\rho U^2 A_\theta) = A_B dP + \tau_w \mathscr{P} dx + (A - A_B) dP_m^0 \qquad (27)$$

where A_B and A_θ are cross-sectional integral parameters which are defined as

$$A_B = \int_0^A \left(1 - \frac{u}{U}\right) dA \qquad (28)$$

$$A_\theta = \int_0^A \left(1 - \frac{u}{U}\right) \frac{u}{U} dA \qquad (29)$$

and $\mathscr{P}$ = wall perimeter
dP_m^0 = the change in stagnation pressure along the streamline or streamlines of
maximum velocity.
The appropriate explicit expressions for dA and $\mathscr{P}$ are determined by the cross-
sectional geometry of the fluid stream.

If the internal flow has an inviscid core the loss term, dP_m^0, is zero and the equation reduces to the momentum integral equation for boundary layer flows. In the
axisymmetric case

$$A_B = 2\pi R \left[\int_0^R \left(1 - \frac{u}{U}\right) \frac{r}{R} dr \right] = 2\pi R \delta_{ax}^* \qquad (24)$$

$$A_\theta = 2\pi R \left[\int_0^R \left(1 - \frac{u}{U}\right) \left(\frac{u}{U}\right) \frac{r}{R} dr \right] = 2\pi R \theta_{ax} \qquad (30)$$

$$\mathscr{P} = 2\pi R \qquad (31)$$

It can be seen that these area-type parameters contain the thickness-type parameters that are conventionally used. Substitution of the expressions into equation
(27) produces the standard form of the axisymmetric momentum integral equation.

References p. 307

For plane-wall boundary layers

$$A_{\rm B} = W\left[\int_0^\infty \left(1 - \frac{u}{U}\right) {\rm d}y \right] = W\delta_{\rm pl}^* \tag{32}$$

$$A_\theta = W\left[\int_0^\infty \left(1 - \frac{u}{U}\right)\left(\frac{u}{U}\right){\rm d}y \right] = W\theta_{\rm pl} \tag{33}$$

$$\mathscr{P} = W \tag{34}$$

Substitution of these expressions into (27) yields the form of the two-dimensional equation, including a term which accounts for any deviation from two-dimensionality in the flow.

The formulation has the following desirable features:

1. It is in a directly recognizable and easily remembered momentum-equation form, i.e., a change in momentum is equated to a summation of forces.
2. With appropriate evaluation of the integral parameters for each type of cross-section, this *single* formulation yields the accepted and complete form of the momentum integral equation for axisymmetric and plane-wall boundary layers.
3. For each flow geometry it specifies the definitions *required* of the thickness-type integral parameters in order to satisfy the momentum equation. The physical concept of wall displacement that is used in defining these thicknesses for plane boundary layers is not generally valid.

CONCLUSIONS

The performance characteristics of the three common geometric types of diffusers have been considered. In each case, the emphasis was placed on the definition of optimum geometries for two frequently occurring diffuser design problems, and on the effect of inlet-boundary-layer thickness on the performance of these geometries.

The specific conclusions obtained are the following:

1. Area ratio and non-dimensional wall length are the principal determinants of optimum geometry for straight-walled annular diffusers.
2. With the appropriate selection of non-dimensional length in each case, the optimum-geometry lines for rectilinear diffusers with rectangular, conical or annular cross-section have a significant degree of similarity.
3. For optimum and near-optimum diffuser geometries the effect of boundary-layer-types of inlet-velocity non-uniformity on performance can be correlated on the basis of area-blockage. The reduction in recovery which occurs with thickening of the inlet boundary layers is primarily the result of insufficient rather than inefficient diffusion.

4. The blockage concept provides a method for equating inlet-velocity profiles in diffusers of different cross-sectional shape. It suggests the possibility of evaluating inlet effects for only one geometric type of diffuser and then applying the results to other cross-sectional forms. This could eliminate the need for vast amounts of data taken with various inlet conditions in diffusers of different geometry.

5. There is a need for detailed diffuser-performance data which can serve as a basis for analytical studies; this data should be complete and consistent within itself. Test geometries should be selected with full awareness of where they lie relative to the optimum lines since the effects of inlet velocity-profile, Reynolds Number, wall contouring, tailpipe, etc., are known to be dependent on this relationship. Too many investigations have been made on diffusers of poor performance and/or of little interest.

ACKNOWLEDGEMENT

The authors would like to acknowledge the assistance of Dr. A. B. Cocanower of the Research Laboratories staff in developing the material reported in the second half of the paper.

REFERENCES

Cockrell, D. J., Diamond, M. J. & Jones, G. D. (1965) *The Diffuser Inlet Flow Parameter.* J. Roy. Aero. Soc. **69**, 350–2.

Cockrell, D. J. & Markland, E. (1963) *A Review of Incompressible Diffuser Flow.* Aircraft Engineering **35**, 286–92.

Kline, S. J., Abbott, D. E. & Fox, R. W. (1959) *Optimum Design of Straight-Walled Diffusers.* J. Basic Engineering, Trans. ASME, Series D, **81**, 321–29.

Ludwieg, H. & Tillmann, W. (1949) *Untersuchungen über die Wandschubspannung in turbulenten Reibungsschichten.* Ing. Arch. **17**, 288–99. (Translation: *Investigation of the Wall Shearing Stress in Turbulent Boundary Layers.* NACA T.M. 1285, May 1950.)

McDonald, A. T. & Fox, R. W. (1965) *An Experimental Investigation of Incompressible Flow in Conical Diffusers.* ASME Preprint 65–FE–25.

Reneau, L. R., Johnston, J. P. & Kline, S. J. (1964) *Performance and Design of Straight Two-Dimensional Diffusers.* Report PD-8, Thermosciences Division, Mechanical Engineering Department, Stanford University, September 1964.

Rippl, E. (1956) *Experimentelle Untersuchungen über Wirkungsgrade und Abreissverhalten von schlanken Kegeldiffusoren.* Maschinenbautechnik, **6**, 241–6. (Translation: *Experimental Investigations Concerning the Efficiency of Slim Conical Diffusers and Their Behavior with Regard to Flow Separation.* Monthly Technical Review, **2**, No. 3, March 1958, 64–70.)

Sprenger, H. (1959) *Experimentelle Untersuchungen an geraden und gekrümmten Diffusoren.* Mitteilung aus dem Institute für Aerodynamik an der ETH, Zürich, No. 27, 1959. (Translation: *Experimental Research on Straight and Curved Diffusers.* Obtainable from the Ministry of Aviation, Gt. Brit.)

von Doenhoff, A. E. & Tetervin, N. (1943) *Determination of General Relations for the Behavior of Turbulent Boundary Layers.* NACA Report 772, 1943.

Winternitz, F. A. L. & Ramsay, W. J. (1957) *Effects of Inlet Boundary Layer on Pressure Recovery, Energy Conversion and Losses in Conical Diffusers.* J. Roy. Aero. Soc. **61**, 116–24.

APPENDIX A

PRESSURE-RECOVERY DATA FOR STRAIGHT-WALLED ANNULAR DIFFUSERS $(B_1 \cong .02)$

$\phi_0-\phi_1-\left(\dfrac{R_H}{R_T}\right)_1-\dfrac{\bar{L}}{\Delta R_1}$	AR	$\bar{C}_{P,i}$	$\bar{C}_P$	$\bar{\mathscr{E}}_0$	Re
+(*) 15–15–.70–2.28	1.167	.266	.256	.964	5.85×10^5
			.261	.980	5.79
3.63	1.286	.396	.367	.928	5.81
5.66	1.465	.534	.450	.844	6.18
			.448	.840	5.94
			.445	.835	5.49
			.431	.807	4.43
8.37	1.704	.656	.541	.825	6.23
			.532	.811	6.08
			.525	.800	5.25
9.72	1.823	.699	.564	.807	6.12
11.07	1.943	.735	.589	.802	6.12
13.10	2.122	.778	.626	.794	6.26
			.609	.783	5.04
● 15–10–.70–2.26	1.373	.470	.404	.858	6.24×10^5
			.392	.835	5.19
2.93	1.506	.559	.441	.789	5.31
3.61	1.645	.630	.520	.825	6.41
			.514	.815	6.21
			.482	.765	5.35
			.488	.775	5.10
			.483	.767	4.82
			.467	.742	4.51
4.96	1.941	.734	.569	.775	5.42
5.64	2.098	.773	.640	.828	6.31
			.638	.825	6.15
			.616	.797	5.62
			.605	.783	5.25
			.581	.751	4.64
6.32	2.261	.804	.616	.767	5.46
8.34	2.787	.871	.672	.770	5.57
10.37	3.368	.912	.714	.783	5.59
13.08	4.228	.944	.729	.773	5.08
▽ 15–8¼–.70–2.25	1.440	.518	.379	.732	4.89×10^5
2.93	1.596	.608	.427	.703	4.88
3.60	1.760	.677	.459	.679	4.84
□ 15–5–.70–2.24	1.558	.588	.356	.606	4.79×10^5
2.91	1.754	.675	.385	.571	4.77
3.59	1.959	.739	.412	.559	4.85
6.29	2.877	.879	.507	.577	4.88
9.68	4.243	.944	.557	.590	4.95
13.06	5.853	.971	.598	.617	4.95

* The data for each diffuser family has been consistently represented by the same symbol in all the figures of the paper.

APPENDIX A (*continued*)

$\phi_o-\phi_i-\left(\dfrac{R_H}{R_T}\right)_1-\dfrac{\bar{L}}{\Delta R_1}$	AR	$\bar{C}_{P,i}$	$\bar{C}_P$	$\bar{\mathscr{E}}_0$	Re
○ 20–15–.70–2.36	1.447	.522	.378	.725	6.25×10^5
			.360	.690	5.03
2.71	1.529	.572	.409	.715	6.24
			.386	.675	5.26
3.05	1.613	.615	.442	.718	6.18
3.40	1.699	.653	.468	.715	6.20
3.75	1.787	.687	.492	.716	6.18
4.44	1.971	.743	.556	.749	6.21
5.14	2.163	.786	.603	.768	6.28
5.83	2.365	.821	.644	.785	6.30
			.609	.742	5.33
◁ 20–10–.70–2.34	1.660	.637	.314	.494	6.06×10^5
2.68	1.779	.684	.336	.492	6.06
3.03	1.902	.723	.348	.480	6.06
3.38	2.028	.757	.362	.478	6.12
3.73	2.158	.785	.369	.470	6.05
4.42	2.430	.831	.403	.485	6.10
5.12	2.717	.865	.434	.503	6.10
5.80	2.965	.886	.459	.519	6.37
◗ 20–8¼–.70–2.33	1.730	.666	.299	.449	5.95×10^5
2.68	1.860	.711	.315	.444	6.00
3.03	1.995	.749	.331	.442	6.04
3.37	2.133	.780	.342	.439	6.10
3.72	2.276	.807	.354	.439	6.18
▷ 20–5–.70–2.32	1.851	.708	.276	.390	6.07×10^5
2.66	2.001	.750	.284	.379	6.08
3.01	2.156	.785	.293	.373	6.11
3.36	2.316	.814	.299	.368	6.15
3.71	2.481	.838	.307	.367	6.20
5.79	3.569	.921	.349	.379	6.26
△ 30–29½–.70–2.42	1.265	.375	.267	.713	6.11×10^5
3.92	1.521	.568	.453	.798	6.28
6.11	1.907	.725	.606	.837	6.36
9.17	2.471	.836	.719	.860	6.60
◖ 5–(−9½)–.55–1.43	1.318	.424	.430	1.014	8.18×10^5
			.431	1.016	7.72
			.401	.945	4.90
2.30	1.500	.555	.518	.933	8.46
			.525	.945	7.97
3.60	1.755	.675	.592	.877	8.49
			.607	.900	7.99
5.34	2.067	.766	.652	.851	8.64
			.686	.896	7.85
			.622	.813	5.31

APPENDIX A (continued)

$\phi_0-\phi_1-\left(\dfrac{R_H}{R_T}\right)_1-\dfrac{\bar{L}}{\Delta R_1}$	AR	$\bar{C}_{P,i}$	$\bar{C}_P$	$\bar{\mathscr{E}}_0$	Re
▽ 5–0–.55–1.47	1.169	.268	.305	1.140	7.57×10^5
			.294	1.100	5.36
2.34	1.274	.384	.403	1.120	7.74
3.64	1.437	.516	.521	1.008	7.83
5.38	1.668	.641	.620	.968	7.99
			.584	.911	5.24
▲ 15–0–.55–1.50	1.531	.574	.352	.613	7.67×10^5
			.340	.593	5.43
1.95	1.713	.659	.362	.550	7.85
2.40	1.902	.723	.385	.533	7.80
2.85	2.099	.773	.403	.521	7.92
3.30	2.304	.812	.421	.519	7.92
3.75	2.517	.842	.438	.520	7.96
4.20	2.738	.867	.448	.517	7.94
4.66	2.967	.886	.462	.522	8.01
5.11	3.205	.903	.471	.522	8.09
5.56	3.450	.916	.477	.522	8.13
			.448	.489	5.48
✕ 15–($13\frac{1}{2}$)–.55–2.01	1.314	.421	.415	.985	8.15×10^5
			.410	.974	6.74
			.402	.955	5.42
2.86	1.462	.532	.516	.970	8.19
3.81	1.650	.633	.587	.927	8.28
4.71	1.827	.701	.643	.918	8.31
6.52	2.200	.793	.720	.908	8.41
7.42	2.396	.826	.749	.906	8.47
8.31	2.595	.851	.781	.919	8.51
◠ 20–0–.55–1.75	1.570	.673	.259	.385	7.80×10^5
			.264	.392	5.55
2.02	2.012	.753	.271	.360	7.73
2.49	2.289	.809	.281	.348	7.68
2.95	2.581	.850	.288	.339	7.75
3.42	2.888	.880	.296	.336	7.73
3.88	3.209	.903	.304	.336	7.65
			.295	.327	5.35
■ 20–($13\frac{1}{2}$)–.55–2.08	1.603	.611	.362	.594	7.75×10^5
			.346	.567	4.87
2.54	1.770	.681	.476	.700	7.98
3.93	2.320	.814	.556	.684	8.01
			.496	.610	5.18

APPENDIX B

GEOMETRIC CHARACTERISTICS OF ANNULAR DIFFUSERS USED IN TURBOMACHINERY APPLICATIONS

Source	AR	$\bar{L}/\Delta R_1$	$(R_H/R_T)_1$	ϕ_o	ϕ_i	Comments*
1. Associated Electrical Industries, Ltd. AP4	2.10	2.49	.580	25	12	TD, SW, 2S
2. Associated Electrical Industries, Ltd. K7	2.00	2.90	.594	21	12	TD, SW
3. Associated Electrical Industries, Ltd. L5IC	1.27	1.66	.643	15	11	TD, SW
4. AiResearch	3.82	4.53	.663	21	−7	TD, SW
5. AiResearch 311	1.37	4.63	.712	4	0	BT, SW
6. Allen 350KW	2.04	4.80	.667	13	6	TD, SW
7. Austin 250	2.20	4.20	.710	12	0	TD, SW
8. Bristol-Siddeley	2.36	8.42	.667	32	32	annular combustor-to-turbine
9. Bristol-Siddeley	2.24	4.00	.725	14	0	TD, 3S
10. Centrax	4.05	9.75	.725	9	−9	TD, 1S
11. Chrysler CR2A	1.33	4.65	.795	30	30	BT
12. Chrysler CR2A	3.0	5.08	.780	30 to 90	30 to 90	TD
13. Clark	1.95	5.50	.66	21 to 90	15 to 90	TD
14. Continental	1.93	4.40	.65	7	−4	TD, SW
15. Cooper-Bessemer	1.77	4.04	.575	27	27	BT
16. Cooper-Bessemer	2.20	5.70	.64	27 to 90	27 to 90	TD
17. Escher Wyss	1.96	5.20	.608	30	30	TD, SW
18. Fiat TG3000	1.51	6.7	.795	0 to 90	0 to 90	CD
19. Fiat TG3000	2.17	3.11	.522	19	10	TD, SW, 1S
20. Fiat TG3000	2.34	5.00	.588	14	8	TD, SW
21. Ford 704	2.20	7.14	.558	6	0	TD, SW
22. General Electric J85	2.26	5.62	.697	5	−10	TD
23. General Electric 8362	2.22	6.04	.873	0	14	BT, SW
24. General Electric 8362	1.86	3.34	.694	12	0	TD, SW
25. General Electric 8362	2.00	5.61	.858	9	0	CD, SW
26. General Motors GT-309	1.85	4.03	.695	15 to 90	2 to 90	TD
27. MAN-Turbolader	2.47	3.25	.720	9	−25	TD

(Continued on next page)

APPENDIX B (continued)

Source	AR	$\bar{L}/\Delta R_1$	$(R_H/R_T)_1$	ϕ_o	ϕ_1	Comments*
28. Parsons 550MW	1.65	1.0	.48	0 to 90	0 to 90	TD, 3S
29. Richardson, Westgarth and Company	2.29	4.77	.794	0 to 90	0 to 90	TD
30. Rover	1.48	2.08	.661	10	0	TD, SW
31. Rover	1.15	2.19	.234			BT, both walls S-shaped
32. Rover IS/60	1.51	2.10	.79	12	0	TD, SW
33. Ruston TE	2.40	8.71	.680	8	3	TD, SW
34. Solar	2.18	4.71	.67	17 to 90	0 to 90	TD
35. Sulzer	2.46	8.61	.607	5	−3	downstream of axial-flow fan stator, SW
36. Sulzer	2.59	6.89	.63	14	8	TD, SW
37. Sulzer	1.04	1.10	.61	17	21	BT, SW
38. Hispano-Suiza THM 1000	2.19	5.24	.63	18	14	TD

* TD – located at turbine discharge
  BT – located between turbines
  CD – located at compressor discharge
  SW – straight walls

1S – one splitter
2S – two splitters
3S – three splitters

Discussion

S. J. KLINE (*Stanford University, Stanford, California*)

Dr. Sovran gave me his paper in advance and so I have had a chance to look at it a bit, and I'd like to make a few comments. I might say first that it is pretty clear from the work, that not only is Dr. Sovran good at organizing an excellent symposium, but he has also done a lot of careful thinking about how to put the diffuser problem together. In spite of his comment about the need for more careful data, it is a pleasure to talk about something in this symposium which is, at least in part, in some reasonable state. I think we can say what it is that is in a reasonable state fairly clearly and Dr. Sovran has said it, mostly. First of all, the class of diffusers which he has described, and this bears repeating, has a straight centerline, a large enough Reynolds number so that the turbulent boundary layer is somewhere near the normal type at the inlet, a potential core at the inlet, unstalled flow, and no choking condition that might plague you with shock-interaction problems. These diffuser cases, which represent perhaps half of the applications which we would like to be able to design, are in some reasonable kind of order. I think, that this has not been the case in the past. The fact that you can correlate the different geometries in a unified way, as Dr. Sovran has shown, will very much speed up the process of getting on with this, and it is a big step forward. The blockage concept which does this I certainly feel is on the right track. A number of people have been aware of it, but Dr. Sovran has put it in an analytical form that certainly makes it much more explicit, useful and clear than it has been before.

I should also comment on the use of ΔR_1 in the non-dimensional length variable for the annular case. The paper by Kline, Abbott & Fox (1962) on the Optimum Design of Straight-Walled Diffusers was wrong in this one connection. We had the right variables for the two-dimensional and conical case, where data were available. At that time there was no data for the annular case. We had the choice of two possibilities, and we took the wrong one; Dr. Sovran has the right one.

I should also like to add a few words of caution on some other points. First of all, it is easy to be misled in doing optimum problems with Reneau's data. All the optimum geometries lie on essentially a single line. It is therefore easy to gain the impression that there is no effect of inlet conditions on the optimum geometry. That is not true. While all the optima in recovery at constant length lie along the same line of geometries, the distance up that line you can go without getting into serious separation problems *is* dependent upon the inlet condition. As you would expect, if you have a thicker boundary layer at the inlet you cannot get to as large an area ratio in a straight-walled diffuser as you can if you have a healthier inlet condition. If you look carefully at the chart you will see that there are marked points which show how far you can go with any given inlet condition.

It is quite clear that the particular optimum line shown by Dr. Sovran is not valid if you have badly distorted inlet conditions of certain kinds. At Stanford we are just beginning to test some of these, and we already have data showing large effects of strong inlet distortion. If you have an inlet core which has a uniform non-zero vorticity, rather than a potential core with zero vorticity, it doesn't take a very large value to knock the maximum performance well below that which you saw on the performance charts. One has to be careful of this sort of thing.

The fact that you can correlate performance for geometries with area ratios as large as those on C_P^*, which in general is after the onset of some appreciable stall, indicates that the same kind of correlation and the boundary layer theory should work up to this line. So this really brings not just the C_P^* line in to order but, unless I am mistaken, also the whole region below the C_P^* line. We can do the calculations that we want in this region.

It is sometimes very tricky to identify diffuser stall from pressure-distribution measurements. The large-transitory-stall states do not have the kind of pressure-distribution curve which the aerodynamicist has historically identified with stall, i.e., a pressure curve which rises and then goes flat, with the flat spot indicating the occurrence of stall. In the large-transitory-stall cases the measured pressure distribution follows the ideal curve fairly closely for some length but then begins to branch away from the ideal curve as the stalls become appreciable in size. However, a continuously rising pressure is observed through the whole diffuser. This indicates the transitory-stall state. The kind of calculations and correlations that have been presented will probably not work for these states.

B. S. STRATFORD (*Rolls Royce Ltd., Derby, England*)

If there is one thing which impresses us about this work it is the massive amount of experimental data that has been obtained and the fact that Dr. Sovran has been able to correlate it. I should like to emphasize what Prof. Kline has just said, in that the particular feature which is of interest is that Dr. Sovran has been able to obtain a unique correlation which brings the annular diffuser into line with both the two-dimensional and the conical diffusers as regards the optimum rate of area change. He has been able to obtain this rather unique line and this does seem to be a particularly valuable contribution.

M. ROGERS (*Air Force Office of Scientific Research, Washington, D.C.*)

Were these tests made with cold gases at the inlet to the diffusers?

G. SOVRAN

Yes.

M. ROGERS

One of the important uses of diffusers is when a hot gas or a mixture of hot gases is the working fluid. I wonder if you think the correlation that you have postulated would work in these cases?

G. SOVRAN

I have no basis for saying yes or no. We did all of our testing with cold air.

S. J. KLINE

Could I ask Mr. Rogers why he feels that temperature should have an effect?

M. ROGERS

You can never get a homogeneous stream of hot gases; if you take exhaust gases and put them through a collector or a plenum you can get local hot spots. A diffuser will amplify these spots, it's not going to smooth them out.

S. J. KLINE

I would agree with you that a diffuser is an amplifier of velocity fluctuations, as Dr. Sovran has expressed very well with the Euler equation. If there is only a temperature distortion and the velocity profile is all right, I don't see that it should make much difference, unless the density difference is large.

E. R. G. ECKERT (*University of Minnesota, Minneapolis, Minnesota*)

If you have uniform velocity at the inlet, but with temperature differences, then you will get non-uniform velocities at the exit.

M. ROGERS

The point I am trying to make is that the optimum diffuser geometry may be entirely different; it may not fall on the optimum curve that has been presented.

S. J. KLINE

The next phase of diffuser research will clearly have to involve a lot more work on inlet conditions than has been done so far. I think Dr. Sovran has pointed his finger specifically at some of the things that need to be done and I think what you are saying is a variation on some of the things to be considered.

W. R. HAWTHORNE (*Cambridge University, Cambridge, England*)

At the risk of being accused of plugging a line, it does occur to me that this is another case of a transition type of device which is combined with flow having turbulence and nonuniformity in it. It might be possible to make some progress by treating at least part of this flow as an inviscid flow. With the use of computers, it seems to me that you could run a whole range of cut-off velocities and so on and handle certainly all the cases of interest having non-uniform entrance flows, using for reference the boundary layer behavior in a good diffuser and the pressure gradient it can stand. There might be possibilities along this line and I want to ask whether you have done any detailed investigations of this sort.

G. SOVRAN

What you are saying is that the distortion effect is primarily inviscid and the pressure forces predominate. This is exactly what the basis of our correlation was. If you have an inlet distortion, the diffuser will amplify it.

W. R. HAWTHORNE

You should be able to calculate it without much trouble.

G. K. SEROVY (*Iowa State University, Ames, Iowa*)

We have written some computer programs to study this distortion effect that you mention for inviscid flow. It is not as easy as it seems at first glance.

G. SOVRAN

I presume that you have a problem at the wall. For instance, if you started with a zero wall velocity at the inlet there would be difficulties in getting the inviscid flow near the walls to accommodate the required diffuser pressure rise.

G. K. SEROVY

That's right.

J. E. FOWLER (*General Electric Company, Schenectady, New York*)

This report represents a very large investment of man-hours and money on the part of General Motors and I would personally like to thank both Dr. Sovran and General Motors for making this information available to the scientific community. It is a major contribution.

G. SOVRAN

Thank you very much.

J. M. ROBERTSON (*University of Illinois, Urbana, Illinois*)

One comment and a suggestion. Having made a number of boundary layer calculations in diffusers I am confused about the displacement thickness comment you made. I think I will have to study your paper to understand the differences.

The suggestion I have is the following. You mentioned the unavailability of any information to study the boundary layer distortion effect (i.e., data with inlet H values other than flat-plate or zero-pressure-gradient ones). Why can't you consider the flow part way down a diffuser, where H has been changed to a higher value, to be the inlet condition for a new diffuser starting at that point? You would have a distorted inlet boundary layer for this diffuser.

G. SOVRAN

The difficulty with doing this is that the local values of H along a diffuser are tied to particular values of cross-sectional blockage, B. The basis of our correlation is that B_1 is the primary parameter controlling the performance of optimum diffusers. Therefore, to properly study the effects of inlet H you have to uncouple it from the blockage.

B. G. NEWMAN (*McGill University, Montreal, Canada*)

I'm not sure of the problem. It seems to me, whether or not you amplify the distortion in a diffuser would depend on whether the rate of diffusion exceeds the self-preserving condition or not. The distortion idea isn't true for all diffusers.

G. SOVRAN

That's right, it isn't. However, we have restricted our discussion to diffusers on the optimum line. This is not as restrictive as it might seem; if there were only one region where I could predict diffuser performance, I couldn't pick a better one than along this line. These are the diffusers that by and large you would want to use in practical applications. If you get off the optimum line then the correlation obviously will not work. For example, if you make a diffuser of given area ratio long enough, a poor inlet velocity profile will actually get more uniform at the exit. It's like putting a tailpipe on the end of a short diffuser. However, I don't think this is the type of diffuser you will normally run into. It is the optimum ones that are of most interest, the ones where you get the maximum pressure rise per unit length. In these, apparently, the pressure forces dominate the viscous forces. The very, very long ones wouldn't be covered by the correlation but they are ones which I think are of much less interest.

J. H. HORLOCK* (*University of Liverpool, Liverpool, England*)

The work of Sovran & Klomp is most useful in providing good experimental data on annular and conical diffusers.

* Written discussion submitted after symposium.

I should like to refer to the effects of inlet non-uniformity in the flow. In two papers in the International Journal of Mechanical Sciences we have shown, analytically and experimentally, that a perturbation (u_1') in the mean entry velocity (U_1) of a two-dimensional diffuser is increased at the outlet (station 2), as

$$\frac{u_2'}{U_2} = \lambda^2 \frac{u_1'}{U_1}$$

where λ is the area ratio.

In a conical or annular diffuser the ratio of perturbation to mean flow again varies as the area ratio squared.

G. SOVRAN

The indicated equation gives the proper qualitative effect that the pressure forces in inviscid flows have on velocity-profile non-uniformities, i.e., diffusers $(AR > 1)$ amplify the non-uniformities and distort the profiles, nozzles $(AR < 1)$ attenuate them. However, the quantitative effect predicted by this particular linearized analysis can be very much in error for diffusers. This is particularly

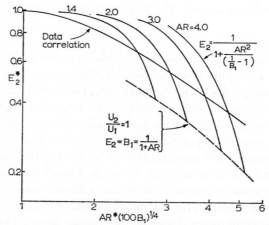

Figure 25. Comparison of Horlock & Lewis prediction of E_2 with data correlation of Sovran & Klomp.

true for the type of inlet flows considered by the correlation presented in this paper (i.e., a uniform central core surrounded by boundary layer). Applying Prof. Horlock's equation to one of the streamlines of the core flow and using the terminology of this paper,

$$E_2 = \cfrac{1}{1 + \cfrac{AR^2}{\left(\cfrac{1}{B_1} - 1\right)}}$$

The comparison between this relationship, which is applicable to the streamlines in any unstalled diffuser, and the data correlation for optimum diffuser geometries on the C_P^* line that we have obtained is shown in figure 25. Although the equation shows that E_2 is dependent on the same variables as the data correlation, it gives a considerably different functional relationship. The curves cannot be collapsed to a single one by the same combination of these variables that proved successful for the data correlation; furthermore, the predicted values are significantly different than those indicated by the actual data. For example, for any area ratio the Horlock & Lewis equation will predict values of U_2/U_1 less than unity if the inlet blockage is excessively large; i.e., it will predict an *acceleration* of the core-flow in the diffuser. The conditions for zero diffusion and the locus line which represents them are shown on the figure.

Some Problems of Recognizing and Defining Separation of the Skewed Boundary Layer

EDWARD S. TAYLOR

Gas Turbine Laboratory, Massachusetts Institute of Technology, Cambridge, Massachusetts

Boundary layer separation continues to be the most troublesome of unsolved problems in turbomachinery. The occurrence of separation can result in very large errors in the flow predicted by calculation. It is very probably responsible for a large part of the losses in many machines operating near their design point, as well as for the incidence of rotating stall and surge.

In turbomachinery virtually all boundary layers are strongly skewed—that is the direction of the velocity vector changes materially as the surface is approached. This adds further elements of difficulty to an already formidable problem. In fact, it is difficult even to define three-dimensional separation in a wholly satisfactory manner.

On the other hand, the effect of a three-dimensional separation on flow is often relative innocuous when compared to that of a two-dimensional separation, and there are undoubtedly opportunities to improve performance and extend the range of turbomachinery which will be opened up by a more complete understanding of the problem.

It seems almost unnecessary to state that one of the first steps in this understanding is to be able to distinguish between separation and non-separation and it is this problem which will be discussed here.

The two-dimensional or collateral boundary layer provides an easily recognized criterion for separation, the vanishing of the shear stress at the surface. For the case of a skewed boundary layer it is only necessary to consider the case of separated flow on a yawed wing of infinite aspect ratio to see that the separation line is no longer a locus of zero shear stress, for here the stress component along the line of separation does not vanish; in fact, there is no point of zero shear stress anywhere on the wing.

Maskell (1955) was one of the first to take a serious look at this problem. He used the device of limiting streamlines. Limiting streamlines can be determined by observing that as the wall is approached, although the velocity approaches zero the direction of the streamlines approaches a limiting direction, which varies in general continuously from point to point on the surface. Lines along these directions are termed "limiting streamlines".

Maskell proposed to distinguish separation by the locus of branching of limiting streamlines. If three-dimensional separation could be so distinguished, it would have a happy relationship to two-dimensional separation which could also be distinguished by the same criterion.

Unfortunately limiting streamlines cannot be assumed to have the properties of ordinary streamlines. Indeed, they are *not streamlines*. Since they lie on the surface, not in the fluid, and the velocity along them is everywhere zero, it is unreasonable to assume that they have the properties of ordinary streamlines. They approximate streamlines close to the surface when the boundary layer thickness is not changing rapidly but are particularly unlike ordinary streamlines close to a separation point.

It seems reasonably clear that limiting streamlines do not join a separation line at an angle, but tangentially. This being the case, it is difficult if not impossible to distinguish the separation line by observing limiting streamlines in the neighborhood of a point since they appear identical to converging limiting streamlines anywhere else on the surface.

Recognizing this fact, Lighthill (1963) gave the situation further study. He introduced the concept of vorticity at the surface. This had several advantages; first, the vorticity at the surface is indeed equal to the vorticity in the fluid next to the surface and, second, the vorticity is a two-dimensional vector having, in general, a non-zero value. It becomes clear that "limiting streamlines" are simply the network perpendicular to the vortex lines. It is also clear that the vorticity (and the shear stress) is continuous over the surface. The introduction of the idea of vorticity has given a greatly improved understanding of the meaning of shear lines or limiting streamlines.

Further, Lighthill recognized the impossibility of distinguishing separation by observations near a single point and proposes to solve this problem by a study of the topology of the entire surface. He introduces the idea of two types of "singularities" (points where the shear stress and surface vorticity go to zero). The first is a "nodal point" where the limiting streamlines are generally radially disposed and, except in the case of "spiral points" which need not concern us here, the vortex lines form closed curves as in figure 1. The second singularity is a "saddle point" which is also sketched in figure 1.

A third situation, here called a "cylindrical point", can be considered a special case of either a saddle point or a nodal point. This latter geometry fits a two-dimensional situation. Cylindrical points of course always occur as a line of such points.

Lighthill identifies the separation line as the line which joins a saddle point to a

References p. 325

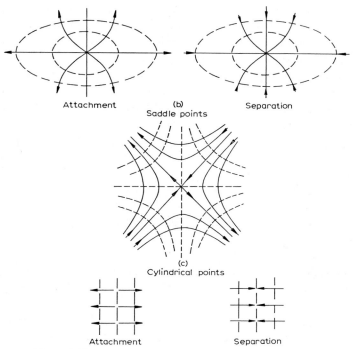

(a)
Nodal points

Attachment   (b)   Separation
                 Saddle points

(c)
Cylindrical points

Attachment   Separation

Figure 1. Types of singular points for limiting streamlines.

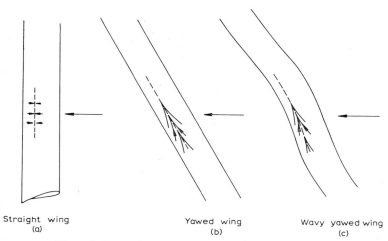

Straight wing   Yawed wing   Wavy yawed wing
    (a)   (b)   (c)

Figure 2. Separation line on wings of various geometries.

nodal point of separation. This idea covers some cases very satisfactorily. Unfortunately it appears not to cover all cases. Furthermore, particularly in internal flows it is often impossible to distinguish the singularities which may be far upstream or far downstream, and consequently it is then impossible to determine the separation line which connects these points. These difficulties can be illustrated by a few examples.

First, let us consider a two-dimensional wing of infinite aspect ratio at a large angle of incidence (figure 2a). In this case the separation line is clearly a series of cylindrical points, any of which can be considered either as saddle points or nodal points. This line is thus a special case of saddle points joined to nodal points and therefore fits Lighthill's criterion.

Furthermore, as Lighthill points out, any small change in the geometry of the wing along the span will in general produce spanwise velocities, nodal and saddle points and retrieve the general case.

If we now consider a yawed wing (figure 2b) we find no singularities on it anywhere, although there is a line on it which we would still very much like to call separation since it is located where the shear layer leaves the surface and is clearly an extension of the case of zero yaw.

If one tries to escape this dilemma by saying that the singularities are now at infinity, this argument can be countered by substituting a spinning projectile for the yawed wing. This latter geometry involves no singularities anywhere on the separation line.

Another possible loophole is that these cases are special and two-dimensional in the sense that all derivatives along the wing (circumferentially around the projectile) are zero. This argument can be easily countered by considering a perturbation of the yawed wing; for example, one could introduce waviness in the wing shape (figure 2c). This procedure creates non-zero derivatives of all properties along the span, but if the waviness is small it appears from physical reasoning that it would introduce no singularities. Since the shear stress along the separation line in this case is not zero but finite, a finite perturbation is required to reduce the stress to zero anywhere along the separation line and thus produce a singularity. Only if the waviness of the wing were large would singularities appear along the separation line and bring the case under Lighthill's separation criterion. It seems that we must recognize the possibility of separation with no associated points of zero shear stress. Here then is a case we would very much like to call separation because of its essential similarity to two-dimensional separation, but which escapes Lighthill's criterion.

The difficulty of locating singularities in internal flow is illustrated by the following photographs taken from the motion picture "Secondary Flow" (Taylor 1965).

Figure 3 shows a horseshoe vortex caused by a boundary layer encountering an

obstruction. It is clear that there is a shear layer which has been lifted from a surface and we would like to call it a case of separation. It is also easy to see that there
must be a saddle point on the wall in front of the obstruction, but where is the
nodal point? Clearly the latter is out of range.

Figure 4 shows a passage vortex—again a shear layer lifted from a wall which we
would like to classify as separation. In this case it is not clear whether there is either
a saddle point or a nodal point associated with the phenomenon.

Neither Maskell's criterion of branching of limiting streamlines (i.e. shear layer
leaving the wall) or Lighthill's of the line joining a saddle point to a nodal point of
separation appears completely satisfactory. Although our understanding of the
geometry of separation has been considerably improved, it is still imperfect. A series
of careful measurements, perhaps with a hot-wire at and in the vicinity of the
separation of a skewed boundary layer, might shed further light on the subject.

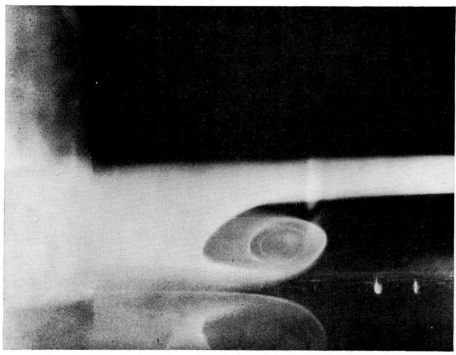

Figure 3. Horseshoe vortex in front of and around a circular cylinder normal to a surface on which
a boundary layer is flowing.

Figure 4. Downstream view of flow in a curved two-dimensional water channel (inside of bend is on the right). A vertical sheet of hydrogen bubbles generated midway between the curved walls and over the height of the channel becomes curved (vertical, white band) as it passes around the bend, and the portion in the boundary layer on the floor of the channel moves towards the inner wall and rolls up into a passage vortex.

REFERENCES

Lighthill, M. J. (1963) *Laminar Boundary Layers* (L. Rosenhead, editor). Oxford University Press, pp. 60–82.

Maskell, E. C. (1955) *Flow Separation in Three Dimensions*. R.A.E. Report No. Aero 2565.

Taylor, E. S. (1965) *Secondary Flow* (motion picture). Educational Services Inc., Watertown, Mass.

Discussion

M. H. BLOOM (*Polytechnic Institute of Brooklyn, Farmingdale, New York*)

Is there a problem of semantics and definition here? That is, are we concerned about how to apply the term "separation" in three-dimensional situations, or is our concern related to the analytic and experimental difficulties in establishing the properties of these flows near surfaces?

E. S. TAYLOR

It isn't the semantics, at least I don't suppose it is that. It certainly is not the calculations; I haven't even arrived anywhere near this yet. It's the difficulty of recognizing separation when it appears. Separation *is* a problem, and we certainly need to be able to distinguish when it exists and when it does not. That's my real difficulty.

M. H. BLOOM

These complex flows are certainly difficult to describe and measure. Perhaps we need not name them.

E. S. TAYLOR

In the two-dimensional case, at least, there is such a big qualitative jump between separation and non-separation that you find it essential to be able to distinguish it. Now it is indeed possible that in the three-dimensional case things can get so foggy in the region of separation and non-separation (where you get a little thickening of the boundary layer but then it goes back down again) that it is unnecessary to make the distinction. This is possible.

E. A. EICHELBRENNER (*Laval University, Quebec, Canada*)

From 1954 to 1964 at Poitiers and the ONERA in France, a long series of experiments and observations were made on skewed boundary layers in which a slightly different viewpoint was taken. We finally explained the problem of the skewed wing as a limiting case constituted by an infinite succession of nodal and saddle points. Consider a finite three-dimensional body with a really three-dimensional flow around it which includes separation (e.g. a flattened ellipsoid with a 10° angle of incidence). When the incidence is progressively reduced to zero you get a line of separation which is in the form of a ring around the body that is perpendicular to the axis of the ellipsoid. This line is constituted by an infinite succession of points which have simultaneously the characteristics of both degenerate saddle and nodal points. This at least permits an explanation of the skewed wing. There were a great number of ONERA reports written on this work which I think can, to a certain extent, clear up the problem; unfortunately, most of them are in French.

E. R. G. ECKERT (*University of Minnesota, Minneapolis, Minnesota*)

The physical consequences of separation disappear in three-dimensional flow. In a two-dimensional flow, when you have this situation the flow usually separates because it accumulates at a particular place. But in the three-dimensional case, as soon as you have this transverse flow it continuously sucks the fluid away so that there is really not the severe consequence that we find with loss of lift or anything like that. One extreme condition would be, for instance, a flow over a curved surface where you have a number of vortices rotating in opposite directions with their axes in the flow direction. Do you call the line where the vortices meet a line of separation or not? I wouldn't.

E. A. EICHELBRENNER

Consider a flat ellipsoid to which you give a growing incidence. There are two pairs of points, nodal and saddle points, having a total intensity of zero which grow together and finally meet when you reach, as I called it in 1957 in an ONERA publication*, the critical incidence of the ellipsoid. At this point a change of regime appears on the upper side of this flattened ellipsoid. This has been shown in a certain number of experiments and photographs; it really exists and it appears at the predicted incidence.

M. V. MORKOVIN (*The Martin Company, Baltimore, Maryland*)

I would like to join Prof. Eichelbrenner and introduce one more example that makes Prof. Eckert's position a little bit more difficult to hold. First, consider a pointed body that is slightly curved and is pointing into an air stream (figure 5). Here you have what I used to call edges of regression, which are infinite sequences of saddle and nodal points, and the very gradual development of separation and double vortices on the side**. This flow situation does have very great technical

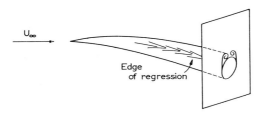

Figure 5. Curved, slender body of revolution at zero incidence.

---

* ONERA publication no. 89 (1957).
** Added in editing: "Such edges of regression are seen in figure 13b of Morkovin *et al.* (J. Aero. Sci. Vol 19, 1952) for a case where a supersonic flow was curved rather than the body. An easily accessible reference treating such streamwise vortex-sheet separation is *Laminar Boundary Layers*, L. Rosenhead editor, Clarendon Press, 1963, chapter II and expecially pp. 488–91 and figure VIII. 15b."

importance. For one thing, the lift is changed very radically in this region. Further-more, should you go to a somewhat larger Reynolds number, depending upon a number of conditions the configuration will be unstable.

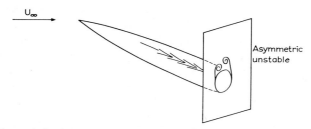

Figure 6. Straight, slender body of revolution at positive incidence.

The transient stability of missiles is also very strongly affected by things of this sort (figure 6). In this case the body is not curved, of course, but it is flying at an angle of attack. The separation in this sense doesn't necessarily start here, but occurs somewhat further downstream.

These are of the same type of separation, I think, that Prof. Taylor was showing. They are certainly far from being technologically unimportant.

E. R. G. ECKERT

Isn't this something quite different from the normal separation that you have in a two-dimensional flow?

M. V. MORKOVIN

Very definitely, but it is not unimportant. Technologically it is a question of real importance.

S. J. KLINE (*Stanford University, Stanford, California*)

I don't think you are in real disagreement with Prof. Eckert. If I understood him correctly, what he said was that with skewed flows you have a gradual change of phenomena, not a sudden change. You indicated yourself that you got a regression of states.

E. R. G. ECKERT

It is difficult to draw a line of separation on your (Dr. Morkovin) configuration.

M. V. MORKOVIN

That is correct, but if you go a short distance downstream you very well know that you've got separation and it grows as you go further downstream. You have to take it into account somewhere. Where is the origin?

R. C. DEAN (*Dartmouth College, Hanover, New Hampshire*)

Prof. Eckert's comments implied to me that he doesn't think three-dimensional separation may be as important as two-dimensional separation. But shear layers are being peeled off the wall and this grossly affects the boundary layer, the location of separation and so on. That's why it is important, not because it leads to unusual effects.

E. R. G. ECKERT

Sure, but let me ask a question. The Görtler vortices, do you call this separation or separation effects?

R. C. DEAN

Yes.

E. R. G. ECKERT

Then this is really semantics.

S. J. KLINE

What about Prof. Hawthorne's classical two-dimensional bend. The boundary layer on the end walls thickens as it goes around the corner and moves towards the inner wall; is that separation or isn't it?

E. S. TAYLOR

Yes.

H. W. LIEPMANN (*California Institute of Technology, Pasadena, California*)

If there is a physical effect, I think I would define it as a physical effect and not as a topological effect. Also, what is separation?

E. A. EICHELBRENNER

There is a surface in the fluid that separates two kinds of flow. I expressed it once in the following way: There are regions on the surface of a finite body (figure 7) where, because of an adverse pressure distribution (not an adverse pressure *gradient* in the two-dimensional sense), the flow cannot arrive from upstream. If you follow back along the shear-stress lines (i.e., opposite to the shear direction) you will find that a certain number of them lead to infinity upstream whereas others do not. The

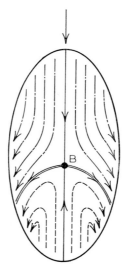

Figure 7. Shear-stress lines ("wall streamlines") on the upper side of a flattened ellipsoid having a positive incidence of, say, 6°.

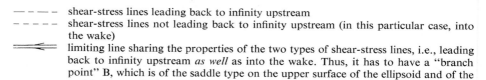

—————— shear-stress lines leading back to infinity upstream

— — — — — shear-stress lines not leading back to infinity upstream (in this particular case, into the wake)

══════ limiting line sharing the properties of the two types of shear-stress lines, i.e., leading back to infinity upstream *as well* as into the wake. Thus, it has to have a "branch point" B, which is of the saddle type on the upper surface of the ellipsoid and of the nodal type on the lower surface.

separation line is the limiting line between these two positions. This leads immediately to the conception of a branch point. This conception of a branch point needs some verification, but some of this work has been done.

E. S. TAYLOR

That's another possible way of distinguishing separation but it also has something the matter with it. Consider the case of the horseshoe vortex in front of a cylinder which protrudes through a boundary layer (figure 8). There is a limiting streamline (A) on the surface which approaches the separation point (S) from the upstream direction. There is also a limiting streamline (B) which, in the vicinity of S, approaches the separation point from the downstream direction. However, this streamline also really comes from upstream, passing over the top of the vortex before it approaches S. It is difficult to make a definition of separation that will include this situation.

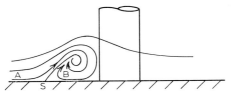

Figure 8. Horseshoe vortex in front of a cylinder protruding through a boundary layer.

R. E. KRONAUER (*Harvard University, Cambridge, Massachusetts*)

I'd like to draw an analogy which may help some people. The field of limiting streamlines is like a two-dimensional phase portrait in nonlinear ordinary differential equations. The singular points under discussion are the linearized singular points of the differential equation set. The problem of the separation line is the same as the problem of finding a limit trajectory of the equations. There is the possibility that this trajectory may be closed on itself in which case it is a limit cycle. Continuity of the vector field requires that there be a singularity with Poincaré index of unity inside the limit cycle. A physical example of this might be a tornado with flow toward the surface in the core and away from the surface at larger radii. It is, of course, more difficult to locate limit cycles than singular points since they are field dependent and cannot be discovered by point-wise analysis.

J. ACKERET (*Eidgenössische Technische Hochschule, Zürich, Switzerland*)

We have now reached a limit where differential equations are superseded by hand-waving mathematics. I would like to thank General Motors for all the hospitality they have shown us, for the excellent facilities and the excellent organization. I am most thankful for having had the opportunity to attend this symposium.

J. H. HORLOCK* (*University of Liverpool, Liverpool, England*)

I should like to query whether the boundary layer flows leading to separation that exist in turbomachines are substantially three-dimensional and whether the emphasis on the semantics of three-dimensional separation is vitally important. It appears that in many cases in turbines and compressors the flow is largely two-dimensional up to separation, but severe cross flows develop after the flow leaves the surface. I should like to give three examples of such flows.

Firstly in the corner separation in compressor cascades, although there is some cross flow into the boundary layer ahead of the separation region, the "stall" appears to be two-dimensional, the fluid leaves the surface and there is clear evidence of back flow.

---

* Written discussion submitted after symposium.

Secondly, consider the flow over a cascade aerofoil subject to a radial or trans-verse pressure gradient—a nozzle guide-vane row, say. We have looked in detail at the laminar and turbulent boundary layers on the surfaces, and the cross flow is small even when the transverse pressure gradient is severe. But when we place a thick aerofoil in a swirling flow, while the radial (transverse) flow is again small up to the separation point, there is a very considerable inward radial flow down-stream of it. Once more the separation itself appears to be controlled mainly by the streamwise pressure gradient, and the separation region itself is the one largely affected by radial pressure gradients.

Finally may I refer to an experiment by Sivaprakasapillai & Jackson at Imperial College, on separation on a rotating cylinder. Although Himmelskamp's earlier work suggested that the stalling lift coefficient of an aerofoil was increased by centrifuging of the boundary layer, Sivaprakasapillai & Jackson find that the separation on the rotating cylinder (observed by flow visualization) occurs sub-stantially two-dimensionally. However radial flow occurs in the separation region, together with a circumferential pressure gradient. The flow is in fact separated although no "flat" appears in the circumferential pressure distribution.

I agree with Professor Taylor that we must have more experimental information on these three-dimensional boundary layers. I am hopeful that more will become available at the second European Mechanics Conference, on three-dimensional boundary layers, at Liverpool in January 1966.

Subject Index

Actuator disc, 244, 245
adverse pressure gradients, 41, 43
airfoils, thin, 250
amplification of disturbances, 60
anemometer, hot-wire, 115, 120
annular diffuser(s), 282, 303
auto-correlation, 155

Backflow, streaks of, 43
band flow, 16
bends, flow in, 257
bent diffusers, 23
— ducts, 247
blocked area, 294, 298
Borda–Carnot pressure rise, 11
boundary layer(s), collateral, 320
— —, equilibrium, 85, 102
— —, three-dimensional, 2, 211
— —, turbulent, see turbulent
— — suction, 23
breakup, 34, 49
—, frequency of, 53
bubbles, separation —, 42
buffer layer, 46

C_P^* line, 277
C_P^{**} line, 277
cascade, flow through, 254, 266
centrifugal force, 1, 10
collateral boundary layer, 320
compressibility, 5
conical diffusers, 278, 297
continuity equation, 1
Coriolis force, 1
correlation(s), 51, 71, 77, 155
— coefficient(s), 131, 143

— length, 131
cross-contamination, 32
crossflow fans, 16
— -velocity profiles, single- and multi-signed, 228
curved tubes, 9

Developed velocity distribution, 215
— — profile, 223
diffuser(s), 17, 26
—, annular, 282, 303
—, bent, 23
—, calculations for, 299
—, conical, 278, 297
—, effectiveness of, 276, 293, 297
—, loss coefficient for, 293
—, two-dimensional, 276, 302
— family, 285
— optimum lines, 277, 289
discrete structures, 162
displacement thickness, 127
dissipation rate, direct-, 138
disturbances, amplification of, 60
—, large, 245
—, small, 243, 245
double structure of turbulence, 167
ducts, bent, 247

Eddies, equilibrium range of, 155
—, large (big), 160, 162, 168, 190
—, small, 160, 162
eddy viscosity, 89, 96, 102, 103, 160, 162, 164, 178
— — Reynolds number, 187
effective area, 294
— — fraction, 297, 300

effectiveness of a diffuser, 276, 293, 297
elbow, flow in, 14
energy, turbulent, 168
— defect, mechanical-, 138
— equation, integral, 192
— —, —, kinetic-, 86
— production, turbulent, 77
— spectrum, 155
entrainment equation, 87
equation of continuity, 1
equilibrium boundary layers, 85, 102
— hypothesis, large-eddy-, 168, 190
— layers, 91
— profiles, 126
— range of eddies, 155

Fans, crossflow, 16
flow about thin airfoils, 250
— in an elbow, 14
— in bends, 257
— in bent ducts, 247
— over thick struts, 248
— regimes, 273
— through a cascade, 254, 266
fluctuations, 30, 60
frequency of breakup, 53
fully turbulent, see turbulent

Geometries, optimum, 313

Half-power law, 220
history, upstream, 91
— effect in skewed turbulent boundary layers,
  231
horseshoe vortex, 323
hot-wire anemometer, 115, 120

Inertial subrange, 155
inlet-profile effects, 301
inlet-velocity profile, non-uniformity of, 292
innermost layer, 46
instability, 59
—, Tollmien–Schlichting, 29
integral equation, energy, 192
— —, kinetic-energy, 86
— —, momentum, 82, 89, 184
— method(s), 107
— —, generalized, 305
— scale, 159

intermittency, 45, 178, 205
internal mixing, 14
inviscid theory, 242

Jet mechanisms for ventilation, 14

Kinetic-energy integral equation, 86

Laminar-turbulent transition, 29
large-eddy-equilibrium hypothesis, 168, 190
large-shear, small-disturbance approximation,
  245
law of the wall, 82, 123, 212, 215
— — — —, logarithmic, 220
— — — —, three-dimensional, 218
limiting streamline(s), 320, 330
line of separation, 321, 326
logarithmic law of the wall, 220
loss coefficient for diffuser, 293

Maximum pressure recovery, 112, 114
mean streak spacing, 52
— -velocity profile, polar plot of, 213
mechanical-energy defect, 138
mixing, internal, 14
— layer, 185
— -length theory, 178
— problems, turbulent, 202
momentum equation, integral, 82, 89, 184
— thickness, 127
multi-signed crossflow-velocity profiles, 228

Natural transition, 29
nodal point(s), 321, 326, 327
non-uniformity of inlet-velocity profile, 292
non-viscous flow, 3

Optimum diffuser lines, 227, 289
— geometries, 313

Passage vortex, 324
peak-and-valley structure, 30
plane defect law, 217
polar plot (of mean-velocity profile), 213, 230,
  236
pressure distributions, 121

— gradients, adverse, 41, 43
— recovery, maximum, 112, 114
— — coefficient, 275

Readjusting zone, 43
reattachment, 2
relaminarization, 39, 79
Reynolds number, eddy-viscosity, 187
— stress, 136, 147, 150, 160
roughness function, 221

Saddle points, 326, 327
secondary flow, 7
— — approximation, 245, 247, 254, 257
self-preserving (self-similar) flows, 174
— - — law, 202
separation, 14
—, incipient, 43
—, line of, 321, 326
—, three-dimensional, 320, 331
—, zones of, 2
— bubbles, 42
shape parameter, 83, 86
shear, large, 245
—, small, 243, 245
— stress distribution(s), 133, 146
— —, turbulent, 134, 178
single-signed crossflow-velocity profiles, 228
skewed turbulent boundary layers, 231
skewness, 52
skin friction, 83, 145
— — coefficient, 124
slip function, 220
small-shear, large-disturbance approximation,
  245
— - —, small-disturbance flows, 243
spiral point, 321
stall, transitory, 115, 130, 143
strain, mean, 60
strain rate, 161
streak(s), 34, 49
— of backflow, 43
— spacing, mean, 52
streaky structure, 33, 34, 35
streamline(s), limiting, 320, 330
stress, Reynolds, 136, 147, 150, 160
—, shear, *see* shear
stretching of vorticity, 156
structure(s), discrete, 162
— of fully turbulent boundary layer, 44
— of turbulence, 161, 167

struts, thick, flow over, 248
suction, boundary layer, 23
surface, vorticity at, 321

Three-dimensional boundary layer(s), 2, 211
— - — law of the wall, 218
— - — separation, 320, 331
threshold level of fluctuations and mean strain,
  60
Tollmien–Schlichting instability, 29
transition, laminar-turbulent, 29
—, natural, 29
— device, 316
— flow, 242
— in adverse pressure gradients, 41
transitional, 28
transitory stall, 115, 130, 143
triangular model, 215
— plot, 227, 279
tubes, curved, 9
turbulence, structure of, 161, 167
— intensity, 128, 143
— level, 113
— production, 57, 60, 69, 74, 137
turbulent, fully, boundary layer, 44
—, —, layer, 33
— boundary layers, skewed, history effect in,
  231
— energy, 168
— mixing problems, 202
— shear stress, 134, 178
— spot formation, 31
— vorticity, 188
two-dimensional diffusers, 276, 302
two-layer model, 82
two-point space correlation, 51

Universal wake function, 212
upstream history, 91

Vector defect, 216
velocity defect law, 82
— distribution, developed, 215
— profile(s), 213, 228, 292
— —, developed, 223
— — data, 123
— — distortion, 296
— — parameter, 295
ventilation, jet mechanisms for, 14

vortex, horseshoe, 323
—, passage, 324
vorticity, stretching of, 156
—, turbulent, 188
— at surface, 321

Wake function, 83
— —, universal, 212
wall, law of, *see* law of the wall

Zones of separation, 2